TEST ITEM FILE

Elementary Statistics
Picturing the World

THIRD EDITION

Larson  Farber

PEARSON

PEARSON

Prentice Hall

Upper Saddle River, NJ 07458

Editor-in-Chief: Sally Yagan
Senior Acquisitions Editor: Petra J. Recter
Supplement Editor: Joanne Wendelken
Executive Managing Editor: Kathleen Schiaparelli
Assistant Managing Editor: Becca Richter
Production Editor: Donna Crilly
Supplement Cover Manager: Paul Gourhan
Supplement Cover Designer: Joanne Alexandris
Manufacturing Buyer: Michael Bell

© 2006 Pearson Education, Inc.
Pearson Prentice Hall
Pearson Education, Inc.
Upper Saddle River, NJ 07458

Pearson Prentice Hall™ is a trademark of Pearson Education, Inc.

The author and publisher of this book have used their best efforts in preparing this book. These efforts include the development, research, and testing of the theories and programs to determine their effectiveness. The author and publisher make no warranty of any kind, expressed or implied, with regard to these programs or the documentation contained in this book. The author and publisher shall not be liable in any event for incidental or consequential damages in connection with, or arising out of, the furnishing, performance, or use of these programs.

Printed in the United States of America

10 9 8 7 6 5 4 3 2 1

ISBN 0-13-148319-6

Pearson Education Ltd., *London*
Pearson Education Australia Pty. Ltd., *Sydney*
Pearson Education Singapore, Pte. Ltd.
Pearson Education North Asia Ltd., *Hong Kong*
Pearson Education Canada, Inc., *Toronto*
Pearson Educación de Mexico, S.A. de C.V.
Pearson Education—Japan, *Tokyo*
Pearson Education Malaysia, Pte. Ltd.

CONTENTS

Ch. 1 Introduction to Statistics

1.1 An Overview of Statistics

Solve the problem.

1) Explain the difference between a sample and a population.

2) Which is used more often, a sample or a population? Why?

3) A recent survey by the alumni of a major university indicated that the average salary of 8000 of its 250,000 graduates was $120,000. Does this value describe a population parameter or a sample statistic? Explain your reasoning.

4) The average salary of all General Motors workers is $42,500. Does this value describe a population parameter or a sample statistic? Explain your reasoning.

5) A survey of 1756 students was taken from a university with 13,000 students. Does this value describe a population parameter or a sample statistic? Explain your reasoning.

6) A survey of 1999 American households found that 94% of the households own a computer. Identify the population and the sample.

7) A survey of 1406 American households found that 79% of the households own two cars. Identify the population and the sample.

8) The average age of the students in a statistics class is 20 years. Does this statement describe:

   A) descriptive statistics?   B) inferential statistics?

9) The chances of winning the California Lottery are one chance in twenty-two million. Does this statement describe:

   A) descriptive statistics?   B) inferential statistics?

10) There is a relationship between smoking cigarettes and getting emphysema. Does this statement describe:

   A) descriptive statistics?   B) inferential statistics?

11) From past figures, it is predicted that 24% of the registered voters in California will vote in the June primary. Does this statement describe:

   A) inferential statistics?   B) descriptive statistics?

12) A survey of 2625 elementary school children found that 28% of the children could be classified as obese. Identify the population and the sample.

13) Based on previous clients, a marriage counselor concludes that the majority of marriages that begin with cohabitation before marriage will result in divorce. Does this statement describe inferential statistics or descriptive statistics?

   A) descriptive statistics   B) inferential statistics

1.2 Data Classification

Solve the problem.

1) Classify the colors of automobiles on a used car lot as qualitative data or quantitative data.

A) quantitative data   B) qualitative data

2) Classify the number of complaint letters received by the United States Postal Service in a given day as qualitative data or quantitative data.

A) qualitative data   B) quantitative data

3) Classify the number of seats in a movie theater as qualitative data or quantitative data.

A) qualitative data   B) quantitative data

4) Classify the numbers on the shirts of a girl's soccer team as qualitative data or quantitative data.

A) qualitative data   B) quantitative data

5) Identify the level of measurement for data that can be classified according to color.

A) ratio   B) ordinal   C) nominal   D) interval

6) Identify the level of measurement for data that are the numbers on the shirts of a girl's soccer team.

A) nominal   B) interval   C) ordinal   D) ratio

7) Identify the level of measurement for data that are the ages of students in a statistic class.

A) nominal   B) ordinal   C) ratio   D) interval

8) Identify the level of measurement for data that are the temperature of 60 refrigerators.

A) ratio   B) ordinal   C) interval   D) nominal

9) Identify the level of measurement for data that are the number of milligrams of tar in 37 cigarettes.

A) interval   B) ratio   C) nominal   D) ordinal

10) Identify the level of measurement for data that are the number of pages in your statistics book.

A) interval   B) nominal   C) ordinal   D) ratio

11) Identify the level of measurement for data that can be classified by marriage status (married, single, or divorced.)

A) interval   B) ordinal   C) nominal   D) ratio

12) Identify the level of measurement for data that are a list of 1275 social security numbers.

A) nominal   B) ratio   C) interval   D) ordinal

13) Identify the level of measurement for data that are the ratings of a movie ranging from poor to good to excellent.

A) nominal   B) ratio   C) ordinal   D) interval

14) Identify the level of measurement for data that are the final grades (A, B, C, D, and F) for students in a statistics class.

A) nominal   B) ordinal   C) ratio   D) interval

15) Identify the level of measurement for data that are the annual salaries for all teachers in California.

    A) interval   B) ordinal   C) nominal   D) ratio

16) Identify the level of measurement for data that are a list of zip codes.

    A) interval   B) nominal   C) ratio   D) ordinal

17) Identify the level of measurement for data that are the nationalities listed in a recent survey (for example, Asian, European, or Hispanic).

    A) nominal   B) ordinal   C) ratio   D) interval

18) Identify the level of measurement for data that are the amount of fat (in grams) in 26 cookies.

    A) nominal   B) interval   C) ratio   D) ordinal

19) Identify the level of measurement for data that are the years the summer Olympics were held in the United States.

    A) ordinal   B) ratio   C) nominal   D) interval

20) The numbers of touchdowns scored by a major university in five randomly selected games are given below. Identify the level of measurement.

2   4   3   5   1

    A) ratio   B) interval   C) ordinal   D) nominal

21) The average daily temperatures (in degrees Fahrenheit) on five randomly selected days are given below. Identify the level of measurement.

22 21 31 36 21

    A) ordinal   B) ratio   C) nominal   D) interval

22) A survey of 2625 elementary school children found that 28% of the children could be classified as obese. Identify the population and the sample.

23) Based on previous clients, a marriage counselor concludes that the majority of marriages that begin with cohabitation before marriage will result in divorce. Does this statement describe inferential statistics or descriptive statistics?

    A) inferential statistics   B) descriptive statistics

24) Identify the level of measurement of the data listed on the horizontal axis in the graph.

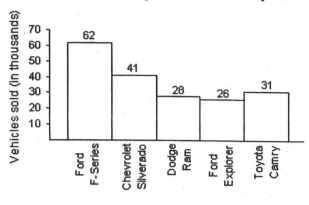

Five Top-Selling Vehicles in January 2004

A) ratio   B) ordinal   C) interval   D) nominal

25) Identify the level of measurement of the data listed on the horizontal axis in the graph.

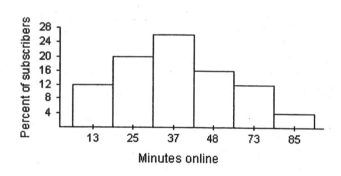

Internet Usage

A) nominal   B) ordinal   C) interval   D) ratio

1.3 Experimental Design

Solve the problem.

1) What method of data collection would you use to collect data for a study where a drug was given to 10 patients and a placebo to another group of 10 patients to determine if the drug has an effect on a patient's illness?

A) use sampling   B) take a census
C) perform an experiment   D) use a simulation

2) What method of data collection would you use to collect data for a study of the salaries of college professors at a particular college?

A) use a simulation   B) perform an experiment
C) use sampling   D) take a census

3) What method of data collection would you use to collect data for a study where a political pollster wishes to determine if his candidate is leading in the polls?

A) use a simulation   B) perform an experiment
C) take a census   D) use sampling

4) What method of data collection would you use to collect data for a study where you would like to determine the chance getting three girls in a family of three children?

    A) take a census   B) use a simulation

    C) perform an experiment   D) use sampling

5) Thirty-five sophomores, 69 juniors and 24 seniors are randomly selected from 461 sophomores, 328 juniors and 558 seniors at a certain high school. What sampling technique is used?

    A) stratified   B) cluster   C) convenience   D) systematic   E) random

6) Every fifth teenager entering a concert is checked for possession of drugs. What sampling technique is used?

    A) stratified   B) cluster   C) random   D) convenience   E) systematic

7) At a local community college, five statistics classes are randomly selected and all of the students from each class are interviewed. What sampling technique is used?

    A) systematic   B) convenience   C) stratified   D) random   E) cluster

8) A researcher randomly selects and interviews fifty male and fifty female teachers. What sampling technique is used?

    A) random   B) cluster   C) stratified   D) convenience   E) systematic

9) A researcher for an airline interviews all of the passengers on five randomly selected flights. What sampling technique is used?

    A) cluster   B) systematic   C) stratified   D) random   E) convenience

10) A community college student interviews everyone in a statistics class to determine who owns a car. What sampling technique is used?

    A) cluster   B) stratified   C) systematic   D) random   E) convenience

11) Based on 8000 responses from 32,500 questionnaires sent to its alumni, a major university estimated that the annual salary of its alumni was $103,000 per year. What sampling technique is used?

    A) random   B) stratified   C) systematic   D) convenience   E) cluster

12) In a recent television survey, participants were asked to answer "yes" or "no" to the question "Are you in favor of the death penalty?" Six thousand five hundred responded "yes" while 4000 responded "no". There was a fifty-cent charge for the call. What sampling technique was used?

    A) cluster   B) convenience   C) stratified   D) systematic   E) random

13) A lobbyist for a major airspace firm assigns a number to each legislator and then uses a computer to randomly generate ten numbers. The lobbyist contacts the legislators corresponding to these numbers. What sampling technique was used?

    A) convenience   B) cluster   C) stratified   D) random   E) systematic

14) To ensure customer satisfaction, every 5th phone call received by customer service will be monitored. What sampling technique was used?

    A) random   B) stratified   C) cluster   D) convenience   E) systematic

15) A market researcher randomly selects 500 drivers under 35 years of age and 300 drivers over 35 years of age. What sampling technique was used?

    A) cluster   B) convenience   C) systematic   D) stratified   E) random

16) To avoid working late, the quality control manager inspects the last 40 items produced that day. What sampling technique was used?

    A) cluster   B) convenience   C) systematic   D) random   E) stratified

17) The names of 70 contestants are written on 70 cards. The cards are placed in a bag, and three names are picked from the bag. What sampling technique was used?

    A) stratified   B) random   C) convenience   D) systematic   E) cluster

18) A researcher for a publisher randomly selects 85 of the nation's middle schools and interviews all of the teachers at each school. What sampling technique was used?

    A) random   B) cluster   C) systematic   D) convenience   E) stratified

19) A report sponsored by the California Citrus Commission concluded that cholesterol levels can be lowered by drinking at least one glass of a citrus product each day. Determine if the report is biased.

20) A local newspaper ran a survey by asking, "Do you support the deployment of a weapon that could kill millions of innocent people?" Determine whether the survey question is biased.

21) After a hurricane, a disaster area is divided into 200 equal grids. Thirty of the grids are selected and every occupied household in the grid is interviewed to help focus relief efforts. Select the numbers of the first five grids that belong to the cluster sample.

    16348   76938   90169   51392   55887   71015   09209   79157

22) There are 750 incoming freshmen attending a university this fall. A researcher wishes to send questionnaires to a sample of 30 of them to complete regarding their drinking habits. Select the numbers of the first five freshmen who belong to the simple random sample.

    16348   76938   90169   51392   55887   71015   09209   79157

23) A college employs 85 faculty members. Without replacement, select the numbers of the five members who will serve on the tenure committee next year.

    16348   76938   90169   51392   55887   71015   09209   79157

24) Of the 5000 outpatients released from a local hospital in the past year, one hundred were contacted and asked their opinion on the care they received. Select the first five patients who belong to the simple random sample.

    16348   76938   90169   51392   55887   71015   09209   79157

Ch. 1 Introduction to Statistics
Answer Key

1.1 An Overview of Statistics
1) A population is the collection of all elements in a population. A sample is a subset of the elements in the population.
2) Sample. It is usually impractical to obtain all the population data.
3) Sample statistic because the number $120,000 is based on a subset of the population.
4) Population parameter because the $42,500 is based on all the workers at GM.
5) Sample statistic because the number 1756 is based on a subset of the population.
6) population: collection of American households; sample: collection of 1999 American households surveyed
7) population: collection of American households; sample: collection of 1406 American households surveyed
8) A
9) B
10) B
11) A
12) population: elementary school children; sample: collection of 2625 elementary school children surveyed.
13) B

1.2 Data Classification
1) B
2) B
3) B
4) A
5) C
6) A
7) C
8) C
9) B
10) D
11) C
12) A
13) C
14) B
15) D
16) B
17) A
18) C
19) D
20) A
21) D
22) population: elementary school children; sample: collection of 2625 elementary school children surveyed.
23) A
24) A
25) D

1.3 Experimental Design
1) C
2) D
3) D
4) B
5) A
6) E
7) E
8) C
9) A
10) E

11) A

12) B

13) D

14) E

15) D

16) B

17) B

18) B

19) A report sponsored by the citrus industry is much more likely to reach conclusions favorable to the industry.

20) The wording of the question is biased, as it tends to encourage negative responses.

21) 163, 169, 15, 92, 97

22) 163, 487, 693, 169, 513

23) 16, 34, 69, 38, 13

24) 1634, 3890, 1695, 1392, 1509

Ch. 2 Descriptive Statistics

2.1 Frequency Distributions and Their Graphs

Solve the problem.

1) Identify the class width used in the frequency distribution.

Height (in inches)	Frequency
50 – 52	5
53 – 55	8
56 – 58	12
59 – 61	13
62 – 64	11

A) 5   B) 3   C) 2   D) 51

2) Identify the midpoint of the first class.

Height (in inches)	Frequency
50 – 52	5
53 – 55	8
56 – 58	12
59 – 61	13
62 – 64	11

A) 49.5   B) 50   C) 51   D) 52

3) Identify the class boundaries of the first class.

Height (in inches)	Frequency
50 – 52	5
53 – 55	8
56 – 58	12
59 – 61	13
62 – 64	11

A) 49 – 53   B) 49.5 – 52.5   C) 50 – 52   D) 50 – 64

4) Identify the class width used in the frequency distribution.

Phone Calls (per day)	Frequency
8 – 11	18
12 – 15	23
16 – 19	38
20 – 23	47
24 – 27	32

A) 3   B) 8   C) 4   D) 11

5) Identify the midpoint of the first class.

Phone Calls (per day)	Frequency
8 – 11	18
12 – 15	23
16 – 19	38
20 – 23	47
24 – 27	32

A) 9   B) 8   C) 22   D) 9.5

6) Identify the class boundaries of the first class.

Phone Calls (per day)	Frequency
8 – 11	18
12 – 15	23
16 – 19	38
20 – 23	47
24 – 27	32

A) 8 – 11   B) 7.5 – 11.5   C) 7 – 12   D) 7.9 – 22.9

7) Identify the class width used in the frequency distribution.

Weight (in pounds)	Frequency
135 – 139	6
140 – 144	4
145 – 149	11
150 – 154	15
155 – 160	8

A) 135   B) 6   C) 5   D) 4

8) Identify the midpoint of the first class.

Weight (in pounds)	Frequency
135 – 139	6
140 – 144	4
145 – 149	11
150 – 154	15
155 – 160	8

A) 135   B) 137   C) 139   D) 11

9) Identify the class boundaries of the first class.

Weight (in pounds)	Frequency
135 – 139	6
140 – 144	4
145 – 149	11
150 – 154	15
155 – 160	8

A) 135 – 159   B) 134.5 – 139.5   C) 135 – 139   D) 134.9 – 139.9

10) Identify the class width used in the frequency distribution.

Miles (per day)	Frequency
1 – 2	9
3 – 4	22
5 – 6	28
7 – 8	15
9 – 10	4

A) 3   B) 2   C) 1   D) 9

11) Identify the midpoint of the first class.

Miles (per day)	Frequency
1 – 2	9
3 – 4	22
5 – 6	28
7 – 8	15
9 – 10	4

A) 5.5   B) 1.5   C) 5   D) 28

12) Identify the class width used in the frequency distribution.

Miles (per day)	Frequency
1 – 7	3
8 – 14	27
15 – 21	29
22 – 28	27

A) 14   B) 6   C) 8   D) 7

13) For the data below, construct a frequency histogram, a relative frequency histogram and a frequency polygon.

Height (in inches)	Frequency
50 – 52	5
53 – 55	8
56 – 58	12
59 – 61	13
62 – 64	11

14) For the data below, construct a frequency histogram, a relative frequency histogram and a frequency polygon.

Weight (in pounds)	Frequency
135 – 139	6
140 – 144	4
145 – 149	11
150 – 154	15
155 – 159	8

15) For the data below, construct a cumulative frequency distribution and an ogive.

Phone Calls (per day)	Frequency
8 – 11	18
12 – 15	23
16 – 19	38
20 – 23	47
24 – 27	32

16) For the data below, construct a cumulative frequency distribution and an ogive.

Height (in inches)	Frequency
50 – 52	5
53 – 55	8
56 – 58	12
59 – 61	13
62 – 64	11

17) For the data below, construct a cumulative frequency distribution and an ogive.

Weight (in pounds)	Frequency
135 – 139	6
140 – 144	4
145 – 149	11
150 – 154	15
155 – 159	8

18) For the data below, construct a cumulative frequency distribution and an ogive.

Miles (per day)	Frequency
1 – 2	9
3 – 4	22
5 – 6	28
7 – 8	15
9 – 10	4

19) A city in the Pacific Northwest recorded its highest temperature at 82 degrees Fahrenheit and its ⌐ ⌐est temperature at 23 degrees Fahrenheit for a particular year. Use this information to find the upper anu ⌐wer limits of the first class if you wish to construct a frequency distribution with 10 classes.

A) 23–27   B) 18–28   C) 23–28   D) 23–29

20) A sample of candies have weights that vary from 2.35 grams to 4.75 grams. Use this information to find the upper and lower limits of the first class if you wish to construct a frequency distribution with 12 classes.

A) 2.35–2.54   B) 2.35–2.65   C) 2.35–2.55   D) 2.35–2.75

21) The grade point averages for 40 students are listed below. Construct a frequency distribution, a relative frequency distribution, and a cumulative frequency distribution using eight classes.

2.0 3.2 1.8 2.9 0.9 4.0 3.3 2.9 3.6 0.8
3.1 2.4 2.4 2.3 1.6 1.6 4.0 3.1 3.2 1.8
2.2 2.2 1.7 0.5 3.6 3.4 1.9 2.0 3.0 1.1
3.0 4.0 4.0 2.1 1.9 1.1 0.5 3.2 3.0 2.2

22) The grade point averages for 40 students are listed below. Construct a frequency histogram, a relative frequency histogram and a frequency polygon using eight classes.

2.0 3.2 1.8 2.9 0.9 4.0 3.3 2.9 3.6 0.8
3.1 2.4 2.4 2.3 1.6 1.6 4.0 3.1 3.2 1.8
2.2 2.2 1.7 0.5 3.6 3.4 1.9 2.0 3.0 1.1
3.0 4.0 4.0 2.1 1.9 1.1 0.5 3.2 3.0 2.2

23) The grade point averages for 40 students are listed below. Construct an ogive using eight classes.

2.0 3.2 1.8 2.9 0.9 4.0 3.3 2.9 3.6 0.8
3.1 2.4 2.4 2.3 1.6 1.6 4.0 3.1 3.2 1.8
2.2 2.2 1.7 0.5 3.6 3.4 1.9 2.0 3.0 1.1
3.0 4.0 4.0 2.1 1.9 1.1 0.5 3.2 3.0 2.2

24) The heights (in inches) of 30 adult males are listed below. Construct a frequency distribution, a relative frequency distribution, and a cumulative frequency distribution using five classes.

70 72 71 70 69 73 69 68 70 71
67 71 70 74 69 68 71 71 71 72
69 71 68 67 73 74 70 71 69 68

25) The heights (in inches) of 30 adult males are listed below. Construct a frequency histogram using five classes.

70 72 71 70 69 73 69 68 70 71
67 71 70 74 69 68 71 71 71 72
69 71 68 67 73 74 70 71 69 68

26) The heights (in inches) of 30 adult males are listed below. Construct a relative frequency histogram using five classes.

70 72 71 70 69 73 69 68 70 71
67 71 70 74 69 68 71 71 71 72
69 71 68 67 73 74 70 71 69 68

Elementary Statistics 13

27) The heights (in inches) of 30 adult males are listed below. Construct a frequency polygon using five classes.

70 72 71 70 69 73 69 68 70 71
67 71 70 74 69 68 71 71 71 72
69 71 68 67 73 74 70 71 69 68

28) The heights (in inches) of 30 adult males are listed below. Construct a ogive using five classes.

70 72 71 70 69 73 69 68 70 71
67 71 70 74 69 68 71 71 71 72
69 71 68 67 73 74 70 71 69 68

29) The Highway Patrol, using radar, checked the speeds (in mph) of 30 passing motorists at a checkpoint. The results are listed below. Construct a frequency distribution, a relative frequency distribution, and a cumulative frequency distribution using six classes.

44 38 41 50 36 36 43 42 49 48
35 40 37 41 43 50 45 45 39 38
50 41 47 36 35 40 42 43 48 33

30) The Highway Patrol, using radar, checked the speeds (in mph) of 30 passing motorists at a checkpoint. The results are listed below. Construct a frequency histogram, a relative frequency histogram and a frequency polygon using six classes.

44 38 41 50 36 36 43 42 49 48
35 40 37 41 43 50 45 45 39 38
50 41 47 36 35 40 42 43 48 33

31) The Highway Patrol, using radar, checked the speeds (in mph) of 30 passing motorists at a checkpoint. The results are listed below. Construct an ogive using six classes.

44 38 41 50 36 36 43 42 49 48
35 40 37 41 43 50 45 45 39 38
50 41 47 36 35 40 42 43 48 33

32) Listed below are the ACT scores of 40 randomly selected students at a major university.

18 22 13 15 24 24 20 19 19 12
16 25 14 19 21 23 25 18 18 13
26 26 25 25 19 17 18 15 13 21
19 19 14 24 20 21 23 22 19 17

a) Construct a relative frequency histogram of the data, using eight classes.
b) If the university wants to accept the top 90% of the applicants, what should the minimum score be?
c) If the university sets the minimum score at 17, what percent of the applicants will be accepted?

33) Use the ogive below to approximate the number in the sample.

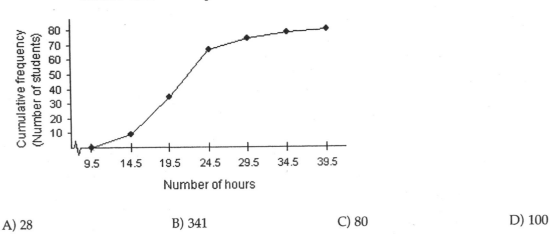

Leisure Time of College Students

A) 28   B) 341   C) 80   D) 100

34) Use the ogive below to approximate the cumulative frequency for 24 hours.

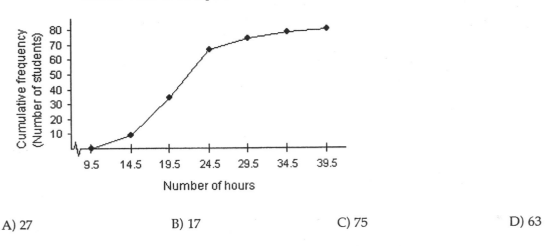

Leisure Time of College Students

A) 27   B) 17   C) 75   D) 63

2.2   More Graphs and Displays

Solve the problem.

1) The numbers of home runs that Sammy Sosa hit in the first 15 years of his major league baseball career are listed below. Make a stem–and–leaf plot for this data.

4   15   10   8   33   25   36   40   36   66   63   50   64   49   40

2) The numbers of home runs that Barry Bonds hit in the first 18 years of his major league baseball career are listed below. Make a stem–and–leaf plot for this data.

16   25   24   19   33   25   34   46   37
33   42   40   37   34   49   73   46   45

3) For the stem-and-leaf plot below, what is the maximum and what is the minimum entry?

```
1 | 2 3
1 | 6 6 6 7 8 9
2 | 0 1 1 2 3 4 4 5 6 6
2 | 7 7 7 8 8 9 9 9
3 | 0 1 1 2 3 4 4 5 5
3 | 6 6 6 7 8 8 9 9
4 | 2 7
```

    A) max: 9; min: 0   B) max: 42; min: 12   C) max: 39; min: 13   D) max: 47; min: 12

4) For the dot plot below, what is the maximum and what is the minimum entry?

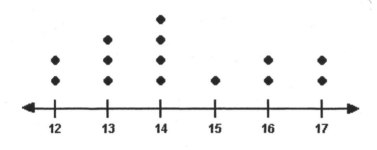

    A) max: 17; min: 12   B) max: 54; min: 12   C) max: 54; min: 15   D) max: 14; min: 12

5) The heights (in inches) of 30 adult males are listed below. Construct a stem-and-leaf chart for the data.

```
70  72  71  70  69  73  69  68  70  71
67  71  70  74  69  68  71  71  71  72
69  71  68  67  73  74  70  71  69  68
```

6) The Highway Patrol, using radar, checked the speeds (in mph) of 30 passing motorists at a checkpoint. The results are listed below. Construct a stem-and-leaf plot for the data.

```
44  38  41  50  36  36  43  42  49  48
35  40  37  41  43  50  45  45  39  38
50  41  47  36  35  40  42  43  48  33
```

7) The Highway Patrol, using radar, checked the speeds (in mph) of 30 passing motorists at a checkpoint. The results are listed below. Construct a dot plot for the data.

```
44  38  41  50  36  36  43  42  49  48
35  40  37  41  43  50  45  45  39  38
50  41  47  36  35  40  42  43  48  33
```

8) The heights (in inches) of 30 adult males are listed below. Construct a dot plot for the data.

```
70  72  71  70  69  73  69  68  70  71
67  71  70  74  69  68  71  71  71  72
69  71  68  67  73  74  70  71  69  68
```

9) A study was conducted to determine how people get jobs. Four hundred subjects were randomly selected and the results are listed below.

Job Sources of Survey Respondents	Frequency
Newspaper want ads	72
Online services	124
Executive search firms	69
Mailings	32
Networking	103

Construct a pie chart of the data.

10) A study was conducted to determine how people get jobs. Four hundred subjects were randomly selected and the results are listed below.

Job Sources of Survey Respondents	Frequency
Newspaper want ads	72
Online services	124
Executive search firms	69
Mailings	32
Networking	103

Construct a Pareto chart of the data.

11) The heights (in inches) of 30 adult males are listed below. Construct a Pareto chart for the data.

```
70  72  71  70  69  73  69  68  70  71
67  71  70  74  69  68  71  71  71  72
69  71  68  67  73  74  70  71  69  68
```

12) Use a scatter plot to display the data below. All measurements are in milligrams per cigarette.

Brand	Tar	Nicotine
Benson & Hedges	16	1.2
Lucky Strike	13	1.1
Marlboro	16	1.2
Viceroy	18	1.4
True	6	0.6

13) The numbers of home runs that Barry Bonds hit in the first 10 years of his major league baseball career are listed below. Use a scatter plot to display the data. Is there a relationship between the home runs and the batting averages?

Home Runs	16	25	24	19	33	25	34	46	37	33
Batting Average	.223	.261	.283	.248	.301	.292	.311	.336	.312	.294

14) The data below represent the numbers of absences and the final grades of 15 randomly selected students from a statistics class. Use a scatter plot to display the data. Is there a relationship between the students' absences and their final grades?

Student	Number of Absences	Final Grade as a Percent
1	5	79
2	6	78
3	2	86
4	12	56
5	9	75
6	5	90
7	8	78
8	15	48
9	0	92
10	1	78
11	9	81
12	3	86
13	10	75
14	3	89
15	11	65

15) The data below represent the infant mortality rates and the life expectancies for seven selected countries in Africa. Use a scatter plot to display the data.

Infant Mortality	63	199	71	61	67	35	194
Life Expectancy	45	31	51	47	39	70	37

16) The data below represent the smoking prevalence among U.S. adults over a 35–year period. Use a time series chart to display the data. Describe any trends shown.

Year	1965	1985	1990	1995	2000
Percent of Smokers	42	30	25	25	23

17) A safety engineer wishes to use the following data to show the number of deaths from the collision of passenger cars with trucks on a particular highway. Use a time series chart to display the data. Describe any trends shown.

Year	Number of Deaths
1930	12
1940	17
1950	22
1960	21
1970	16
1980	13
1990	11
2000	12

18) Women were allowed to enter the Boston Marathon for the first time in 1972. Listed below are the winning women's times (in minutes) for the first 10 years. Use a time series chart to display the data.

Year	1972	1973	1974	1975	1976	1977	1978	1979	1980	1981
Time	190	186	167	162	167	168	165	155	154	147

19) The five longest winning streaks for NCAA Men's Division I Basketball are listed below. Construct a Pareto chart for the data.

University	Number of Games
Indiana	57
San Francisco	51
UCLA	76
Marquette	56
Kentucky	54

20) The lengths, in kilometers, of the world's largest subway systems are listed below. Construct a Pareto chart for the data.

City	Length
Moscow	340
Paris	211
London	415
Tokyo	281
New York City	371

21) The number of beds in a sample of 24 hospitals are listed below. Construct a stem-and-leaf plot for the data.

149	167	162	127	130	180	160	167
221	145	137	194	207	150	254	262
244	287	137	204	166	174	180	151

22) The number of minutes that a dentist kept 20 patients waiting beyond their appointment times are listed below. Construct a stem-and-leaf plot for the data.

12.9	12.1	9.6	9.8	11.5	13.0	10.5	10.3	15.7	11.3
10.7	10.0	13.0	9.7	11.4	12.8	11.9	9.3	9.6	10.1

23) A study was conducted to determine how certain families pay on their credit card balances. Two hundred families with a household annual income between $25,000 and $49,999 were randomly selected and the results are listed below. Construct a pie chart of the data.

Payment schedule	Frequency
Almost always pay off balance	97
Sometimes pay off balance	41
Hardly ever pay off balance	62

24) Of the 55 tornado fatalities in a recent year, the locations of the victims are listed below. Construct a pie chart of the data.

Location	Fatalities
Mobile home	37
Permanent home	10
Vehicle	4
Business	2
Unknown	2

25) The data below represent the alcohol–related driving fatalities, in thousands, in the United States over a 20–year period. Use a time series chart to display the data. Describe any trends shown.

Year	1983	1985	1987	1989	1991	1993	1995	1997	1999	2001
Fatalities	25	23	24	22	20	18	18	17	17	17

2.3 Measures of Central Tendency

Solve the problem.

1) Find the mean, median, and mode of the following numbers:

52 55 48 52 45 53 52 46 47 50

2) The top 14 speeds, in miles per hour, for Pro-Stock drag racing over the past two decades are listed below. Find the mean speed.

181.1 202.2 190.1 201.4 191.3 201.4 192.2
201.2 193.2 201.2 194.5 199.2 196.0 196.2

A) 210.9   B) 201.2   C) 195.8   D) 196.1

3) The scores of the top ten finishers in a recent LPGA Valley of the Stars Tournament are listed below. (Source: Los Angeles Times) Find the mean score.

71   67   67   72   76   72   73   68   72   72

A) 72   B) 68   C) 71   D) 67

4) The numbers of runs batted in that Sammy Sosa hit in the first 15 years of his major league baseball career are listed below. Find the mean and median number of runs batted in. Round the mean to the nearest whole number.

13   70   33   25   93   70   119   100
119   158   141   138   160   108   103

5) The numbers of home runs that Barry Bonds hit in the first 18 years of his major league baseball career are listed below. Find the mean and median number of home runs. Round the mean to the nearest whole number. Which measure of central tendency– the mean or the median– best represents the data? Explain your reasoning.

16   25   24   19   33   25   34   46   37
33   42   40   37   34   49   73   46   45

6) The top 14 speeds, in miles per hour, for Pro-Stock drag racing over the past two decades are listed below. Find the median speed.

181.1   202.2   190.1   201.4   191.3   201.4   192.2
201.2   193.2   201.2   194.5   199.2   196.0   196.2

   A) 192.2   B) 196.7   C) 196.1   D) 201.2

7) The scores of the top ten finishers in a recent LPGA Valley of the Stars Tournament are listed below. (Source: Los Angeles Times)

71 67 67 72 76 72 73 68 72 72

Find the median score.

   A) 72   B) 71   C) 67   D) 73

8) The top 14 speeds, in miles per hour, for Pro-Stock drag racing over the past two decades are listed below. Find the mode speed.

181.1   202.2   190.1   201.4   191.3   201.4   192.2
201.2   193.2   201.2   194.5   199.2   196.0   196.2

   A) 201.2   B) 201.4   C) bimodal   D) no mode

9) The scores of the top ten finishers in a recent LPGA Valley of the Stars Tournament are listed below. (Source: Los Angeles Times)

71 67 67 72 76 72 73 68 72 72

Find the mode score.

   A) 67   B) 73   C) 72   D) 76

10) The amounts of money won by the top ten finishers in a recent Daytona 500 are listed below. Find the mean and median winnings. Round to the nearest dollar. Which measure– the mean or the median– best represents the data? Explain your reasoning.

$2,194,246 $464,084 $164,096 $199,209 $438,834
$613,659 $142,884 $240,731 $145,809 $290,596

11) A student receives test scores of 62, 83, and 91. The student's final exam score is 88 and homework score is 76. Each test is worth 20% of the final grade, the final exam is 25% of the final grade, and the homework grade is 15% of the final grade. What is the student's mean score in the class?

    A) 76.6   B) 85.6   C) 80.6   D) 90.6

12) Grade points are assigned as follows: A = 4, B = 3, C = 2, D = 1, and F = O. Grades are weighted according to credit hours. If a student receives an A in a four–unit class, a D in a two–unit class, a B in a three–unit class and a C in a three–unit class, what is the student's grade point average?

    A) 3.00   B) 2.75   C) 1.75   D) 2.50

13) For the following data, approximate the mean miles per day.

Miles (per day)	Frequency
1–2	21
3–4	8
5–6	15
7–8	13
9–10	6

    A) 6   B) 5   C) 4   D) 13

14) For the following data, approximate the mean number of phone calls per day.

Phone calls (per day)	Frequency
8–11	5
12–15	28
16–19	21
20–23	37
24–27	17

    A) 19   B) 17   C) 18   D) 22   E) 20

15) For the following data, approximate the mean weight.

Weight (in pounds)	Frequency
135–139	11
140–144	10
145–149	9
150–154	6
155–159	15

    A) 10   B) 149   C) 145   D) 147

16) The cost of five homes in a certain area is given.

$133,000 $141,000 $161,000 $131,000 $1,211,000

Which measure of central tendency should be used?

    A) mode   B) median   C) mean   D) midrange

17) The cost of five homes in a certain area is given.

$155,000 $163,000 $183,000 $153,000 $1,233,000

Which is the midrange?

   A) $1,080,000   B) $377,400   C) $163,000   D) $540,000

18) For the data below, construct a frequency histogram using five classes. Describe the shape of the histogram. The data set: California Pick Three Lottery

3 6 7 6 0 6 1 7 8 4
1 5 7 5 9 1 5 3 9 9
2 2 3 0 8 8 4 0 2 4

   A) symmetric   B) negatively skewed   C) uniform   D) positively skewed

19) For the data below, construct a frequency histogram using five classes. Describe the shape of the histogram. The data set: ages of 20 cars randomly selected in a student parking lot

12   6   4   9 11   1   7   8   9   8
 9 13   5 15   7   6   8   8   2   1

   A) symmetric   B) negatively skewed   C) positively skewed   D) uniform

20) For the data below, construct a frequency histogram using five classes. Describe the shape of the histogram. The data set: systolic blood pressures of 20 randomly selected patients at a blood bank

135 120 115 132 136 124 119 145   98 110
125 120 115 130 140 105 116 121 125 108

   A) positively skewed   B) negatively skewed   C) symmetric   D) uniform

21) Use the histogram below to approximate the mode heart rate of adults in the gym.

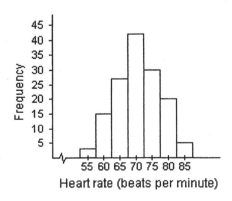

Heart Rates of Adults

   A) 2   B) 55   C) 70   D) 42

22) Use the histogram below to approximate the median heart rate of adults in the gym.

Heart Rates of Adults

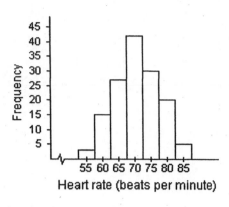

A) 65   B) 42   C) 70   D) 75

23) Use the histogram below to approximate the mean heart rate of adults in the gym.

Heart Rates of Adults

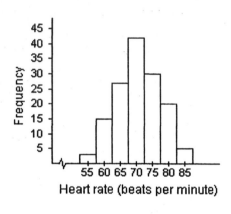

A) 70   B) 1425.7   C) 31.6   D) 70.8

2.4 Measures of Variation

Solve the problem.

1) For the stem–and–leaf plot below, find the range of the data set.

```
1 | 2 5
2 | 6 6 6 7 8 9
2 | 7 7 7 8 8 9 9 9
3 | 0 1 1 2 3 4 4 5
3 | 6 6 6 7 8 8 9
4 | 0 1
```

A) 41   B) 12   C) 33   D) 29

2) Find the range of the data set represented by the graph.

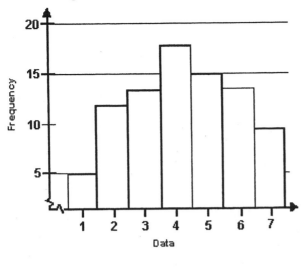

A) 17   B) 6   C) 5   D) 20

3) The grade point averages for 10 students are listed below. Find the range of the data.

2.0 3.2 1.8 2.9 0.9 4.0 3.3 2.9 3.6 0.8

A) 1.4   B) 2.8   C) 3.2   D) 2.45

4) The heights (in inches) of 20 adult males are listed below. Find the range of the data.

70 72 71 70 69 73 69 68 70 71
67 71 70 74 69 68 71 71 71 72

A) 5   B) 6.5   C) 6   D) 7

5) The heights (in inches) of 10 adult males are listed below. Find the sample standard deviation.

70 72 71 70 69 73 69 68 70 71

A) 1.49   B) 3   C) 2.38   D) 70

6) The heights (in inches) of 10 adult males are listed below. Find the population standard deviation and the population variance.

70 72 71 70 69 73 69 68 70 71

7) In a random sample, 10 students were asked to compute the distance they travel one way to school to the nearest tenth of a mile. The data is listed below. Compute the range, sample standard deviation and sample variance of the data.

1.1 5.2 3.6 5.0 4.8 1.8 2.2 5.2 1.5 0.8

8) You need to purchase a battery for your car. There are two types available. Type A has a mean life of five years and a standard deviation of one year. Type B has a mean life of five years and a standard deviation of one month. Both batteries cost the same. Which one should you purchase? Explain your reasoning.

Elementary Statistics 25

9) Here are the batting averages of Sammy Sosa and Barry Bonds for 13 recent years. Which player is more consistent? Explain your reasoning.

Sammy Sosa .203 .260 .261 .300 .268 .273 .251 .308 .288 .320 .328 .288 .279
Barry Bonds .292 .311 .336 .312 .294 .308 .291 .303 .262 .306 .328 .370 .341

10) You are the maintenance engineer for a local high school. You must purchase fluorescent light bulbs for the classrooms. Should you choose Type A with $\mu = 3000$ hours and $\sigma = 200$ hours, or Type B with $\mu = 3000$ hours and $\sigma = 250$ hours?

11) Adult IQ scores have a bell-shaped distribution with a mean of 100 and a standard deviation of 15. Use the Empirical Rule to find the percentage of adults with scores between 70 and 130.

A) 100%   B) 95%   C) 68%   D) 99.7%

12) A placement exam for entrance into a math class yields a mean of 80 and a standard deviation of 10. The distribution of the scores is roughly bell-shaped. Use the Empirical Rule to find the percentage of scores that lie between 60 and 80.

A) 34%   B) 68%   C) 95%   D) 47.5%

13) The average IQ of students in a particular calculus class is 110, with a standard deviation of 5. The distribution is roughly bell-shaped. Use the Empirical Rule to find the percentage of students with an IQ above 120.

A) 11.15%   B) 2.5%   C) 13.5%   D) 15.85%

14) Heights of adult women have a mean of 63.6 in. and a standard deviation of 2.5 in. What does Chebyshev's Theorem say about the percentage of women with heights between 58.6 in. and 68.6 in.?

15) Heights of adult women have a mean of 63.6 in. and a standard deviation of 2.5 in. What does Chebyshev's Theorem say about the percentage of women with heights between 56.1 in. and 71.1 in.?

16) A competency test has scores with a mean of 70 and a standard deviation of 6. A histogram of the data shows that the distribution is normal. Use the Empirical Rule to find the percentage of scores between 58 and 82.

A) 50%   B) 68%   C) 99.7%   D) 95%

17) Lengths of pregnancies of humans are normally distributed with a mean of 270 days and a standard deviation of 12 days. Use the Empirical Rule to determine the percentage of women whose pregnancies are between 258 and 282 days.

A) 68%   B) 50%   C) 99.7%   D) 95%

18) SAT verbal scores are normally distributed with a mean of 460 and a standard deviation of 91. Use the Empirical Rule to determine what percent of the scores lie between 460 and 551.

A) 49.9%   B) 34%   C) 47.5%   D) 68%

19) SAT verbal scores are normally distributed with a mean of 404 and a standard deviation of 95. Use the Empirical Rule to determine what percent of the scores lie between 309 and 404.

A) 47.5%   B) 68%   C) 49.9%   D) 34%

20) SAT verbal scores are normally distributed with a mean of 422 and a standard deviation of 96. Use the Empirical Rule to determine what percent of the scores lie between 422 and 614.

    A) 49.9%   B) 47.5%   C) 68%   D) 34%

21) SAT verbal scores are normally distributed with a mean of 444 and a standard deviation of 95. Use the Empirical Rule to determine what percent of the scores lie between 254 and 539.

    A) 83.9%   B) 68%   C) 34%   D) 81.5%

22) For the following data set, approximate the sample standard deviation.

Miles (per day)	Frequency
1–2	9
3–4	22
5–6	28
7–8	15
9–10	4

    A) 2.1   B) 1.6   C) 2.9   D) 5.1

23) For the following data set, approximate the sample standard deviation of phone calls per day.

Phone calls (per day)	Frequency
8–11	18
12–15	23
16–19	38
20–23	47
24–27	32

    A) 18.8   B) 5.1   C) 2.9   D) 3.2

24) For the following data set, approximate the sample standard deviation.

Height (in inches)	Frequency
50–52	5
53–55	8
56–58	12
59–61	13
62–64	11

    A) 3.85   B) 2.57   C) 1.86   D) 0.98

25) In a random sample, 10 students were asked to compute the distance they travel one way to school to the nearest tenth of a mile. The data is listed below. Compute the coefficient of variation.

    1.1 5.2 3.6 5.0 4.8 1.8 2.2 5.2 1.5 0.8

26) For the data below, find Pearson's index of skewness. The data set: The systolic blood pressures of 20 randomly selected patients at a blood bank.

    130 120 115 132 136 124 119 145   98 110
    125 120 115 130 140 105 116 121 125 108

27) In a random sample, 10 students were asked to compute the distance they travel one way to school to the nearest tenth of a mile. The data is listed below.

a) If a constant value k is added to each value, how will the standard deviation be affected?

b) If each value is multiplied by a constant k, how will the standard deviation be affected?

1.1 5.2 3.6 5.0 4.8 1.8 2.2 5.2 1.5 0.8

A) The standard deviation will be multiplied by the constant k.

B) The standard deviation will not be affected.

28) Without performing any calculations, use the stem-and-leaf plots to determine which statement is accurate.

(i) 0 | 9
     1 | 5 8
     2 | 3 3 7 7
     3 | 2 5
     4 | 1

(ii) 10 | 9
      11 | 5 8
      12 | 3 3 7 7
      13 | 2 5
      14 | 1

(iii) 0 |
       1 | 5
       2 | 3 3 3 3 7 7 7 7
       3 | 5
       4 |

A) Data set (ii) has the greatest standard deviation.

B) Data sets (i) and (ii) have the same standard deviation.

C) Data sets (i) and (iii) have the same range.

D) Data set (i) has the smallest standard deviation.

2.5 Measures of Position

Solve the problem.

1) The test scores of 30 students are listed below. Find Q_3.

```
31  41  45  48  52  55  56  56  63  65
67  67  69  70  70  74  75  78  79  79
80  81  83  85  85  87  90  92  95  99
```

A) 78   B) 83   C) 85   D) 31

2) The weights (in pounds) of 30 preschool children are listed below. Find Q_1.

```
25  25  26  26.5  27    27  27.5  28  28   28.5
29  29  30  30    30.5  31  31    32  32.5 32.5
33  33  34  34.5  35    35  37    37  38   38
```

A) 27   B) 25   C) 38   D) 28

3) A student's score on the SAT-1 placement test for U.S. history is in the 90th percentile. What can you conclude about the student's test score?

4) The weights (in pounds) of 30 preschool children are listed below. Find the interquartile range of the 30 weights listed below. What can you conclude from the result?

```
25  25  26  26.5  27    27  27.5  28  28   28.5
29  29  30  30    30.5  31  31    32  32.5 32.5
33  33  34  34.5  35    35  37    37  38   38
```

5) The cholesterol levels (in milligrams per deciliter) of 30 adults are listed below. Find D_6.

154 156 165 165 170 171 172 180 184 185
189 189 190 192 195 198 198 200 200 200
205 205 211 215 220 220 225 238 255 265

A) 171   B) 265   C) 205   D) 200

6) The test scores of 30 students are listed below. Find P_{30}.

31 41 45 48 52 55 56 56 63 65
67 67 69 70 70 74 75 78 79 79
80 81 83 85 85 87 90 92 95 99

A) 67   B) 56   C) 63   D) 90

7) The weights (in pounds) of 30 preschool children are listed below. Find D_7.

25 25 26 26.5 27 27 27.5 28 28 28.5
29 29 30 30 30.5 31 31 32 32.5 32.5
33 33 34 34.5 35 35 37 37 38 38

A) 27   B) 31   C) 33   D) 37

8) The cholesterol levels (in milligrams per deciliter) of 30 adults are listed below. Find Q_1.

154 156 165 165 170 171 172 180 184 185
189 189 190 192 195 198 198 200 200 200
205 205 211 215 220 220 225 238 255 265

A) 180   B) 171   C) 184.5   D) 200

9) The cholesterol levels (in milligrams per deciliter) of 30 adults are listed below. Find the interquartile range for the cholesterol level of the 30 adults.

154 156 165 165 170 171 172 180 184 185
189 189 190 192 195 198 198 200 200 200
205 205 211 215 220 220 225 238 255 265

A) 180   B) 31   C) 30   D) 211

10) A teacher gives a 20-point quiz to 10 students. The scores are listed below. What percentile corresponds to the score of 12?

20 8 10 7 15 16 12 19 14 9

A) 12   B) 13   C) 40   D) 25

11) In a data set with a minimum value of 54.5 and a maximum value of 98.6 with 300 observations, there are 186 points less than 81.2. Find the percentile for 81.2.

A) 53   B) 71   C) 68   D) 62

12) The cholesterol levels (in milligrams per deciliter) of 30 adults are listed below. Find the percentile that corresponds to cholesterol level of 195.

154 156 165 165 170 171 172 180 184 185
189 189 190 192 195 198 198 200 200 200
205 205 211 215 220 220 225 238 255 265

  A) 33   B) 58   C) 12   D) 50

13) The test scores of 30 students are listed below. Draw a box-and-whisker plot that represents the data.

31 41 45 48 52 55 56 56 63 65
67 67 69 70 70 74 75 78 79 79
80 81 83 85 85 87 90 92 95 99

14) The cholesterol levels (in milligrams per deciliter) of 30 adults are listed below. Draw a box-and-whisker plot that represents the data.

154 156 165 165 170 171 172 180 184 185
189 189 190 192 195 198 198 200 200 200
205 205 211 215 220 220 225 238 255 265

15) Find the z-score for the value 97, when the mean is 60 and the standard deviation is 7.

  A) $z = -1.50$ B) $z = 5.14$ C) $z = 1.50$ D) $z = 5.29$

16) Test scores for a history class had a mean of 79 with a standard deviation of 4.5. Test scores for a physics class had a mean of 69 with a standard deviation of 3.7. Suppose a student gets a 58 on the history test and a 100 on the physics test. Calculate the z-score for each test. On which test did the student perform better?

17) The ages of 10 grooms at their first marriage are listed below. Find the midquartile.

35.1 24.3 46.6 41.6 32.9 26.8 39.8 21.5 45.7 33.9

  A) 34.5   B) 34.2   C) 34.1   D) 43.7

18) Use the box-and-whisker plot below to determine which statement is accurate.

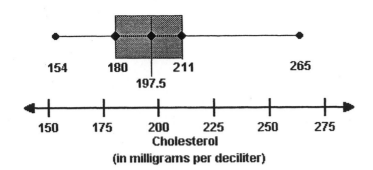

A) About 75% of the adults have cholesterol levels less than 180.

B) About 25% of the adults have cholesterol levels of at least 211.

C) One half of the cholesterol levels are between 180 and 211.

D) One half of the cholesterol levels are between 180 and 197.5.

19) The birth weights for twins are normally distributed with a mean of 2353 grams and a standard deviation of 647 grams. Use z-scores to determine which birth weight could be considered unusual.

A) 2353 g   B) 3600 g   C) 1200 g   D) 2000 g

20) For the mathematics part of the SAT the mean is 514 with a standard deviation of 113, and for the mathematics part of the ACT the mean is 20.6 with a standard deviation of 5.1. Bob scores a 660 on the SAT and a 27 on the ACT. Use z-scores to determine on which test he performed better.

A) SAT   B) ACT

Ch. 2 Descriptive Statistics
Answer Key

2.1 Frequency Distributions and Their Graphs

1) B
2) C
3) B
4) C
5) D
6) B
7) C
8) B
9) B
10) B
11) B
12) D
13)

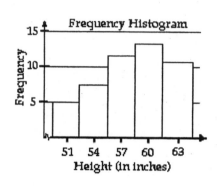

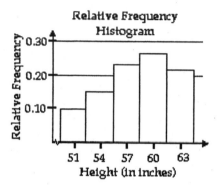

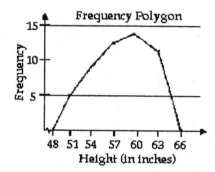

14)

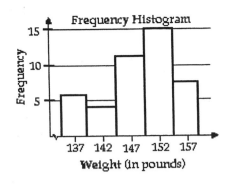

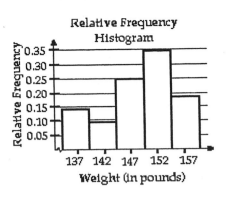

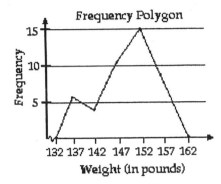

15)

Phone calls (per day)	Frequency	Cumulative Frequency
8 – 11	18	18
12 – 15	23	41
16 – 19	38	79
20 – 23	47	126
24 – 27	32	158

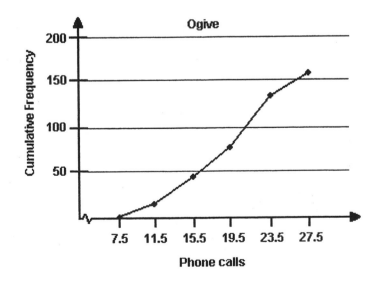

16)

Height (in inches)	Frequency	Cumulative Frequency
50 – 52	5	5
53 – 55	8	13
56 – 58	12	25
59 – 61	13	38
62 – 64	11	49

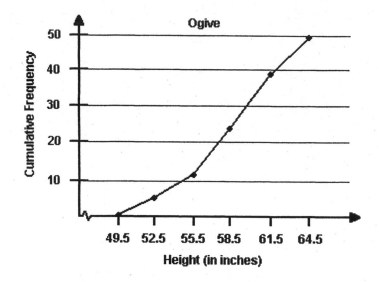

17)

Weight (in pounds)	Frequency	Cumulative Frequency
135 – 139	6	6
140 – 144	4	10
145 – 149	11	21
150 – 154	15	36
155 – 159	8	44

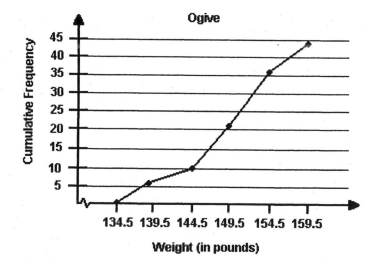

18)

Miles (per day)	Frequency	Cumulative Frequency
1 – 2	9	9
3 – 4	22	31
5 – 6	28	59
7 – 8	15	74
9 – 10	4	78

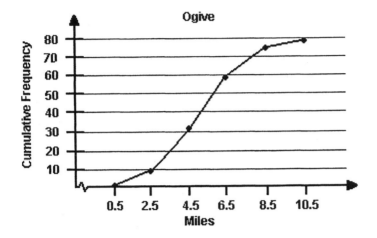

19) D

20) A

21)

GPA	Frequency	Relative Frequency	Cumulative Frequency
0.5–0.9	4	0.10	4
1.0–1.4	2	0.05	6
1.5–1.9	7	0.175	13
2.0–2.4	9	0.225	22
2.5–2.9	2	0.05	24
3.0–3.4	10	0.25	34
3.5–3.9	2	0.05	36
4.0–4.4	4	0.10	40

22)

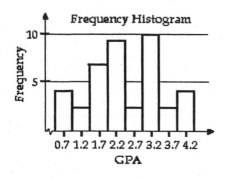

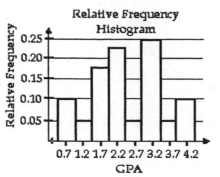

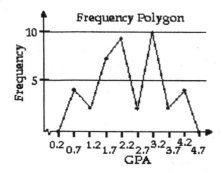

23)

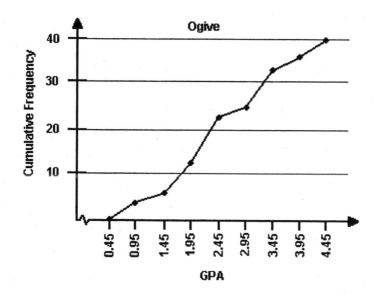

24)

Height (in inches)	Frequency	Relative Frequency	Cumulative Frequency
67.0–68.4	6	0.20	6
68.5–69.9	5	0.167	11
70.0–71.4	13	0.433	24
71.5–72.9	2	0.067	26
73.0–74.4	4	0.133	30

25)

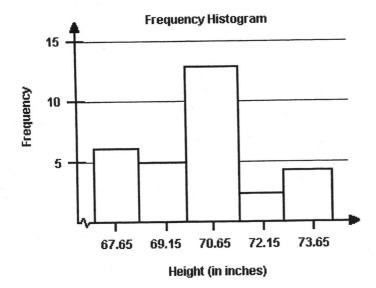

26)

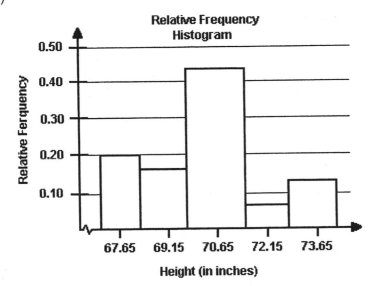

27)

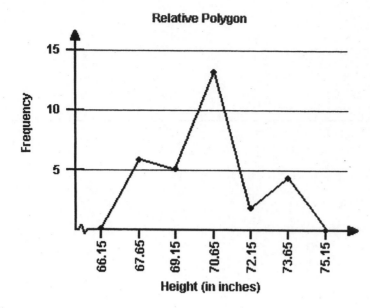

Relative Polygon

28)

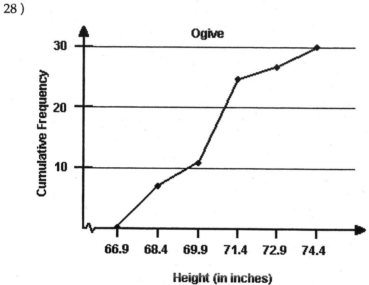

Ogive

29)

Speed (in mph)	Frequency	Relative Frequency	Cumulative Frequency
33–35	3	0.10	3
36–38	6	0.20	9
39–41	6	0.20	15
42–44	6	0.20	21
45–47	3	0.10	24
48–50	6	0.20	30

30)

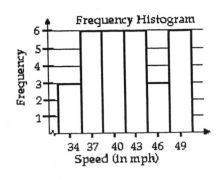

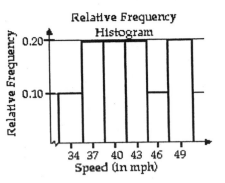

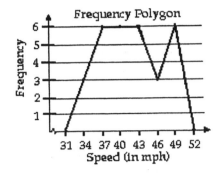

31)

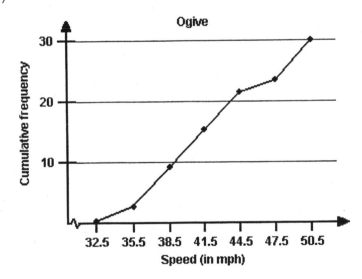

32) a) See graph below
    b) The minimum score = 14
    c) The university will accept 76.57% of the applicants.

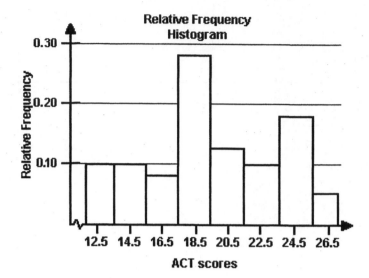

33) C
34) D

2.2 More Graphs and Displays

1)

```
0 | 4 8
1 | 0 5
2 | 5
3 | 3 6 6
4 | 0 0 9
5 | 0
6 | 3 4 6
```

2)

```
1 | 6 9
2 | 4 5 5
3 | 3 3 4 4 7 7
4 | 0 2 5 6 6 9
5 |
6 |
7 | 3
```

3) D
4) A
5)

```
6 | 7 7 8 8 8 8 9 9 9 9 9 9
7 | 0 0 0 0 0 1 1 1 1 1 1 1 1 2 2 3 3 4 4
```

6)

```
3 | 3 5 5 6 6 6 7 8 8 9
4 | 0 0 1 1 1 2 2 3 3 3 4 5 5 7 8 8 9
5 | 0 0 0
```

7)

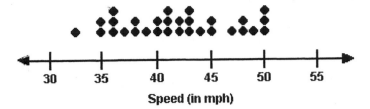

Speed (in mph)

Height (in inches)

8)

9)

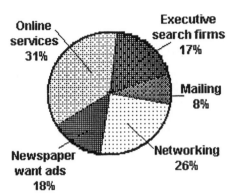

10)

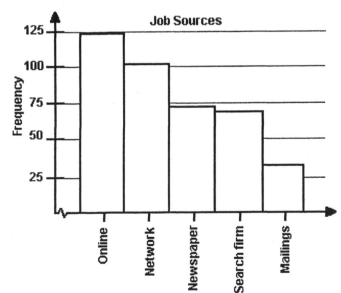

11)

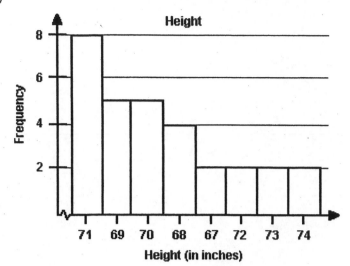

12)

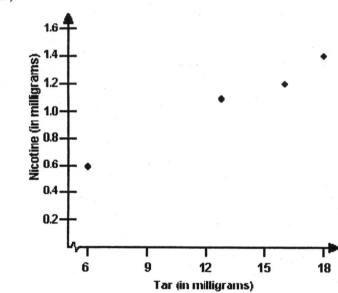

13)

Barry Bonds: Hitting Statistics

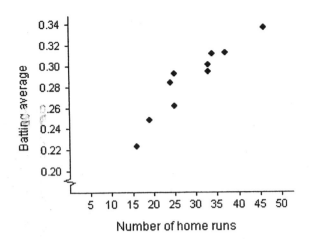

In general, there appears to be a relationship between the home runs and batting averages. As the number of home runs increased, the batting averages increased.

14)

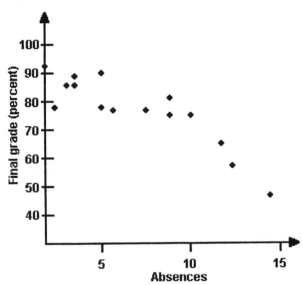

In general, there appears to be a relationship between the absences and the final grades. As the number of absences increased, the students' final grades decreased.

15)

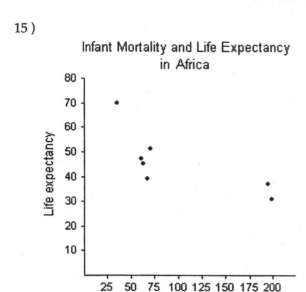

16)

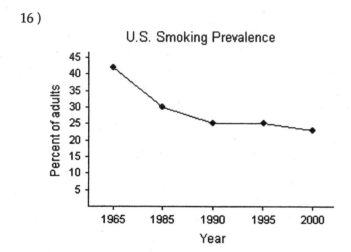

It appears the percent of U.S. adults who smoke is declining.

17)

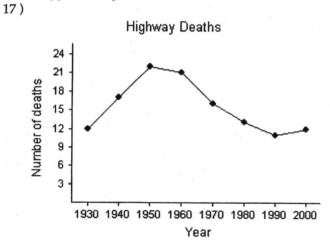

It appears the number of deaths peaked in 1950.

18)

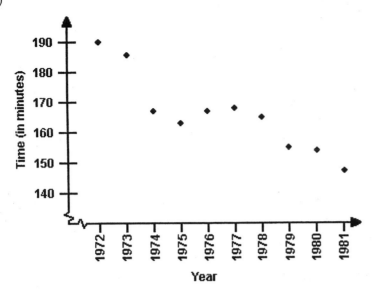

19)

NCAA Men's Basketball Winning Streaks

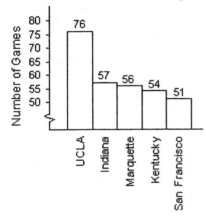

20)

World's Largest Subway Systems

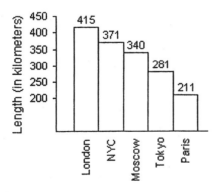

21)

```
12 | 7
13 | 0 7 7
14 | 5 9
15 | 0 1
16 | 0 2 6 7 7
17 | 4
18 | 0 0
19 | 4
20 | 4 7
21 |
22 | 1
23 |
24 | 4
25 | 4
26 | 2
27 |
28 | 7
```

22)

```
 9 | 3 6 6 7 8
10 | 0 1 3 5 7
11 | 3 4 5 9
12 | 1 8 9
13 | 0 0
14 |
15 | 7        Key: 9 | 3 = 9.3
```

23)

Credit Card Payment Habits

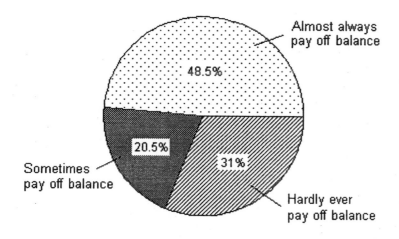

Almost always pay off balance 48.5%

Sometimes pay off balance 20.5%

Hardly ever pay off balance 31%

24)

U.S. Tornado Fatalities

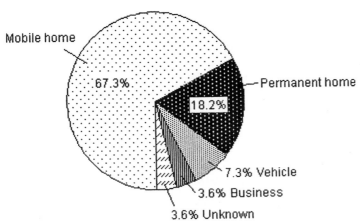

Mobile home

67.3%

18.2% ─ Permanent home

7.3% Vehicle

3.6% Business

3.6% Unknown

25) It appears the number of alcohol–related fatalities is gradually declining.

2.3 Measures of Central Tendency

1) mean 50, median 51, mode 52

2) C

3) C

4) mean: 97; median 103

5) mean: 37; median: 35.5; the median

6) C

7) A

8) C

9) C

10) mean: $489,415; median: $265,664; the median

11) C

12) B

13) B

14) A

15) D

16) B

17) D

18) C

19) A

20) C

21) C

22) C

23) D

2.4 Measures of Variation

1) D

2) B

3) C

4) D

5) A

6) $\sigma = 1.42$, $\sigma^2 = 2.01$

7) range = 4.4, s = 1.8, $s^2 = 3.324$

8) Battery Type B has less variation. As a result, it is less likely to fail before its mean life is up.

9) Sosa: $\bar{x} = 0.279$ and s = 0.033; Bonds: $\bar{x} = 0.312$ and s = 0.027.
   Bonds is more consistent since his standard deviation is less.

10) The bulbs with the lower standard deviation are more consistent and it is easier to plan for their replacement.

11) B

12) D

13) B

14) At least 75% of the heights should fall between 58.6 in. and 68.6 in.

15) At least 89% of the heights should fall between 56.1 in. and 71.1 in.

16) D

17) A

18) B

19) D

20) B

21) D

22) A

23) B

24) A

25) coefficient of variation $= \dfrac{1.82}{3.12} \times 100\% = 58.3\%$

26) $\bar{x} = 121.7$, s = 11.82, P = 0.31. Since $-1 \le P \le 1$, there is no significant skewness.

27) B

28) B

2.5 Measures of Position

1) B

2) D

3) The student's score was higher than the scores of 90% of the students who took the test.

4) IQR $= Q_3 - Q_1 = 34 - 28 = 6$. This means that the weights of the middle half of the data set vary by 6 pounds.

5) D

6) C

7) C

8) A

9) B

10) C

11) D

12) D

13)

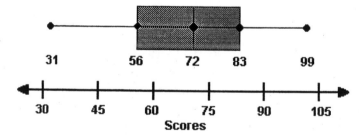

14)

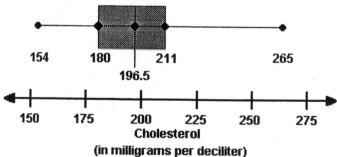

15) D

16) history z–score = –4.67; physics z–score = 8.38; The student performed better on the physics test.

17) B

18) C
19) B
20) A

Ch. 3 Probability

3.1 Basic Concepts of Probability

Solve the problem.

1) Which of the following cannot be a probability?

   A) 0   B) –49   C) $\frac{\sqrt{3}}{3}$ D) 0.001

2) Which of the following cannot be a probability?

   A) 1   B) 85%   C) 0.0002   D) $\frac{4}{3}$

3) Rank the probabilities of 10%, $\frac{1}{5}$, and 0.06 from the least likely to occur to the most likely to occur.

   A) 10%, $\frac{1}{5}$, 0.06   B) 0.06, $\frac{1}{5}$, 10%   C) 0.06, 10%, $\frac{1}{5}$ D) $\frac{1}{5}$, 10%, 0.06

4) Rank the probabilities of 10%, $\frac{1}{5}$, and 0.06 from the most likely to occur to the least likely to occur.

   A) 10%, $\frac{1}{5}$, 0.06   B) 0.06, 10%, $\frac{1}{5}$ C) $\frac{1}{5}$, 10%, 0.06   D) 0.06, $\frac{1}{5}$, 10%

5) Explain why the following statement is incorrect:
   He gave 110% effort.

6) Identify the sample space of the probability experiment: shooting a free throw in basketball.

7) Identify the sample space of the probability experiment: answering a true or false question

8) Identify the sample space of the probability experiment: recording the number of days it snowed in Cleveland in the month of January.

9) Identify the sample space of the probability experiment: answering a multiple choice question with A, B, C, and D as the possible answers

10) Identify the sample space of the probability experiment: determining the children's gender for a family of three children (Use B for boy and G for girl.)

11) Identify the sample space of the probability experiment: rolling a single 12–sided die with sides numbered 1–12

12) Identify the sample space of the probability experiment: rolling a pair of 12–sided dice (with sides numbered 1–12) and observing the total number of points of each roll

13) Identify the sample space of the probability experiment: A calculator has a function button to generate a random integer from –5 to 5

14) Identify the sample space of the probability experiment: recording a response to the survey question and the gender of the respondent.

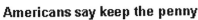

Source: Harris interactive poll of 2136 adults taken June 10-16.
By Shannon Reilly and Robert W. Ahrens, USA Today

15) Identify the sample space of the probability experiment: recording the day of the week and whether or not it rains.

16) A coin is tossed. Find the probability that the result is heads.

    A) 0.5   B) 1   C) 0.9   D) 0.1

17) A single six–sided die is rolled. Find the probability of rolling a number less than 3.

    A) 0.333   B) 0.25   C) 0.1   D) 0.5

18) A single six–sided die is rolled. Find the probability of rolling a seven.

    A) 0.1   B) 1   C) 0.5   D) 0

19) A study of 1000 randomly selected flights of a major airline showed that 784 of the flights arrived on time. What is the probability of a flight arriving on time?

    A) $\dfrac{125}{27}$ B) $\dfrac{98}{125}$ C) $\dfrac{125}{98}$ D) $\dfrac{27}{125}$

20) If one card is drawn from a standard deck of 52 playing cards, what is the probability of drawing an ace?

    A) $\dfrac{1}{4}$ B) $\dfrac{1}{52}$ C) $\dfrac{1}{13}$ D) $\dfrac{1}{2}$

21) If one card is drawn from a standard deck of 52 playing cards, what is the probability of drawing a red card?

    A) $\dfrac{1}{52}$ B) $\dfrac{1}{4}$ C) $\dfrac{1}{2}$ D) $\dfrac{1}{13}$

22) If one card is drawn from a standard deck of 52 playing cards, what is the probability of drawing a heart?

    A) $\dfrac{1}{4}$ B) 1   C) $\dfrac{1}{2}$ D) $\dfrac{3}{4}$

23) Classify the statement as an example of classical probability, empirical probability, or subjective probability. The probability that a train will be in an accident on a specific route is 1%.

A) classical probability   B) empirical probability   C) subjective probability

24) Classify the statement as an example of classical probability, empirical probability, or subjective probability. The probability that interest rates will rise during the summer is 0.05.

A) classical probability   B) empirical probability   C) subjective probability

25) Classify the statement as an example of classical probability, empirical probability, or subjective probability. In California's Pick Three lottery, a person selects a 3-digit number. The probability of winning California's Pick Three lottery is $\frac{1}{1000}$.

A) empirical probability   B) classical probability   C) subjective probability

26) Classify the statement as an example of classical probability, empirical probability, or subjective probability. The probability that a newborn baby is a boy is $\frac{1}{2}$.

A) subjective probability   B) classical probability   C) empirical probability

27) Classify the statement as an example of classical probability, empirical probability, or subjective probability. The probability that it will rain tomorrow is 28%.

A) empirical probability   B) subjective probability   C) classical probability

28) In a survey of college students, 809 said that they have cheated on an exam and 1793 said that they have not. If one college student is selected at random, find the probability that the student has cheated on an exam.

A) $\frac{2602}{1793}$ B) $\frac{2602}{809}$ C) $\frac{809}{2602}$ D) $\frac{1793}{2602}$

29) If an individual is selected at random, what is the probability that he or she has a birthday in July? Ignore leap years.

A) $\frac{31}{365}$ B) $\frac{12}{365}$ C) $\frac{1}{365}$ D) $\frac{364}{365}$

30) The data in the table represent the number of consumer complaints against major U.S. airlines. If one complaint from the table is randomly selected, find the probability that it was filed against United Airlines.

Airline	Number of Complaints
United	1172
Northwest	765
Continental	563

31) The data in the table represent the number of consumer complaints against major U.S. airlines. If one complaint from the table is randomly selected, find the probability that it was filed against Northwest Airlines.

Airline	Number of Complaints
United	1172
Northwest	765
Continental	563

32) The data in the table represent the number of consumer complaints against major U.S. airlines. If one complaint from the table is randomly selected, find the probability that it was filed against Continental Airlines.

Airline	Number of Complaints
United	1172
Northwest	765
Continental	563

33) The distribution of blood types for 100 Americans is listed in the table. If one donor is selected at random, find the probability of selecting a person with blood type A+.

Blood Type	O+	O-	A+	A-	B+	B-	AB+	AB-
Number	37	6	34	6	10	2	4	1

   A) 0.68   B) 0.4   C) 0.45   D) 0.34

34) The distribution of blood types for 100 Americans is listed in the table. If one donor is selected at random, find the probability of selecting a person with blood type A+ or A-.

Blood Type	O+	O-	A+	A-	B+	B-	AB+	AB-
Number	37	6	34	6	10	2	4	1

   A) 0.60   B) 0.4   C) 0.34   D) 0.45

35) The distribution of blood types for 100 Americans is listed in the table. If one donor is selected at random, find the probability of not selecting a person with blood type B+.

Blood Type	O+	O-	A+	A-	B+	B-	AB+	AB-
Number	37	6	34	6	10	2	4	1

   A) 0.90   B) 0.82   C) 0.10   D) 0.12

36) The distribution of blood types for 100 Americans is listed in the table. If one donor is selected at random, find the probability of selecting a person with blood type AB-.

Blood Type	O+	O-	A+	A-	B+	B-	AB+	AB-
Number	37	6	34	6	10	2	4	1

   A) 0.99   B) 0.01   C) 0.05   D) 0.10

37) The distribution of Master's degrees conferred by a university is listed in the table.

Major	Frequency
Mathematics	216
English	207
Engineering	75
Business	176
Education	222

What is the probability that a randomly selected student graduating with a Master's degree has a major of Engineering? Round your answer to three decimal places.

A) 0.084   B) 0.013   C) 0.916   D) 0.987

38) The distribution of Master's degrees conferred by a university is listed in the table.

Major	Frequency
Mathematics	216
English	207
Engineering	86
Business	176
Education	221

What is the probability that a randomly selected student graduating with a Master's degree has a major of Education? Round your answer to three decimal places.

A) 0.323   B) 0.005   C) 0.244   D) 0.756

39) Use the following graph, which shows the types of incidents encountered with drivers using cell phones, to find the probability that a randomly chosen incident involves cutting off a car.

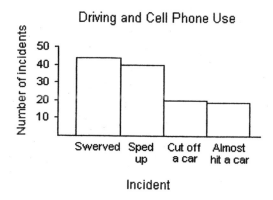

40) Use the following graph, which shows the types of incidents encountered with drivers using cell phones, to find the probability that a randomly chosen incident did not involve cutting off a car.

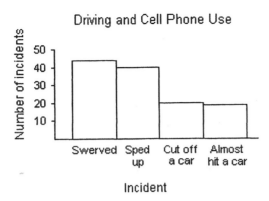

41) Use the pie chart, which shows the number of Congressional Medal of Honor recipients in the United States, to find the probability that a randomly chosen recipient served in the Navy.

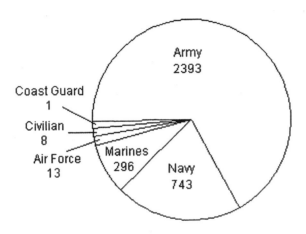

42) Use the pie chart, which shows the number of Congressional Medal of Honor recipients in the United States, to find the probability that a randomly chosen recipient did not serve in the Marines.

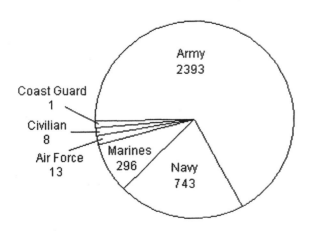

43) A question has five multiple-choice answers. Find the probability of guessing an incorrect answer.

A) $\frac{1}{5}$ B) $\frac{5}{2}$ C) $\frac{4}{5}$ D) $\frac{3}{5}$

44) A question has five multiple-choice questions. Find the probability of guessing the correct answer.

A) $\frac{1}{5}$ B) $\frac{2}{5}$ C) $\frac{5}{4}$ D) $\frac{4}{5}$

45) At the local racetrack, the favorite in a race has odds 3:2 in favor of winning. What is the probability that the favorite wins the race?

A) 0.8 B) 0.6 C) 0.2 D) 0.4

46) At the local racetrack, the favorite in a race has odds 3:2 against winning. What is the probability that the favorite wins the race?

A) 0.2 B) 0.4 C) 0.6 D) 0.8

47) The P(A) = $\frac{3}{5}$. Find the odds in favor of A.

A) 2:3 B) 3:2 C) 5:2 D) 2:5

48) If a card is picked at random from a standard deck of 52 playing cards, find the odds that the card is not a heart.

A) 1:4 B) 4:1 C) 3:1 D) 1:3

49) The distribution of Master's degrees conferred by a university is listed in the table.

Major	Frequency
Mathematics	216
English	207
Engineering	86
Business	176
Education	222

Find the probability of randomly choosing a person graduating with a Master's degree who did not major in Education. Round your answer to three decimal places.

50) The data in the table represent the number of consumer complaints against major U.S. airlines. If one complaint from the table is randomly selected, find the probability that it was not filed against Continental Airlines. (Round to three decimal places.)

Airline	Number of Complaints
United	287
Northwest	256
Continental	246

3.2 Conditional Probability and the Multiplication Rule

Solve the problem.

1) A group of students were asked if they carry a credit card. The responses are listed in the table.

Class	Credit Card Carrier	Not a Credit Card Carrier	Total
Freshman	33	27	60
Sophomore	6	34	40
Total	39	61	100

If a student is selected at random, find the probability that he or she owns a credit card given that the student is a freshman. Round your answer to three decimal places.

   A) 0.846   B) 0.330   C) 0.550   D) 0.450

2) A group of students were asked if they carry a credit card. The responses are listed in the table.

Class	Credit Card Carrier	Not a Credit Card Carrier	Total
Freshman	48	12	60
Sophomore	22	18	40
Total	70	30	100

If a student is selected at random, find the probability that he or she owns a credit card given that the student is a sophomore. Round your answer to three decimal places.

   A) 0.220   B) 0.450   C) 0.550   D) 0.314

3) A group of students were asked if they carry a credit card. The responses are listed in the table.

Class	Credit Card Carrier	Not a Credit Card Carrier	Total
Freshman	45	15	60
Sophomore	21	19	40
Total	66	34	100

If a student is selected at random, find the probability that he or she is a freshman given that the student owns a credit card. Round your answers to three decimal places.

   A) 0.318   B) 0.750   C) 0.450   D) 0.682

4) A group of students were asked if they carry a credit card. The responses are listed in the table.

Class	Credit Card Carrier	Not a Credit Card Carrier	Total
Freshman	12	48	60
Sophomore	19	21	40
Total	31	69	100

If a student is selected at random, find the probability that he or she is a sophomore given that the student owns a credit card. Round your answers to three decimal places.

   A) 0.775   B) 0.613   C) 0.190   D) 0.387

5) Classify the events as dependent or independent. Events A and B where
P(A) = 0.2, P(B) = 0.4, and P(A and B) = 0.08

   A) dependent   B) independent

6) Classify the events as dependent or independent. Events A and B where
P(A) = 0.2, P(B) = 0.3, and P(A and B) = 0.05

   A) independent   B) dependent

7) Classify the events as dependent or independent.
The events of getting two aces when two cards are drawn from a deck of playing cards and the first card is
replaced before the second card is drawn.

   A) dependent   B) independent

8) Classify the events as dependent or independent. The events of getting two aces when two cards are drawn
from a deck of playing cards and the first card is not replaced before the second card is drawn.

   A) independent   B) dependent

9) Classify the events as dependent or independent. Event A: A red candy is selected from a package with 30
colored candies and eaten. Event B: A blue candy is selected from the same package and eaten.

   A) independent   B) dependent

10) You are dealt two cards successively without replacement from a standard deck of 52 playing cards. Find the
probability that the first card is a two and the second card is a ten. Round your answer to three decimal places.

   A) 0.006   B) 0.250   C) 0.500   D) 0.994

11) Find the probability of answering two true or false questions correctly if random guesses are made. Only one of
the choices is correct.

   A) 0.75   B) 0.25   C) 0.5   D) 0.1

12) Find the probability of answering the two multiple choice questions correctly if random guesses are made.
Assume the questions each have five choices for the answer. Only one of the choices is correct.

   A) 0.004   B) 0.02   C) 0.4   D) 0.04

13) Find the probability of getting four consecutive aces when four cards are drawn without replacement from a
standard deck of 52 playing cards.

14) Find the probability of selecting two consecutive threes when two cards are drawn without replacement from a
standard deck of 52 playing cards. Round your answer to four decimal places.

15) A multiple-choice test has five questions, each with five choices for the answer. Only one of the choices is
correct. You randomly guess the answer to each question. What is the probability that you answer the first two
questions correctly?

   A) 0.04   B) 0.02   C) 0.2   D) 0.4

16) A multiple-choice test has five questions, each with five choices for the answer. Only one of the choices is
correct. You randomly guess the answer to each question. What is the probability that you answer all five
questions correctly?

17) A multiple-choice test has five questions, each with five choices for the answer. Only one of the choices is correct. You randomly guess the answer to each question. What is the probability that you do not answer any of the questions correctly?

18) A multiple-choice test has five questions, each with five choices for the answer. Only one of the choices is correct. You randomly guess the answer to each question. What is the probability that you answer at least one of the questions correctly?

19) The probability it will rain is 40% each day over a three-day period. What is the probability it will rain at least one of the three days?

20) The probability it will rain is 40% each day over a three-day period. What is the probability it will not rain at least one of the three days?

21) Four students drive to school in the same car. The students claim they were late to school and missed a test because of a flat tire. On the makeup test, the instructor asks the students to identify the tire that went flat; front driver's side, front passenger's side, rear driver's side, or rear passenger's side. If the students didn't really have a flat tire and each randomly selects a tire, what is the probability that all four students select the same tire?

A) $\frac{1}{4}$　　　　　　B) $\frac{1}{8}$　　　　　　C) $\frac{1}{64}$　　　　　　D) $\frac{1}{256}$

22) Use Bayes' theorem to solve this problem. A storeowner purchases stereos from two companies. From Company A, 250 stereos are purchased and 1% are found to be defective. From Company B, 550 stereos are purchased and 9% are found to be defective. Given that a stereo is defective, find the probability that it came from Company A.

A) $\frac{11}{104}$　　　　　　B) $\frac{99}{104}$　　　　　　C) $\frac{5}{104}$　　　　　　D) $\frac{45}{104}$

23) Use Baye's Theorem to solve this problem, A paper bag contains two red balls and one blue ball. A plastic bag contains three blue balls and one red ball. A coin is tossed. If it falls heads up, the paper bag is selected and a ball is drawn. If the coin falls tails up, the plastic bag is selected and a ball is drawn. If a red ball is selected, what is the probability that it came from the paper bag?

A) $\frac{8}{11}$　　　　　　B) $\frac{1}{8}$　　　　　　C) $\frac{1}{3}$　　　　　　D) $\frac{3}{8}$

24) Find the probability that of 25 randomly selected students, no two share the same birthday.
A) 0.995　　　　　B) 0.431　　　　　C) 0.569　　　　　D) 0.068

25) Find the probability that of 25 randomly selected students, at least two share the same birthday.
A) 0.432　　　　　B) 0.995　　　　　C) 0.569　　　　　D) 0.068

26) What is the probability that a husband, wife, and daughter have the same birthday?

3.3 The Addition Rule

Solve the problem.

1) Decide if the events A and B are mutually exclusive or not mutually exclusive. A die is rolled.
A: The result is an odd number.
B: The result is an even number.

A) not mutually exclusive　　　　　　　　B) mutually exclusive

2) Decide if the events A and B are mutually exclusive or not mutually exclusive, A die is rolled.
   A: The result is a 3.
   B: The result is an odd number.

   A) mutually exclusive   B) not mutually exclusive

3) Decide if the events A and B are mutually exclusive or not mutually exclusive. A date in Philadelphia is selected.
   A: It rains that day.
   B: It snows that day.

   A) not mutually exclusive   B) mutually exclusive

4) Decide if the events A and B are mutually exclusive or not mutually exclusive. A card is drawn from a standard deck of 52 playing cards.
   A: The result is a 7.
   B: The result is a jack.

   A) mutually exclusive   B) not mutually exclusive

5) Decide if the events A and B are mutually exclusive or not mutually exclusive. A card is drawn from a standard deck of 52 playing cards.
   A: The result is a club.
   B: The result is a king.

   A) not mutually exclusive   B) mutually exclusive

6) Decide if the events A and B are mutually exclusive or not mutually exclusive. A person is selected at random.
   A: Their birthday is in the fall.
   B: Their birthday is in October.

   A) mutually exclusive   B) not mutually exclusive

7) Decide if the events A and B are mutually exclusive or not mutually exclusive. A student is selected at random.
   A: The student is taking a math course.
   B: The student is a business major.

   A) not mutually exclusive   B) mutually exclusive

8) A card is drawn from a standard deck of 52 playing cards. Find the probability that the card is an ace or a king.

   A) $\dfrac{1}{13}$ B) $\dfrac{8}{13}$ C) $\dfrac{2}{13}$ D) $\dfrac{4}{13}$

9) A card is drawn from a standard deck of 52 playing cards. Find the probability that the card is an ace or a heart.

   A) $\dfrac{7}{52}$ B) $\dfrac{2}{13}$ C) $\dfrac{3}{13}$ D) $\dfrac{4}{13}$

10) A card is drawn from a standard deck of 52 playing cards. Find the probability that the card is an ace or a black card.

   A) $\dfrac{7}{13}$ B) $\dfrac{29}{52}$ C) $\dfrac{4}{13}$ D) $\dfrac{15}{26}$

11) The events A and B are mutually exclusive. If P(A) = 0.6 and P(B) = 0.2, what is P(A and B)?

   A) 0   B) 0.5   C) 0.8   D) 0.12

12) The events A and B are mutually exclusive. If P(A) = 0.2 and P(B) = 0.4, what is P(A or B)?

    A) 0.6   B) 0.08   C) 0.2   D) 0

13) Given that $P(A \text{ or } B) = \frac{1}{2}$, $P(A) = \frac{1}{8}$, and $P(A \text{ and } B) = \frac{1}{9}$, find P(B).

    A) $\frac{19}{144}$ B) $\frac{35}{72}$ C) $\frac{37}{72}$ D) $\frac{53}{72}$

14) Use the pie chart, which shows the number of Congressional Medal of Honor recipients, to find the probability that a randomly chosen recipient served in the Army, Navy, or Marines.

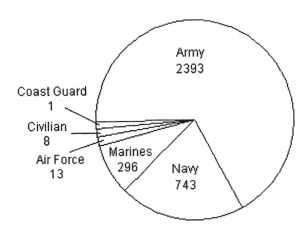

Medal of Honor Recipients

15) Use the following graph, which shows the types of incidents encountered with drivers using cell phones, to find the probability that a randomly chosen incident involves either swerving or almost hitting a car.

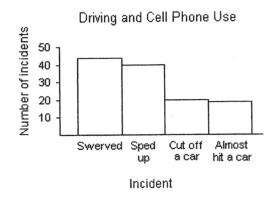

Driving and Cell Phone Use

16) The table lists the smoking habits of a group of college students.

Sex	Non-smoker	Regular Smoker	Heavy Smoker	Total
Man	135	44	5	184
Woman	187	21	13	221
Total	322	65	18	405

If a student is chosen at random, find the probability of getting someone who is a regular or heavy smoker. Round your answer to three decimal places.

A) 0.239   B) 0.687   C) 0.141   D) 0.205

17) The table lists the smoking habits of a group of college students.

Sex	Non-smoker	Regular Smoker	Heavy Smoker	Total
Man	135	55	5	195
Woman	187	21	9	217
Total	322	76	14	412

If a student is chosen at random, find the probability of getting someone who is a man or a non-smoker. Round your answer to three decimal places.

A) 0.927   B) 0.816   C) 0.941   D) 0.948

18) The table lists the smoking habits of a group of college students.

Sex	Non-smoker	Regular Smoker	Heavy Smoker	Total
Man	135	34	5	174
Woman	187	21	11	219
Total	322	55	16	393

If a student is chosen at random, find the probability of getting someone who is a woman or a heavy smoker. Round your answer to three decimal places.

A) 0.598   B) 0.919   C) 0.115   D) 0.860

19) The table lists the smoking habits of a group of college students.

Sex	Non-smoker	Regular Smoker	Heavy Smoker	Total
Man	135	58	5	198
Woman	187	21	12	220
Total	322	79	17	418

If a student is chosen at random, find the probability of getting someone who is a man or a woman. Round your answer to three decimal places.

A) 0.921   B) 0.230   C) 1   D) 0.770

20) The distribution of Master's degrees conferred by a university is listed in the table.
(assume that a student majors in only one subject)

Major	Frequency
Mathematics	223
English	205
Engineering	86
Business	176
Education	222

What is the probability that a randomly selected student with a Master's degree majored in English or Mathematics? Round your answer to three decimal places.

A) 0.225   B) 0.245   C) 0.531   D) 0.469

21) The distribution of Master's degrees conferred by a university is listed in the table.
(assume that a student majors in only one subject)

Major	Frequency
Mathematics	216
English	207
Engineering	75
Business	175
Education	221

What is the probability that a randomly selected student with a Master's degree majored in Business, Education or Engineering? Round your answer to three decimal places.

A) 0.280   B) 0.473   C) 0.331   D) 0.527

22) In the Venn diagram below, event A represents the adults who drink coffee, event B represents the adults who drink tea, and event C represents the adults who drink cola. List the region(s) which represent the adults who drink both coffee and tea.

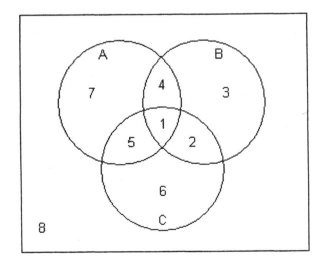

7) Seven guests are invited for dinner. How many ways can they be seated at a dinner table if the table is straight with seats only on one side?

    A) 5040   B) 720   C) 4   D) 40,320

8) The Environmental Protection Agency must visit nine factories for complaints of air pollution. In how many different ways can a representative visit five of these to investigate this week?

    A) 5   B) 45   C) 15,120   D) 362,880

9) How many ways can a jury of three men and six women be selected from twelve men and ten women?

10) How many ways can two Republicans, one Democrat, and one Independent be chosen from nine Republicans, five Democrats, and two Independents to fill four positions on city council?

11) How many different permutations of the letters in the word PROBABILITY are there?

12) How many different permutations of the letters in the word STATISTICS are there?

13) If a couple plans to have eleven children, how many gender sequences are possible?

    A) 2.853116706e+11   B) 11   C) 121   D) 2048

14) If a couple has two boys and seven girls, how many gender sequences are possible?

    A) 36   B) 8   C) 16   D) 9

15) A student must answer seven questions on an exam that contains twelve questions.

    a) How many ways can the student do this?
    b) How many ways are there if the student must answer the first and last question?

16) How many versions of a test are required to cover all possible question arrangements if there are seven open-ended questions on the test?

17) How many ways can five people, A, B, C, D, and E, sit in a row at a movie theater if A and B must sit together?

    A) 24   B) 48   C) 120   D) 12

18) How many ways can five people, A, B, C, D, and E, sit in a row at a movie theater if C must sit to the right of but not necessarily next to B?

    A) 60   B) 20   C) 48   D) 24

19) How many ways can five people, A, B, C, D, and E, sit in a row at a movie theater if D and E will not sit next to each other?

    A) 72   B) 48   C) 60   D) 24

20) The access code to a house's security system consists of five digits. How many different codes are available if the first digit cannot be zero and the arrangement of five fives is excluded?

21) In the California State lottery, you must select six numbers from fifty-two numbers to win the big prize. The numbers do not have to be in a particular order. What is the probability that you will win the big prize if you buy one ticket?

22) In California, each automobile license plate consists of a single digit followed by three letters, followed by three digits. How many distinct license plates can be formed if there are no restrictions on the digits or letters?

23) In California, each automobile license plate consists of a single digit followed by three letters, followed by three digits. How many distinct license plates can be formed if the first number cannot be zero and the three letters cannot form "GOD"?

Ch. 3 Probability
Answer Key

3.1 Basic Concepts of Probability

1) B
2) D
3) C
4) C
5) Maximum effort is 100%.
6) (hit, miss)
7) (true, false)
8) (0, 1, 2, 3, 4, 5, 6, 7, 8, 9, 10, . . . , 30, 31)
9) (A, B, C, D)
10) (BBB), (BBG), (BGB), (GBB), (BGG), (GBG), (GGB), (GGG)
11) (1, 2, 3, 4, 5, 6, 7, 8, 9, 10, 11, 12)
12) (2, 3, 4, 5, 6, 7, 8, 9, 10, 11, 12, 13, 14, 15, 16, 17, 18, 19, 20, 21, 22, 23, 24)
13) (−5, −4, −3, −2, −1, 0, 1, 2, 3, 4, 5)
14) (YM, YF, NM, NF, UM, UF)
15) (MR, TR, WR, HR, FR, SAR, SUR, MN, TN, WN, HN, FN, SAN, SUN)

16) A
17) A
18) D
19) B
20) C
21) C
22) A
23) B
24) C
25) B
26) B
27) B
28) C
29) A
30) $\dfrac{1172}{2500}$

31) $\dfrac{765}{2500}$

32) $\dfrac{563}{2500}$

33) D
34) B
35) A
36) B
37) A
38) C
39) 0.163
40) 0.837
41) 0.215
42) 0.914

43) C
44) A
45) B
46) B
47) B

48) C

49) Let E = Master's degree in Education.

$$P(E) = \frac{222}{907}. \; P(E') = 1 - P(E) = \frac{685}{907} = 0.755$$

50) Let E = the event the complaint was against Continental

$$P(E) = \frac{82}{263}$$

$$P(E') = 1 - P(E) = 1 - \frac{82}{263} = \frac{181}{263} = 0.688$$

3.2 Conditional Probability and the Multiplication Rule

1) C

2) C

3) D

4) B

5) B

6) B

7) B

8) B

9) B

10) A

11) B

12) D

13) $P(4\text{–Aces}) = \left(\frac{4}{52}\right)\left(\frac{3}{51}\right)\left(\frac{2}{50}\right)\left(\frac{1}{49}\right) = 0.00000369$

14) $P(2\text{–threes}) = \left(\frac{4}{52}\right)\left(\frac{3}{51}\right) = 0.0045$

15) A

16) $P(\text{all five questions answered correctly}) = \left(\frac{1}{5}\right)\left(\frac{1}{5}\right)\left(\frac{1}{5}\right)\left(\frac{1}{5}\right)\left(\frac{1}{5}\right) = 0.00032$

17) $P(\text{all five questions answers incorrect}) = \left(\frac{4}{5}\right)\left(\frac{4}{5}\right)\left(\frac{4}{5}\right)\left(\frac{4}{5}\right)\left(\frac{4}{5}\right) = 0.32768$

18) $P(\text{at least one correct}) = 1 - P(\text{all five anwers incorrect})$

$$= 1 - \left(\frac{4}{5}\right)\left(\frac{4}{5}\right)\left(\frac{4}{5}\right)\left(\frac{4}{5}\right)\left(\frac{4}{5}\right) = 1 - 0.32768 = 0.67232$$

19) $P(\text{rain at least one day}) = 1 - P(\text{no rain all three days})$

$$= 1 - (0.60)(0.60)(0.60)$$

$$= 0.784$$

20) $P(\text{not rain at least one day}) = 1 - P(\text{rain all three days})$

$$= 1 - (0.40)(0.40)(0.40)$$

$$= 0.936$$

21) C

22) C

23) A

24) B

25) C

26) $\left(\frac{365}{365}\right)\left(\frac{1}{365}\right)\left(\frac{1}{365}\right) = 0.00000751$

3.3 The Addition Rule

1) B

2) B

3) A

4) A

5) A
6) B
7) A
8) C
9) D
10) A
11) A
12) A
13) B
14) 0.994
15) 0.512
16) D
17) A
18) A
19) C
20) D
21) D
22) 1 and 4
23) 6
24) B

3.4 Counting Principles

1) A

2) $\dfrac{1}{1,000,000} = 0.000001$

3) C
4) A
5) D
6) A
7) A
8) C

9) $(_{12}C_3)(_{10}C_6) = 46,200$

10) $(_9C_2)(_5C_1)(_2C_1) = 360$

11) $11!/(2!2!) = 9,979,200$

12) $10!/(3!3!2!) = 50,400$

13) D

14) A

15) (a) $_{12}C_7 = 792$; (b) $_{10}C_5 = 252$

16) $7! = 5040$

17) B

18) A

19) A

20) $9 \times 10^4 - 1 = 89,999$

21) $\dfrac{1}{_{52}C_6} = \dfrac{1}{20,358,520} = 0.0000000491$

22) $10(26^3)(10^3) = 175,760,000$

23) $9(26^3)(10^3) - 9,000 = 158,175,000$

Ch. 4   Discrete Probability Distributions

4.1   Probability Distributions

Solve the problem.

1) State whether the variable is discrete or continuous.
   The number of cups of coffee sold in a cafeteria during lunch

   A) continuous   B) discrete

2) State whether the variable is discrete or continuous.
   The height of a player on a basketball team

   A) discrete   B) continuous

3) State whether the variable is discrete or continuous.
   The cost of a Statistics textbook

   A) continuous   B) discrete

4) State whether the variable is discrete or continuous.
   The blood pressures of a group of students the day before their final exam

   A) discrete   B) continuous

5) State whether the variable is discrete or continuous.
   The temperature in degrees Fahrenheit on July 4th in Juneau, Alaska

   A) continuous   B) discrete

6) State whether the variable is discrete or continuous.
   The number of goals scored in a soccer game

   A) continuous   B) discrete

7) State whether the variable is discrete or continuous.
   The speed of a car on a Los Angeles freeway during rush hour traffic

   A) continuous   B) discrete

8) State whether the variable is discrete or continuous.
   The number of phone calls to the attendance office of a high school on any given school day

   A) discrete   B) continuous

9) State whether the variable is discrete or continuous.
   The age of the oldest student in a statistics class

   A) discrete   B) continuous

10) State whether the variable is discrete or continuous.
    The number of pills in a container of vitamins

    A) continuous   B) discrete

11) Determine whether the distribution represents a probability distribution. If not, identify any requirements that are not satisfied.

x	P(x)
1	0.2
2	0.2
3	0.2
4	0.2
5	0.2

12) Determine whether the distribution represents a probability distribution. If not, identify any requirements that are not satisfied.

x	P(x)
3	-0.3
6	0.5
9	0.1
12	0.3
15	0.4

13) Determine whether the distribution represents a probability distribution. If not, identify any requirements that are not satisfied. Also, the sum of the probabilities does not equal one.

x	P(x)
1	1.2
2	1.2
3	1.4
4	1.1
5	1.1

14) Determine whether the distribution represents a probability distribution. If not, any requirements that are not satisfied. Also, the sum of the probabilities does not equal one.

x	P(x)
1	0.49
2	0.05
3	0.32
4	0.07
5	0.07

15) Determine whether the distribution represents a probability distribution. If not, identify any requirements that are not satisfied. Also, the sum of the probabilities does not equal one.

x	P(x)
1	-0.2
2	-0.2
3	-0.2
4	-0.2
5	-0.2

16) A sports analyst records the winners of NASCAR Winston Cup races for a recent season. The random variable x represents the races won by a driver in one season. Use the frequency distribution to construct a probability distribution.

Wins	1	2	3	4	5	6	7
Drivers	12	2	0	2	0	0	1

17) An insurance actuary asked a sample of senior citizens the cause of their automobile accidents over a two-year period. The random variable x represents the number of accidents caused by their failure to yield the right of way. Use the frequency distribution to construct a probability distribution.

Accidents	0	1	2	3	4	5
Senior Citizens	4	3	12	3	2	1

18) A sports announcer researched the performance of baseball players in the World Series. The random variable x represents the number of of hits a player had in the series. Use the frequency distribution to construct a probability distribution.

Hits	0	1	2	3	4	5	6	7
Players	7	9	7	4	1	1	2	1

19) Determine the probability distribution's missing value.
The probability that a tutor will see 0, 1, 2, 3, or 4 students

x	0	1	2	3	4
P(x)	$\frac{5}{26}$	$\frac{4}{13}$	$\frac{3}{13}$	?	$\frac{5}{26}$

A) $\frac{3}{26}$ B) $\frac{1}{13}$ C) $-\frac{5}{13}$ D) $\frac{12}{13}$

20) Determine the probability distribution's missing value.
The probability that a tutor will see 0, 1, 2, 3, or 4 students

x	0	1	2	3	4
P(x)	0.32	0.15	0.22	0.29	?

A) 0.02   B) 0.53   C) –0.49   D) 0.98

21) Determine the probability distributions's missing value.
The probability that a tutor sees 0, 1, 2, 3, or 4 students on a given day.

x	0	1	2	3	4
P(x)	?	0.15	0.20	0.20	0.25

A) 0.80   B) 0.20   C) 0.50   D) 1.0

22) The random variable x represents the number of boys in a family of three children. Assuming that boys and girls are equally likely, (a) construct a probability distribution, and (b) graph the distribution.

23) The random variable x represents the number of boys in a family of three children. Assuming that boys and girls are equally likely, find the mean and standard deviation for the random variable x.

A) mean: 1.50; standard deviation: 0.87

B) mean: 2.25; standard deviation: 0.87

C) mean: 2.25; standard deviation: 0.76

D) mean: 1.50; standard deviation: 0.76

24) The random variable x represents the number of tests that a patient entering a hospital will have along with the corresponding probabilities. Graph the probability distribution.

x	0	1	2	3	4
P(x)	$\frac{3}{17}$	$\frac{5}{17}$	$\frac{6}{17}$	$\frac{2}{17}$	$\frac{1}{17}$

25) The random variable x represents the number of tests that a patient entering a hospital will have along with the corresponding probabilities. Find the mean and standard deviation.

x	0	1	2	3	4
P(x)	$\frac{3}{17}$	$\frac{5}{17}$	$\frac{6}{17}$	$\frac{2}{17}$	$\frac{1}{17}$

A) mean: 2.52; standard deviation: 1.93

B) mean: 1.59; standard deviation: 1.09

C) mean: 1.59; standard deviation: 3.72

D) mean: 3.72; standard deviation: 2.52

26) The random variable x represents the number of credit cards that adults have along with the corresponding probabilities. Graph the probability distribution.

x	P(x)
0	0.07
1	0.68
2	0.21
3	0.03
4	0.01

27) The random variable x represents the number of credit cards that adults have along with the corresponding probabilities. Find the mean and standard deviation.

x	P(x)
0	0.07
1	0.68
2	0.21
3	0.03
4	0.01

A) mean: 1.23; standard deviation: 0.33

B) mean: 1.30; standard deviation: 0.32

C) mean: 1.23; standard deviation: 0.44

D) mean: 1.30; standard deviation: 0.44

28) In a pizza takeout restaurant, the following probability distribution was obtained. The random variable x represents the number of toppings for a large pizza. Graph the probability distribution.

x	P(x)
0	0.30
1	0.40
2	0.20
3	0.06
4	0.04

29) In a pizza takeout restaurant, the following probability distribution was obtained. The random variable x represents the number of toppings for a large pizza. Find the mean and standard deviation.

x	P(x)
0	0.30
1	0.40
2	0.20
3	0.06
4	0.04

A) mean: 1.54; standard deviation: 1.30

B) mean: 1.30; standard deviation: 1.54

C) mean: 1.30; standard deviation: 2.38

D) mean: 1.14; standard deviation: 1.04

30) A twenty–five–year–old man decides to pay $369 for a one–year insurance policy with coverage for $1,000,000. The probability of him living through the year is 0.9988. What is his expected value for the insurance policy?

31) One thousand tickets are sold at $5 each. One ticket will be randomly selected and the winner will receive a color television valued at $392. What is the expected value if a person buys one ticket?

    A) $4.60   B) $1.00   C) –$4.60   D) –$1.00

32) If a person rolls doubles when tossing two dice, the roller profits $55. If the game is fair, how much should the person pay to play the game?

    A) $11   B) $54   C) $55   D) $52

33) At a raffle, 10,000 tickets are sold at $5 each for three prizes valued at $4,800, $1,200, and $400. What is the expected value of one ticket?

    A) –$4.36   B) –$0.64   C) $0.64   D) $4.36

34) At a raffle, 10,000 tickets are sold at $10 each for three prizes valued at $4,800, $1,200, and $400. What is the expected value of one ticket?

    A) –$0.64   B) $0.64   C) –$9.36   D) $9.36

35) In a raffle, 1,000 tickets are sold for $2 each. One ticket will be randomly selected and the winner will receive a laptop computer valued at $1200. What is the expected value if a person buys one ticket?

    A) –$1.20   B) $0.8   C) $1.20   D) –$0.80

36) Use the frequency distribution to (a) construct a probability distribution for the random variable x represents the number of cars per household in a town of 1000 households, and (b) graph the distribution.

Cars	Households
0	125
1	428
2	256
3	108
4	83

37) From the probability distribution, find the mean and standard deviation for the random variable x, which represents the number of cars per household in a town of 1000 households.

x	P(x)
0	0.125
1	0.428
2	0.256
3	0.108
4	0.083

38) The random variable x represents the number of cars per household in a town of 1000 households. Find the probability of randomly selecting a household that has less than two cars.

Cars	Households
0	125
1	428
2	256
3	108
4	83

A) 0.809   B) 0.428   C) 0.125   D) 0.553

39) The random variable x represents the number of cars per household in a town of 1000 households. Find the probability of randomly selecting a household that has at least one car.

Cars	Households
0	125
1	428
2	256
3	108
4	83

A) 0.125   B) 0.500   C) 0.083   D) 0.875

40) The random variable x represents the number of cars per household in a town of 1000 households. Find the probability of randomly selecting a household that has between one and three cars, inclusive.

Cars	Households
0	125
1	428
2	256
3	108
4	83

A) 0.125   B) 0.792   C) 0.256   D) 0.208

41) A student has five motor vehicle accidents in one year and claims that having five accidents is not unusual. Use the frequency distribution below to determine if the student is correct.

Accidents	0	1	2	3	4	5
Students	260	500	425	305	175	45

42) A baseball player gets four hits during the World Series and a sports announcer claims that getting four hits is not unusual. Use the frequency distribution below to determine if the sports announcer is correct.

Hits	0	1	2	3	4	5	6	7
Players	7	9	7	4	1	1	2	1

4.2 Binomial Distributions

Solve the problem.

1) Decide whether the experiment is a binomial experiment. If it is not, explain why. You observe the gender of the next 950 babies born at a local hospital. The random variable represents the number of girls.

2) Decide whether the experiment is a binomial experiment. If it is not, explain why. You roll a die 400 times. The random variable represents the number that appears on each roll of the die.

3) Decide whether the experiment is a binomial experiment. If it is not, explain why. You spin a number wheel that has 11 numbers 100 times. The random variable represents the winning numbers on each spin of the wheel.

4) Decide whether the experiment is a binomial experiment. If it is not, explain why. You test four pain relievers. The random variable represents the pain reliever that is most effective.

5) Decide whether the experiment is a binomial experiment. If it is not, explain why. Testing a pain reliever using 200 people to determine if it is effective. The random variable represents the number of people who find the pain reliever to be effective.

6) Decide whether the experiment is a binomial experiment. If it is not, explain why. Surveying 400 prisoners to see how many crimes on which they were convicted. The random variable represents the number of crimes on which each prisoner was convicted.

7) Decide whether the experiment is a binomial experiment. If it is not, explain why. Surveying 150 prisoners to see whether they are serving time for their first offense. The random variable represents the number of prisoners serving time for their first offense.

8) Decide whether the experiment is a binomial experiment. If it is not, explain why. Each week, a man plays a game in which he has a 21% chance of winning. The random variable is the number of times he wins in 64 weeks.

9) Decide whether the experiment is a binomial experiment. If it is not, explain why. Each week, a lottery player plays the Daily Three in the California lottery. The random variable is the number of times per year the player wins.

10) Decide whether the experiment is a binomial experiment. If it is not, explain why. Selecting five cards, one at a time without replacement, from a standard deck of cards. The random variable is the number of red cards obtained.

11) You observe the gender of the next 100 babies born at a local hospital. You count the number of girls born. Identify the values of n, p, and q, and list the possible values of the random variable x.

12) Twenty-six percent of people in the United States with Internet access go online to get news. A random sample of five Americans with Internet access is selected. Identify the values of n, p, and q, and list the possible values of the random variable x.

13) Fifty-seven percent of families say that their children have an influence on their vacation plans. Consider a sample of eight families who are asked if their children influence their vacation plans. Identify the values of n, p, and q, and list the possible values of the random variable x.

14) Thirty-eight percent of people in the United States have type O+ blood. You randomly select 30 Americans and ask them if their blood type is O+. Identify the values of n, p, and q, and list the possible values of the random variable x.

15) Assume that male and female births are equally likely and that the birth of any child does not affect the probability of the gender of any other children. Find the probability of exactly seven boys in ten births.
    A) 0.938   B) 0.7   C) 0.117   D) 0.07

16) Assume that male and female births are equally likely and that the birth of any child does not affect the probability of the gender of any other children. Find the probability of at most three boys in ten births.
    A) 0.333   B) 0.172   C) 0.300   D) 0.003

17) A test consists of 10 true or false questions. To pass the test a student must answer at least eight questions correctly. If the student guesses on each question, what is the probability that the student will pass the test?
    A) 0.20   B) 0.055   C) 0.08   D) 0.8

18) A test consists of 10 multiple choice questions, each with five possible answers, one of which is correct. To pass the test a student must get 60% or better on the test. If a student randomly guesses, what is the probability that the student will pass the test?
    A) 0.377   B) 0.060   C) 0.205   D) 0.006

19) In a recent survey, 61% of the community favored building a police substation in their neighborhood. If 14 citizens are chosen, find the probability that exactly 11 of them favor the building of the police substation.
    A) 0.786   B) 0.003   C) 0.094   D) 0.610

20) The probability that an individual is left-handed is 0.14. In a class of 45 students, what is the probability of finding five left-handers?
    A) 0.14   B) 0.158   C) 0.111   D) 0.000

21) A recent survey found that 70% of all adults over 50 wear glasses for driving. In a random sample of 10 adults over 50, what is the probability that at least six wear glasses?
    A) 0.006   B) 0.700   C) 0.850   D) 0.200

22) According to government data, the probability that a woman between the ages of 25 and 29 was never married is 40%. In a random survey of 10 women in this age group, what is the probability that two or fewer were never married?
    A) 0.161   B) 0.167   C) 0.013   D) 1.002

23) According to government data, the probability that a woman between the ages of 25 and 29 was never married is 40%. In a random survey of 10 women in this age group, what is the probability that at least eight were married?

A) 1.002   B) 0.013   C) 0.167   D) 0.161

24) According to police sources a car with a certain protection system will be recovered 85% of the time. Find the probability that 4 of 9 stolen cars will be recovered.

A) 0.444   B) 0.15   C) 0.005   D) 0.85

25) The probability that a tennis set will go to a tie–breaker is 19%. What is the probability that two of three sets will go to tie–breakers?

A) 0.0361   B) 0.088   C) 0.19   D) 0.374

26) Fifty percent of the people that get mail–order catalogs order something. Find the probability that only two of 9 people getting these catalogs will order something.

A) 0.070   B) 0.222   C) 9.000   D) 0.002

27) The probability that a house in an urban area will be burglarized is 3%. If 45 houses are randomly selected, what is the probability that none of the houses will be burglarized?

A) 0.254   B) 0.000   C) 0.030   D) 0.001

28) An airline has a policy of booking as many as 150 persons on a plane that seats 140. Past studies indicate that only 85% of booked passengers show up for their flight. Find the probability that if the airline books 150 persons for a 140-seat plane, not enough seats will be available.

29) Sixty-five percent of men consider themselves knowledgeable football fans. If 10 men are randomly selected, find the probability that exactly four of them will consider themselves knowledgeable fans.

A) 0.400   B) 0.65   C) 0.069   D) 0.238

30) Assume that male and female births are equally likely and that the birth of any child does not affect the probability of the gender of any other children. Suppose that 350 couples each have a baby; find the mean and standard deviation for the number of girls in the 350 babies.

31) A test consists of 540 true or false questions. If the student guesses on each question, what is the mean number of correct answers?

A) 108   B) 0   C) 270   D) 540

32) A test consists of 870 true or false questions. If the student guesses on each question, what is the standard deviation of the number of correct answers?

A) 0.70710678   B) 2   C) 0   D) 14.7478812

33) A test consists of 50 multiple choice questions, each with five possible answers, only one of which is correct. Find the mean and the standard deviation of the number of correct answers.

A) mean: 10; standard deviation: 3.16227766   B) mean: 25; standard deviation: 5

C) mean: 10; standard deviation: 2.82842712   D) mean: 25; standard deviation: 2.82842712

34) In a recent survey, 80% of the community favored building a police substation in their neighborhood. If 15 citizens are chosen, what is the mean number favoring the substation?

A) 12   B) 15   C) 10   D) 8

Elementary Statistics 78

35) In a recent survey, 80% of the community favored building a police substation in their neighborhood. If 15 citizens are chosen, what is the standard deviation of the number favoring the substation?

  A) 1.55   B) 0.98   C) 2.40   D) 0.55

36) The probability that an individual is left-handed is 0.19. In a class of 60 students, what is the mean and standard deviation of the number of left-handers in the class?

  A) mean: 60; standard deviation: 3.03874974   B) mean: 11.4; standard deviation: 3.3763886

  C) mean: 11.4; standard deviation: 3.03874974   D) mean: 60; standard deviation: 3.3763886

37) A recent survey found that 66% of all adults over 50 wear glasses for driving. In a random sample of 90 adults over 50, what is the mean and standard deviation of those that wear glasses?

  A) mean: 59.4; standard deviation: 4.49399599   B) mean: 30.6; standard deviation: 4.49399599

  C) mean: 30.6; standard deviation: 7.70713955   D) mean: 59.4; standard deviation: 7.70713955

38) According to government data, the probability that a woman between the ages of 25 and 29 was never married is 40%. In a random survey of 10 women in this age group, what is the mean and standard deviation of the number that never married?

  A) mean: 4; standard deviation: 2.4   B) mean: 4; standard deviation: 1.55

  C) mean: 6; standard deviation: 155   D) mean: 6; standard deviation: 1.55

39) According to police sources, a car with a certain protection system will be recovered 89% of the time. If 500 stolen cars are randomly selected, what is the mean and standard deviation of the number of cars recovered after being stolen?

  A) mean: 445; standard deviation: 6.99642766   B) mean: -2055: standard deviation: 6.99642766

  C) mean: -2055: standard deviation: 48.95   D) mean: 445; standard deviation: 48.95

40) The probability that a tennis set will go to a tiebreaker is 16%. In 220 randomly selected tennis sets, what is the mean and the standard deviation of the number of tiebreakers?

  A) mean: 33; standard deviation: 5.43764655   B) mean: 33; standard deviation: 5.93295879

  C) mean: 35.2; standard deviation: 5.93295879   D) mean: 35.2; standard deviation: 5.43764655

41) The probability that a house in an urban area will be burglarized is 5%. If 20 houses are randomly selected, what is the mean of the number of houses burglarized?

  A) 0.5   B) 1.5   C) 1   D) 2

4.3 More Discrete Probability Distributions

Solve the problem.

1) A company ships computer components in boxes that contain 10 items. Assume that the probability of a defective computer component is 0.18. Find the probability that the first defect is found in the seventh component tested. Round your answer to four decimal places.

2) Basketball player Chauncey Billups of the Detroit Pistons makes free throw shots 88% of the time. Find the probability that he misses his first shot and makes the second.

  A) 0.0144   B) 0.50   C) 0.7744   D) 0.1056

3) A statistics professor finds that when he schedules an office hour at the 10:30 a.m. time slot, an average of three students arrive. Use the Poisson distribution to find the probability that in a randomly selected office hour in the 10:30 a.m. time slot exactly four students will arrive.

    A) 0.1680   B) 0.0489   C) 0.1328   D) 0.0618

4) A statistics professor finds that when he schedules an office hour at the 10:30 a.m. time slot, an average of three students arrives. Use the Poisson distribution to find the probability that in a randomly selected office hour no students will arrive.

    A) 0.1225   B) 0.0743   C) 0.1108   D) 0.0498

5) A sales firm receives an average of four calls per hour on its toll-free number. For any given hour, find the probability that it will receive exactly eight calls. Use the Poisson distribution.

    A) 302.5764   B) 0.0005   C) 0.0298   D) 0.0019

6) A sales firm receives an average of three calls per hour on its toll-free number. For any given hour, find the probability that it will receive at least three calls. Use the Poisson distribution.

    A) 0.1891   B) 0.4232   C) 0.5768   D) 0.6138

7) A mail-order company receives an average of five orders per 500 solicitations. If it sends out 100 advertisements, find the probability of receiving at least two orders. Use the Poisson distribution.

    A) 0.9596   B) 0.2642   C) 0.1839   D) 0.9048

8) A local fire station receives an average of 0.55 rescue calls per day. Use the Poisson distribution to find the probability that on a randomly selected day, the fire station will receive fewer than two calls.

    A) 0.087   B) 0.894   C) 0.317   D) 0.106

9) A car towing service company averages two calls per hour. Use the Poisson distribution to determine the probability that in a randomly selected hour the number of calls is three.

    A) 0.0747   B) 0.1805   C) 0.2030   D) 0.0664

10) A book contains 500 pages. If there are 200 typing errors randomly distributed throughout the book, use the Poisson distribution to determine the probability that a page contains exactly two errors.

    A) 0.0536   B) 0.0893   C) 0.4423   D) 0.0108

11) A company ships computer components in boxes that contain 20 items. Assume that the probability of a defective computer component is 0.2. Use the geometric mean to find the mean number of defective parts. Interpret the results.

12) A company ships computer components in boxes that contain 70 items. Assume that the probability of a defective computer component is 0.1. Use the geometric variance to find the variance of defective parts.

    A) 90   B) 8100   C) 0.12345679   D) 0

13) Given: The probability that a federal income tax return is filled out incorrectly with an error in favor of the taxpayer is 20%. Question: What is the probability that of the ten tax returns randomly selected for an audit, three returns will contain only errors favoring the taxpayer? Determine which distribution best describes the situation.

    A) Poisson   B) geometric   C) binomial

14) Given: The probability that a federal income tax return is filled out incorrectly with an error in favor of the taxpayer is 20%. Question: What is the probability that of the ten tax returns randomly selected for an audit in a given week, three returns will contain only errors favoring the taxpayer? Determine which distribution best describes the situation.

    A) binomial   B) geometric   C) Poisson

15) Given: The probability that a federal income tax return is filled out incorrectly with an error in favor of the taxpayer is 20%. Question: What is the probability that when the ten tax returns are randomly selected for an audit, the sixth return will contain only errors favoring the taxpayer? Determine which distribution best describes the situation.

    A) Poisson   B) geometric   C) binomial

16) Given: The probability that a federal income tax return is filled out incorrectly with an error in favor of the taxpayer is 20%. Question: What is the probability that of the ten tax returns randomly selected for an audit, five returns will contain only errors favoring the taxpayer, one return will contain only errors favoring the government, and four returns will contain no errors? Determine which distribution best describes the situation.

    A) Poisson   B) binomial   C) multinomial   D) geometric

Ch. 4 Discrete Probability Distributions
Answer Key

4.1 Probability Distributions

1) B
2) B
3) B
4) B
5) A
6) B
7) A
8) A
9) B
10) B
11) probability distribution
12) Not a probability distribution. A probability value cannot be negative.
13) Not a probability distribution. A probability value cannot be greater than one.
14) probability distribution
15) Not a probability distribution. A probability value cannot be negative.
16)

x	1	2	3	4	5	6	7
P(x)	0.71	0.12	0	0.12	0	0	0.06

17)

x	0	1	2	3	4	5
P(x)	0.16	0.12	0.48	0.12	0.08	0.04

18)

x	P(x)
0	0.21875
1	0.28125
2	0.21875
3	0.125
4	0.03125
5	0.03125
6	0.0625
7	0.03125

19) B
20) A
21) B

22) (a)

x	P(x)
0	$\frac{1}{8}$
1	$\frac{3}{8}$
2	$\frac{3}{8}$
3	$\frac{1}{8}$

(b)

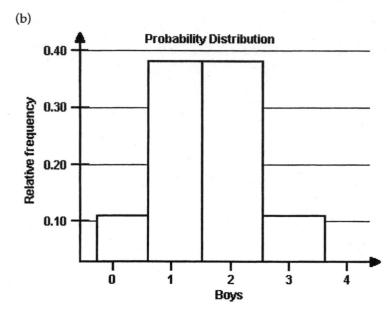

23) A

24)

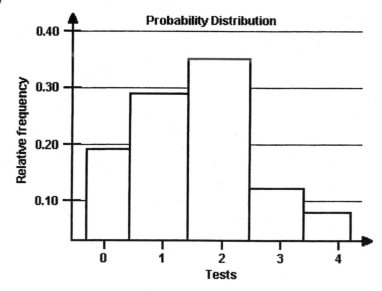

25) B

26)

Probability Distribution

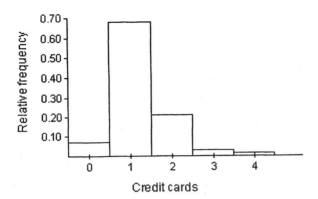

27) C
28)

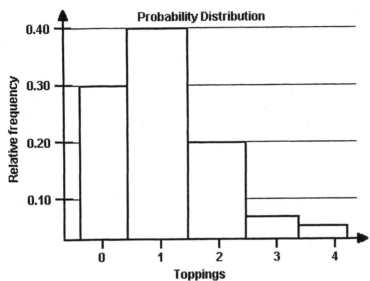

29) D
30) $(999{,}631 \times 0.9988) - (369 \times 0.0012) = \$998{,}431.00$

31) C
32) A
33) A
34) C
35) D

36) (a)

x	P(x)
0	0.125
1	0.428
2	0.256
3	0.108
4	0.083

(b)

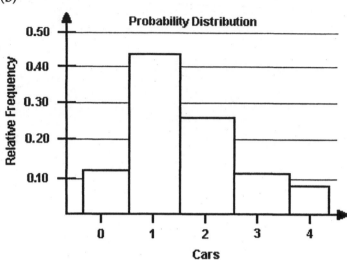

37) $\mu = 1.596$; $\sigma = 1.098$

38) D

39) D

40) B

41) The student is not correct. For a student to have five accidents is unusual because the probability of this event is 0.026.

42) The sports announcer is correct. For a baseball player to get four hits during a World Series is not unusual because the probability is 0.125.

4.2 Binomial Distributions

1) binomial experiment

2) Not a binomial experiment. There are more than two outcomes.

3) Not a binomial experiment. There are more than two outcomes.

4) Not a binomial experiment. There are more than two outcomes.

5) binomial experiment.

6) Not a binomial experiment. There are more than two outcomes.

7) binomial experiment.

8) binomial experiment.

9) Not a binomial experiment. There are more than two outcomes.

10) Not a binomial experiment. The probability of success is not the same for each trial.

11) $n = 100$; $p = 0.5$; $q = 0.5$; $x = 0, 1, 2, \ldots, 99, 100$

12) $n = 5$; $p = 0.26$; $q = 0.84$; $x = 0, 1, 2, 3, 4, 5$

13) $n = 8$; $p = 0.57$; $q = 0.43$; $x = 0, 1, 2, 3, 4, 5, 6, 7, 8$

14) $n = 30$; $p = 0.38$; $q = 0.62$; $x = 0, 1, 2, \ldots, 29, 30$

15) C

16) B

17) B

18) D

19) C

20) B

21) C

22) B

23) C

24) C

25) B

26) A

27) A

28) 0.0005

29) C

30) $\mu = np = 350(0.5) = 175;\ \sigma = \sqrt{npq} = \sqrt{350(0.5)(0.5)} = 9.35$

31) C

32) D

33) C

34) A

35) A

36) C

37) A

38) B

39) A

40) D

41) C

4.3 More Discrete Probability Distributions

1) $(0.82)^6(0.18) = 0.0547$

2) D

3) A

4) D

5) C

6) C

7) B

8) B

9) B

10) A

11) Geometric mean = 5; on average, 5 items will be examined before finding one that is defective.

12) A

13) C

14) C

15) B

16) C

Ch. 5 Normal Probability Distributions

5.1 Introduction to Normal Distributions and the Standard Normal Distribution

Solve the problem.

1) Find the area under the standard normal curve between $z = 0$ and $z = 3$.
  A) 0.9987   B) 0.4987   C) 0.4641   D) 0.0010

2) Find the area under the standard normal curve to the right of $z = 1$.
  A) 0.1397   B) 0.5398   C) 0.1587   D) 0.8413

3) Find the area under the standard normal curve between $z = 1$ and $z = 2$.
  A) 0.1359   B) 0.5398   C) 0.2139   D) 0.8413

4) Find the area under the standard normal curve to the left of $z = 1.5$.
  A) 0.5199   B) 0.9332   C) 0.0668   D) 0.7612

5) Find the area under the standard normal curve between $z = -1.5$ and $z = 2.5$.
  A) 0.9831   B) 0.6312   C) 0.9270   D) 0.7182

6) Find the area under the standard normal curve to the right of $z = -1.25$.
  A) 0.7193   B) 0.8944   C) 0.5843   D) 0.6978

7) Find the area under the standard normal curve to the left of $z = 1.25$.
  A) 0.1056   B) 0.2318   C) 0.8944   D) 0.7??2

8) Find the area under the standard normal curve between $z = 1.5$ and $z = 2.5$.
  A) 0.0606   B) 0.9938   C) 0.9816   D) 0.9332

9) Find the area under the standard normal curve between $z = -1.25$ and $z = 1.25$.
  A) 0.6412   B) 0.8817   C) 0.2112   D) 0.7888

10) Find the sum of the areas under the standard normal curve to the left of $z = -1.25$ and to the right of $z = 1.25$.
  A) 0.2112   B) 0.7888   C) 0.3944   D) 0.1056

11) Use the standard normal distribution to find $P(0 < z < 2.25)$.
  A) 0.5122   B) 0.8817   C) 0.4878   D) 0.7888

12) Use the standard normal distribution to find $P(-2.25 < z < 0)$.
  A) 0.5122   B) 0.4878   C) 0.0122   D) 0.6831

13) Use the standard normal distribution to find $P(-2.25 < z < 1.25)$.
  A) 0.8944   B) 0.4878   C) 0.0122   D) 0.8822

14) Use the standard normal distribution to find $P(-2.50 < z < 1.50)$.
  A) 0.6167   B) 0.9270   C) 0.8822   D) 0.5496

15) Use the standard normal distribution to find $P(z < -2.33 \text{ or } z > 2.33)$.

    A) 0.9809   B) 0.0198   C) 0.7888   D) 0.0606

16) For the standard normal curve, find the z–score that corresponds to the third quartile.

    A) 0.67   B) –0.23   C) 0.77   D) –0.67

17) For the standard normal curve, find the z–score that corresponds to the first quartile.

    A) –0.23   B) 0.77   C) –0.67   D) 0.67

18) For the standard normal curve, find the z–score that corresponds to the first decile.

    A) 0.16   B) 1.28   C) –1.28   D) –2.33

19) Find the area of the indicated region under the standard normal curve.

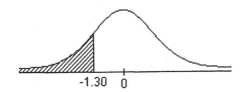

    A) 0.0823   B) 0.0968   C) 0.4032   D) 0.9032

20) Find the area of the indicated region under the standard normal curve.

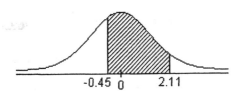

    A) 0.309   B) 0.3438   C) 0.6562   D) 1.309

21) Find the area of the indicated region under the standard normal curve.

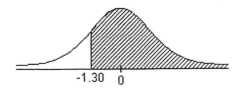

    A) 0.9032   B) 0.0823   C) 0.9177   D) 0.0968

22) Find the area of the indicated region under the standard normal curve.

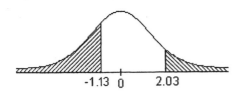

    A) 0.1292   B) 0.8489   C) 0.0212   D) 0.1504

Elementary Statistics 88

5.2 Normal Distributions: Finding Probabilities

Solve the problem.

1) IQ test scores are normally distributed with a mean of 100 and a standard deviation of 15. An individual's IQ score is found to be 110. Find the z–score corresponding to this value.

    A) –1.33   B) 0.67   C) –0.67   D) 1.33

2) IQ test scores are normally distributed with a mean of 100 and a standard deviation of 15. An individual's IQ score is found to be 90. Find the z–score corresponding to this value.

    A) 1.33   B) –1.33   C) 0.67   D) –0.67

3) IQ test scores are normally distributed with a mean of 100 and a standard deviation of 15. An individual's IQ score is found to be 120. Find the z–score corresponding to this value.

    A) 0.67   B) –1.33   C) 1.33   D) –0.67

4) IQ test scores are normally distributed with a mean of 100 and a standard deviation of 15. Find the x–score that corresponds to a z–score of 1.96.

    A) 115.6   B) 122.4   C) 132.1   D) 129.4

5) IQ test scores are normally distributed with a mean of 101 and a standard deviation of 13. An individual's IQ score is found to be 110. Find the z–score corresponding to this value.

    A) 0.69   B) –1.44   C) 1.44   D) –0.69

6) IQ test scores are normally distributed with a mean of 100 and a standard deviation of 12. An individual's IQ score is found to be 105. Find the z–score corresponding to this value.

    A) –2.40   B) 2.40   C) 0.42   D) –0.42

7) The lengths of pregnancies of humans are normally distributed with a mean of 268 days and a standard deviation of 15 days. A baby is premature if it is born three weeks early. What percentage of babies are born prematurely?

    A) 8.08%   B) 10.31%   C) 9.21%   D) 6.81%

8) The lengths of pregnancies of humans are normally distributed with a mean of 268 days and a standard deviation of 15 days. Find the probability of a pregnancy lasting more than 300 days.

    A) 0.2375   B) 0.3189   C) 0.9834   D) 0.0166

9) The lengths of pregnancies of humans are normally distributed with a mean of 268 days and a standard deviation of 15 days. Find the probability of a pregnancy lasting less than 250 days.

    A) 0.0606   B) 0.1151   C) 0.0066   D) 0.1591

10) The distribution of cholesterol levels in teenage boys is approximately normal with $\mu = 170$ and $\sigma = 30$ (Source: U.S. National Center for Health Statistics). Levels above 200 warrant attention. Find the probability that a teenage boy has a cholesterol level greater than 200.

    A) 0.2138   B) 0.1587   C) 0.3419   D) 0.8413

11) The distribution of cholesterol levels in teenage boys is approximately normal with $\mu = 170$ and $\sigma = 30$ (Source: U.S. National Center for Health Statistics). Levels above 200 warrant attention. Find the probability that a teenage boy has a cholesterol level greater than 225.

    A) 0.0012   B) 0.0718   C) 0.0336   D) 0.0606

12) The distribution of cholesterol levels in teenage boys is approximately normal with $\mu = 170$ and $\sigma = 30$ (Source: U.S. National Center for Health Statistics). Levels above 200 warrant attention. What percentage of teenage boys have levels between 170 and 225?

A) 0.0606   B) 0.5613   C) 0.4664   D) 0.0336

13) An airline knows from experience that the distribution of the number of suitcases that get lost each week on a certain route is approximately normal with $\mu = 15.5$ and $\sigma = 3.6$. What is the probability that during a given week the airline will lose less than 20 suitcases?

A) 0.3944   B) 0.8944   C) 0.1056   D) 0.4040

14) An airline knows from experience that the distribution of the number of suitcases that get lost each week on a certain route is approximately normal with $\mu = 15.5$ and $\sigma = 3.6$. What is the probability that during a given week the airline will lose more than 20 suitcases?

A) 0.3944   B) 0.1056   C) 0.8944   D) 0.4040

15) An airline knows from experience that the distribution of the number of suitcases that get lost each week on a certain route is approximately normal with $\mu = 15.5$ and $\sigma = 3.6$. What is the probability that during a given week the airline will lose between 10 and 20 suitcases?

A) 0.1056   B) 0.3944   C) 0.4040   D) 0.8314

16) Assume that blood pressure readings are normally distributed with $\mu = 120$ and $\sigma = 8$. A blood pressure reading of 145 or more may require medical attention. What percentage of people have a blood pressure reading greater than 145?

A) 99.91%   B) 0.09%   C) 6.06%   D) 11.09%

17) Assume that the salaries of elementary school teachers in the United States are normally distributed with a mean of $32,000 and a standard deviation of $3000. If a teacher is selected at random, find the probability that he or she makes more than $36,000.

A) 0.1056   B) 0.4040   C) 0.0918   D) 0.9082

18) Assume that the salaries of elementary school teachers in the United States are normally distributed with a mean of $32,000 and a standard deviation of $3000. If a teacher is selected at random, find the probability that he or she makes less than $28,000.

A) 0.9981   B) 0.9827   C) 0.2113   D) 0.0228

19) Assume that the heights of women are normally distributed with a mean of 63.6 inches and a standard deviation of 2.5 inches. The cheerleaders for a local professional basketball team must be between 65.5 and 68.0 inches. If a woman is randomly selected, what is the probability that her height is between 65.5 and 68.0 inches?

A) 0.9608   B) 0.3112   C) 0.1844   D) 0.7881

20) Assume that the heights of women are normally distributed with a mean of 63.6 inches and a standard deviation of 2.5 inches. The U.S. Army requires that the heights of women be between 58 and 80 inches. If a woman is randomly selected, what is the probability that her height is between 58 and 80 inches?

21) Assume that the heights of men are normally distributed with a mean of 69.0 inches and a standard deviation of 2.8 inches. The U.S. Marine Corps requires that men have heights between 64 and 78 inches. Find the percentage of men meeting these height requirements.

A) 96.26%   B) 31.12%   C) 3.67%   D) 99.93%

22) The lengths of pregnancies are normally distributed with a mean of 268 days and a standard deviation of 15 days. Out of 50 pregnancies, how many would you expect to last less than 250 days?

23) The distribution of cholesterol levels in teenage boys is approximately normal with $\mu = 170$ and $\sigma = 30$. Levels above 200 warrant attention. If 95 teenage boys are examined, how many would you expect to have cholesterol levels greater than 225?

24) An airline knows from experience that the distribution of the number of suitcases that get lost each week on a certain route is approximately normal with $\mu = 15.5$ and $\sigma = 3.6$. In one year, how many weeks would you expect the airline to lose between 10 and 20 suitcases?

25) Assume that the heights of women are normally distributed with a mean of 63.6 inches and a standard deviation of 2.5 inches. The U.S. Army requires that the heights of women be between 58 and 80 inches. If 200 women want to enlist in the U.S. Army, how many would you expect to meet the height requirements?

26) Assume that the heights of men are normally distributed with a mean of 69.0 inches and a standard deviation of 2.8 inches. The U.S. Marine Corps requires that the heights of men be between 64 and 78 inches. If 500 men want to enlist in the U.S. Marine Corps, how many would you not expect to meet the height requirements?

5.3 Normal Distributions: Finding Values

Solve the problem.

1) Find the z–score that corresponds to the given area under the standard normal curve.

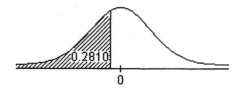

2) Find the z–score that corresponds to the given area under the standard normal curve.

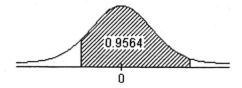

3) Find the z–score that corresponds to the given area under the standard normal curve.

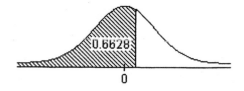

4) Find the z-score that corresponds to the given area under the standard normal curve.

0.0011

0

5) IQ test scores are normally distributed with a mean of 100 and a standard deviation of 15. Find the x-score that corresponds to a z-score of 2.33.

    A) 125.95   B) 139.55   C) 134.95   D) 142.35

6) IQ test scores are normally distributed with a mean of 100 and a standard deviation of 15. Find the x-score that corresponds to a z-score of −1.645.

    A) 79.1   B) 91.0   C) 75.3   D) 82.3

7) The scores on a mathematics exam have a mean of 74 and a standard deviation of 8. Find the x-value that corresponds to the z-score 2.575.

    A) 82.0   B) 94.6   C) 53.4   D) 76.6

8) For the standard normal curve, find the z-score that corresponds to the 90th percentile.

    A) 1.28   B) 1.52   C) 2.81   D) 0.28

9) For the standard normal curve, find the z-score that corresponds to the 30th percentile.

    A) −0.47   B) −0.98   C) −0.53   D) −0.12

10) For the standard normal curve, find the z-score that corresponds to the 7th decile.

    A) 0.47   B) 0.98   C) 0.12   D) 0.53

11) Find the z-scores for which 90% of the distribution's area lies between −z and z.

    A) (−2.33, 2.33)   B) (−0.99, 0.99)   C) (−1.645, 1.645)   D) (−1.96, 1.96)

12) Find the z-scores for which 98% of the distribution's area lies between −z and z.

    A) (−1.96, 1.96)   B) (−1.645, 1.645)   C) (−0.99, 0.99)   D) (−2.33, 2.33)

13) Find the z-score that is less than the mean and for which 70% of the distribution's area lies to its right.

    A) −0.53   B) −0.81   C) −0.47   D) −0.98

14) Find the z-score that is greater than the mean and for which 70% of the distribution's area lies to its left.

    A) 0.98   B) 0.53   C) 0.47   D) 0.81

15) Use a standard normal table to find the z-score that corresponds to the cumulative area of 0.4286.

    A) −1.465   B) −0.18   C) 0.18   D) 1.465

16) Use a standard normal table to find the z-score that corresponds to the 5th percentile.

    A) 0.00   B) −2.575   C) −1.645   D) 4

17) Find the z-score that has 70.54% of the distribution's area to its right.

    A) 0.82   B) –0.54   C) 0.54   D) –0.82

18) Find the z-score for which 99% of the distribution's area lies between –z and z.

    A) (-1.28, 1.28)   B) (-1.96, 1.96)   C) (-1.645, 1.645)   D) (-2.575, 2.575)

19) A mathematics professor gives two different tests to two sections of his college algebra courses. The first class has a mean of 56 with a standard deviation of 9 while the second class has a mean of 75 with a standard deviation of 15. A student from the first class scores a 62 on the test while a student from the second class scores an 83 on the test. Compare the scores.

20) Compare the scores: a score of 75 on a test with a mean of 65 and a standard deviation of 8 and a score of 75 on a test with a mean of 70 and a standard deviation of 4.

    A) A score of 75 with a mean of 65 and a standard deviation of 8 is better.

    B) You cannot determine which score is better from the given information.

    C) A score of 75 with a mean of 70 and a standard deviation of 4 is better.

    D) The two scores are statistically the same.

21) Compare the scores: a score of 220 on a test with a mean of 200 and a standard deviation of 21 and a score of 90 on a test with a mean of 80 and a standard deviation of 8.

    A) A score of 220 with a mean of 200 and a standard deviation of 21 is better.

    B) The two scores are statistically the same.

    C) You cannot determine which score is better from the given information.

    D) A score of 90 with a mean of 80 and a standard deviation of 8 is better.

22) Two high school students took equivalent language tests, one in German and one in French. The student taking the German test, for which the mean was 66 and the standard deviation was 8, scored an 82, while the student taking the French test, for which the mean was 27 and the standard deviation was 5, scored a 35. Compare the scores.

    A) The two scores are statistically the same.

    B) You cannot determine which score is better from the given information.

    C) A score of 82 with a mean of 66 and a standard deviation of 8 is better.

    D) A score of 35 with a mean of 27 and a standard deviation of 5 is better.

23) SAT scores have a mean of 1026 and a standard deviation of 209. ACT scores have a mean of 20.8 and a standard deviation of 4.8. A student takes both tests and scores 1130 on the SAT and 25 on the ACT. Compare the scores.

    A) The two scores are statistically the same.

    B) You cannot determine which score is better from the given information.

    C) A score of 1130 on the SAT test was better.

    D) A score of 25 on the ACT test was better.

24) SAT scores have a mean of 1026 and a standard deviation of 209. ACT scores have a mean of 20.8 and a standard deviation of 4.8. A student takes both tests and scores 860 on the SAT and 16 on the ACT. Compare the scores.

   A) You cannot determine which score is better from the given information.

   B) The two scores are statistically the same.

   C) A score of 16 on the ACT test was better.

   D) A score of 860 on the SAT test was better.

25) Assume that blood pressure readings are normally distributed with $\mu = 117$ and $\sigma = 5$. A researcher wishes to select people for a study but wants to exclude the top and bottom 10 percent. What would be the upper and lower readings to qualify people to participate in the study?

26) Assume that the salaries of elementary school teachers in the United States are normally distributed with a mean of $36,000 and a standard deviation of $5000. What is the cutoff salary for teachers in the top 10%?

27) Assume that the salaries of elementary school teachers in the United States are normally distributed with a mean of $41,000 and a standard deviation of $4000. What is the cutoff salary for teachers in the bottom 10%?

   A) $34,420   B) $35,880   C) $46,120   D) $47,580

28) The times for completing one circuit of a bicycle course are normally distributed with a mean of 78.9 minutes and a standard deviation of 5.8 minutes. An association wants to sponsor a race but only wants the top 25% of riders included. In a trial run, what should be the cutoff time?

29) Assume that the heights of men are normally distributed with a mean of 69.7 inches and a standard deviation of 2.3 inches. If the top 5 percent and bottom 5 percent are excluded for an experiment, what are the cutoff heights to be eligible for this experiment? Round your answers to one decimal place.

30) Assume that the heights of women are normally distributed with a mean of 65.0 inches and a standard deviation of 2.8 inches. Find Q_3, the third quartile that separates the bottom 75% from the top 25%.

   A) 66.9   B) 68.2   C) 63.1   D) 68.6

31) The body temperatures of adults are normally distributed with a mean of 98.6° F and a standard deviation of 0.86° F. What temperature represents the 95th percentile?

   A) 100.29° F   B) 97.19° F   C) 99.70° F   D) 100.01° F

32) In a certain normal distribution, find the standard deviation σ when $\mu = 50$ and 10.56% of the area lies to the right of 55.

   A) 2   B) 5   C) 3   D) 4

33) In a certain normal distribution, find the mean μ when $\sigma = 5$ and 5.48% of the area lies to the left of 78.

   A) 62   B) 70   C) 94   D) 86

34) In a certain normal distribution, 6.3% of the area lies to the left of 36 and 6.3% of the area lies to the right of 42. Find the mean μ and the standard deviation σ.

35) A tire company finds the lifespan for one brand of its tires is normally distributed with a mean of 49,800 miles and a standard deviation of 4000 miles. If the manufacturer is willing to replace no more than 10% of the tires, what should be the approximate number of miles for a warranty?

   A) 44,680   B) 54,920   C) 56,380   D) 43,220

5.4 Sampling Distributions and the Central Limit Theorem

Solve the problem.

1) The distribution of room and board expenses per year at a four-year college is normally distributed with a mean of $5850 and standard deviation of $1125. Random samples of size 20 are drawn from this population and the mean of each sample is determined. Which of the following mean expenses would be considered unusual?

    A) $6180   B) $5180   C) $6350   D) none of these

2) The lengths of pregnancies are normally distributed with a mean of 273 days and a standard deviation of 20 days. If 64 women are randomly selected, find the probability that they have a mean pregnancy between 273 days and 275 days.

    A) 0.2881   B) 0.2119   C) 0.7881   D) 0.5517

3) The lengths of pregnancies are normally distributed with a mean of 268 days and a standard deviation of 15 days. If 64 women are randomly selected, find the probability that they have a mean pregnancy between 266 days and 268 days.

    A) 0.7881   B) 0.3577   C) 0.5517   D) 0.2881

4) Assume that the heights of women are normally distributed with a mean of 63.6 inches and a standard deviation of 2.5 inches. If 100 women are randomly selected, find the probability that they have a mean height greater than 63.0 inches.

    A) 0.9918   B) 0.8989   C) 0.0082   D) 0.2881

5) Assume that the heights of women are normally distributed with a mean of 63.6 inches and a standard deviation of 2.5 inches. If 75 women are randomly selected, find the probability that they have a mean height between 63 and 65 inches.

    A) 0.0188   B) 0.9811   C) 0.3071   D) 0.2119

6) Assume that the heights of men are normally distributed with a mean of 68.0 inches and a standard deviation of 3.5 inches. If 100 men are randomly selected, find the probability that they have a mean height greater than 69 inches.

    A) 9.9671   B) 0.9005   C) 0.8188   D) 0.0021

7) Assume that the heights of men are normally distributed with a mean of 69.0 inches and a standard deviation of 2.8 inches. If 64 men are randomly selected, find the probability that they have a mean height between 68 and 70 inches.

    A) 0.9015   B) 0.0021   C) 0.9958   D) 0.9979

8) The body temperatures of adults are normally distributed with a mean of 98.6° F and a standard deviation of 0.60° F. If 25 adults are randomly selected, find the probability that their mean body temperature is less than 99° F.

9) The body temperatures of adults are normally distributed with a mean of 98.6° F and a standard deviation of 0.60° F. If 36 adults are randomly selected, find the probability that their mean body temperature is greater than 98.4° F.

    A) 0.0228   B) 0.9772   C) 0.9360   D) 0.8188

10) Assume that the salaries of elementary school teachers in the United States are normally distributed with a mean of $32,000 and a standard deviation of $3000. If 100 teachers are randomly selected, find the probability that their mean salary is less than $32,500.

11) Assume that the salaries of elementary school teachers in the United States are normally distributed with a mean of $32,000 and a standard deviation of $3000. If 100 teachers are randomly selected, find the probability that their mean salary is greater than $32,500.

    A) 0.0475   B) 0.3312   C) 0.1312   D) 0.9525

12) Assume that blood pressure readings are normally distributed with a mean of 117 and a standard deviation of 6.4. If 64 people are randomly selected, find the probability that their mean blood pressure will be less than 119.

    A) 0.0062   B) 0.8615   C) 0.9938   D) 0.8819

13) Assume that blood pressure readings are normally distributed with a mean of 120 and a standard deviation of 8. If 100 people are randomly selected, find the probability that their mean blood pressure will be greater than 122.

    A) 0.8615   B) 0.8819   C) 0.0062   D) 0.9938

14) The average number of pounds of red meat a person consumes each year is 196 with a standard deviation of 22 pounds (Source: American Dietetic Association). If a sample of 50 individuals is randomly selected, find the probability that the mean of the sample will be less than 200 pounds.

    A) 0.9015   B) 0.7613   C) 0.8815   D) 0.0985

15) The average number of pounds of red meat a person consumes each year is 196 with a standard deviation of 22 pounds (Source: American Dietetic Association). If a sample of 50 individuals is randomly selected, find the probability that the mean of the sample will be greater than 200 pounds.

    A) 0.0985   B) 0.8815   C) 0.7613   D) 0.9015

16) A coffee machine dispenses normally distributed amounts of coffee with a mean of 12 ounces and a standard deviation of 0.2 ounce. If a sample of 9 cups is selected, find the probability that the mean of the sample will be less than 12.1 ounces.

    A) 0.2123   B) 0.9332   C) 0.0668   D) 0.3216

17) A coffee machine dispenses normally distributed amounts of coffee with a mean of 12 ounces and a standard deviation of 0.2 ounce. If a sample of 9 cups is selected, find the probability that the mean of the sample will be greater than 12.1 ounces.

    A) 0.9332   B) 0.3216   C) 0.0668   D) 0.2123

18) A study of 800 homeowners in a certain area showed that the average value of the homes is $182,000 and the standard deviation is $15,000. If 50 homes are for sale, find the probability that the mean value of these homes is less than $185,000. Remember: check to see if the finite correction factor applies.

19) A study of 800 homeowners in a certain area showed that the average value of the homes is $182,000 and the standard deviation is $15,000. If 50 homes are for sale, find the probability that the mean value of these homes is greater than $185,000. Remember: check to see if the finite correction factor applies.

20) A soda machine dispenses normally distributed amounts of soda with a mean of 20 ounces and a standard deviation of 0.2 ounce. Are you more likely to randomly select one bottle with more than 20.3 ounces or are you more likely to select a sample of eight bottles with a mean amount of more than 20.3 ounces? Explain.

21) A soda machine dispenses normally distributed amounts of soda with a mean of 20 ounces and a standard deviation of 0.2 ounce. Are you more likely to randomly select one bottle with an amount between 19.8 ounces and 20.2 ounces or are you more likely to select a sample of eight bottles with a mean amount between 19.8 ounces and 20.2 ounces? Explain.

5.5 Normal Approximations to Binomial Distributions

Solve the problem.

1) In a recent survey, 83% of the community favored building a police substation in their neighborhood. You randomly select 20 citizens and ask each if he or she thinks the community needs a police substation. Decide whether you can use the normal distribution to approximate the binomial distribution. If so, find the mean and standard deviation. If not, explain why.

2) A recent survey found that 74% of all adults over 50 wear glasses for driving. You randomly select 30 adults over 50, and ask if he or she wears glasses. Decide whether you can use the normal distribution to approximate the binomial distribution. If so, find the mean and standard deviation, If not, explain why.

3) According to government data, the probability than an adult was never married is 12%. You randomly select 45 adults and ask if he or she was ever married. Decide whether you can use the normal distribution to approximate the binomial distribution, If so, find the mean and standard deviation, If not, explain why.

4) For the following conditions, determine if it is appropriate to use the normal distribution to approximate a binomial distribution with n = 7 and p = 0.2.

5) For the following conditions, determine if it is appropriate to use the normal distribution to approximate a binomial distribution with n = 33 and p = 0.6.

6) For the following conditions, determine if it is appropriate to use the normal distribution to approximate a binomial distribution with n = 25 and p = 0.2.

7) Match the binomial probability P(x < 23) with the correct statement.

    A) P(there are more than 23 successes)   B) P(there are at least 23 successes)

    C) P(there are fewer than 23 successes)   D) P(there are at most 23 successes)

8) Match the binomial probability P(x < 54) with the correct statement.

    A) P(there are at most 54 successes)   B) P(there are fewer than 54 successes)

    C) P(there are at least 54 successes)   D) P(there are more than 54 successes)

9) Match the binomial probability P(x ≤ 23) with the correct statement.

    A) P(there are more than 23 successes)   B) P(there are at least 23 successes)

    C) P(there are at most 23 successes)   D) P(there are fewer than 23 successes)

10) Match the binomial probability P(x > 23) with the correct statement.

    A) P(there are at least 23 successes)   B) P(there are at most 23 successes)

    C) P(there are more than 23 successes)   D) P(there are fewer than 23 successes)

11) Ten percent of the population is left-handed. In a class of 100 students, write the binomial probability for the statement "There are at least 12 left-handed students in the class."

    A) P(x ≤ 12)   B) P(x > 12)   C) P(x < 12)   D) P(x ≥ 12)

12) Ten percent of the population is left-handed. In a class of 100 students, write the binomial probability for the statement "There are more than 12 left-handed students in the class."

    A) $P(x = 12)$ B) $P(x < 12)$ C) $P(x > 12)$ D) $P(x \le 12)$

13) Ten percent of the population is left-handed. In a class of 100 students, write the binomial probability for the statement "There are at most 12 left-handed students in the class."

    A) $P(x < 12)$ B) $P(x \ge 12)$ C) $P(x \le 12)$ D) $P(x = 12)$

14) Ten percent of the population is left-handed. In a class of 70 students, write the binomial probability for the statement "There are more than 24 left-handed students in the class."

    A) $P(x > 24)$ B) $P(x < 24)$ C) $P(x \ge 24)$ D) $P(x \le 24)$

15) Ten percent of the population is left-handed. In a class of 100 students, write the binomial probability for the statement "There are exactly 12 left-handed students in the class."

    A) $P(x > 12)$ B) $P(x \le 12)$ C) $P(x = 12)$ D) $P(x \ge 12)$

16) Ten percent of the population is left-handed. A class of 100 students is selected. Convert the binomial probability $P(x > 12)$ to a normal probability by using the correction for continuity.

    A) $P(x < 11.5)$ B) $P(x \le 12.5)$ C) $P(x \ge 11.5)$ D) $P(x > 12.5)$

17) Ten percent of the population is left-handed. A class of 7500 students is selected. Convert the binomial probability $P(x < 20)$ to a normal probability by using the correction for continuity.

    A) $P(x \le 19.5)$ B) $P(x > 20.5)$ C) $P(x < 20.5)$ D) $P(x \ge 19.5)$

18) Ten percent of the population is left-handed. A class of 100 students is selected. Convert the binomial probability $P(x < 12)$ to a normal probability by using the correction for continuity.

    A) $P(x \ge 11.5)$ B) $P(x \le 12.5)$ C) $P(x > 12.5)$ D) $P(x < 11.5)$

19) Ten percent of the population is left-handed. A class of 8550 students is selected. Convert the binomial probability $P(x \le 14)$ to a normal probability by using the correction for continuity.

    A) $P(x \le 14.5)$ B) $P(x \ge 13.5)$ C) $P(x < 13.5)$ D) $P(x > 14.5)$

20) The failure rate in a statistics class is 10%. In a class of 40 students, find the probability that exactly five students will fail. Use the normal distribution to approximate the binomial distribution.

21) A local motel has 200 rooms. The occupancy rate for the winter months is 60%. Find the probability that in a given winter month at least 140 rooms will be rented. Use the normal distribution to approximate the binomial distribution.

22) A local motel has 50 rooms. The occupancy rate for the winter months is 60%. Find the probability that in a given winter month fewer than 35 rooms will be rented. Use the normal distribution to approximate the binomial distribution.

23) A student answers all 48 questions on a multiple-choice test by guessing. Each question has four possible answers, only one of which is correct. Find the probability that the student gets exactly 15 correct answers. Use the normal distribution to approximate the binomial distribution.

    A) 0.8577   B) 0.0823   C) 0.0606   D) 0.7967

24) If the probability of a newborn child being female is 0.5, find the probability that in 100 births, 55 or more will be female. Use the normal distribution to approximate the binomial distribution.

    A) 0.7967   B) 0.8159   C) 0.1841   D) 0.0606

25) An airline reports that it has been experiencing a 15% rate of no-shows on advanced reservations. Among 150 advanced reservations, find the probability that there will be fewer than 20 no-shows.

    A) 0.7967   B) 0.3187   C) 0.7549   D) 0.2451

26) Find the probability that in 200 tosses of a fair six-sided die, a five will be obtained at least 40 times.

    A) 0.3875   B) 0.1210   C) 0.0871   D) 0.8810

27) Find the probability that in 200 tosses of a fair six-sided die, a five will be obtained at most 40 times.

    A) 0.8810   B) 0.1190   C) 0.0853   D) 0.9131

28) A telemarketer found that there was a 1% chance of a sale from his phone solicitations. Find the probability of getting 5 or more sales for 1000 telephone calls.

    A) 0.8810   B) 0.0871   C) 0.0401   D) 0.9599

29) The author of a statistics book has trouble deciding whether to use the words "he" or "she" in the book's examples. To solve the problem, the author flips a coin each time the problem arises. If a head shows, the author uses "he" and if a tail shows, the author uses "she". If this problem occurs 100 times in the book, what is the probability that "she" will be used 58 times?

Ch. 5 Normal Probability Distributions
Answer Key

5.1 Introduction to Normal Distributions and the Standard Normal Distribution
1) B
2) C
3) A
4) B
5) C
6) B
7) C
8) A
9) D
10) A
11) C
12) B
13) D
14) B
15) B
16) A
17) C
18) C
19) B
20) C
21) A
22) D

5.2 Normal Distributions: Finding Probabilities
1) B
2) D
3) C
4) D
5) A
6) C
7) A
8) D
9) B
10) B
11) C
12) D
13) B
14) B
15) D
16) B
17) C
18) D
19) C
20) If x = 58, then z = –2.24 and P(x) = 0.0125. If x = 80, then z = 6.56 and P(x) = 0.9999.
P(58 < x < 80) = 0.9999 – 0.0125 = 0.9874.

21) A
22) About 6 pregnancies
23) About 8 teenage boys
24) About 43 weeks
25) About 197 women
26) About 19 men

5.3 Normal Distributions: Finding Values

1) $z = -0.58$

2) $z = -1.71$

3) $z = 0.42$

4) $z = 3.07$

5) C

6) C

7) B

8) A

9) C

10) D

11) C

12) D

13) A

14) B

15) B

16) C

17) B

18) D

19) $z = (62 - 56)/9 = 0.667$; $z = (83 - 75)/15 = 0.533$. The student with the score of 62 has the better score.

20) D

21) D

22) C

23) D

24) D

25) (110.6, 123.4)

26) $x = \mu + z\sigma = 36{,}000 + (1.28)(5000) = \$42{,}400$

27) B

28) $x = \mu + z\sigma = 78.9 + (0.675)(5.8) = 82.82$

29) 65.9 inches, 73.5 inches

30) A

31) D

32) D

33) D

34) $\mu = 39$, $\sigma = 1.96$

35) A

5.4 Sampling Distributions and the Central Limit Theorem

1) B

2) A

3) B

4) A

5) B

6) D

7) C

8) 0.9996

9) B

10) 0.9525

11) A

12) C

13) C

14) A

15) A

16) B

17) C

18) $50/800 = 0.0625 = 6.25\%$, hence the finite correction factor applies; $P(x < 185{,}000) = 0.9279$

19) $50/800 = 0.0625 = 6.25\%$, hence the finite correction factor applies; $P(x > 185{,}000) = 1 - 0.9279 = 0.0721$

20) It is more likely to select one bottle with more than 20.3 ounces because the probability is higher.

21) It is more likely to select a sample of eight bottles with an amount between 19.8 ounces and 20.2 ounces because the probability is higher.

5.5 Normal Approximations to Binomial Distributions

1) cannot use normal distribution, $nq = (20)(0.17) = 3.4 < 5$

2) use normal distribution, $\mu = 22.2$ and $\sigma = 2.40$.

3) use normal distribution, $\mu = 5.4$ and $\sigma = 2.18$.

4) cannot use normal distribution

5) can use normal distribution

6) can use normal distribution

7) C

8) B

9) C

10) C

11) D

12) C

13) C

14) A

15) C

16) D

17) A

18) D

19) A

20) $P(4.5 < X < 5.5) = P(0.27 < z < 0.78) = 0.7823 - 0.6064 = 0.1759$

21) $P(x \geq 139.5) = 0.0025$

22) $P(x \leq 34.5) = 0.9032$

23) B

24) C

25) D

26) B

27) D

28) D

29) $P(57.5 < x < 58.5) = P(1.50 < z < 1.70) = 0.9554 - 0.9332 = 0.0222$

Ch. 6 Confidence Intervals

6.1 Confidence Intervals for the Mean (Large Samples)

Solve the problem.

1) A random sample of 100 high school seniors is given the SAT–V test. The mean score for this sample is $\bar{x} = 492$. What can you say about the mean score μ of all high school seniors?

2) The grade point averages for 10 randomly selected students in a statistics class with 125 students are listed below. What can you say about the mean score μ of all 125 students?

   3.6 3.9 2.1 3.2 3.8 2.0 3.5 3.4 2.5 2.9

3) A certain confidence in interval is $8.95 < \mu < 10.25$. Find the sample mean $\bar{x}$ and the error of estimate E.

4) Given the same sample statistics, which level of confidence will produce the narrowest confidence interval?
   A) 75%   B) 85%   C) 95%   D) 90%

5) The grade point averages for 10 randomly selected students in a statistics class with 125 students are listed below.

   2.0 3.2 1.8 2.9 0.9 4.0 3.3 2.9 3.6 0.8

   What is the effect on the width of the confidence interval if the sample size is increased to 20?
   A) The width increases.   B) It is impossible to tell without more information.
   C) The width decreases.   D) The width remains the same.

6) Find the critical value z_c that corresponds to a 94% confidence level.
   A) ±1.96   B) ±2.33   C) ±1.88   D) ±1.645

7) Determine the margin of error if the grade point averages for 10 randomly selected students from a class of 125 students has a mean of $\bar{x} = 2.4$. Assume the grade point average of the 125 students has a mean of $\mu = 2.9$.
   A) 2.65   B) –0.5   C) 0.5   D) 2.15

8) A random sample of 120 students has a test score average with a standard deviation of 9.1. Find the margin of error if c = 0.95.
   A) 1.63   B) 0.79   C) 0.83   D) 0.15

9) A random sample of 150 students has a grade point average with a standard deviation of 0.78. Find the margin of error if c = 0.98.
   A) 0.08   B) 0.12   C) 0.15   D) 0.11

10) A random sample of 40 students has a mean annual earnings of $3120 and a standard deviation of $677. Find the margin of error if c = 0.95.
   A) $2891   B) $7   C) $210   D) $77

11) A random sample of 150 students has a grade point average with a mean of 2.86 and with a standard deviation of 0.78. Construct the confidence interval for the population mean, μ, if c = 0.98.
   A) (2.71, 3.01)   B) (2.31, 3.88)   C) (2.43, 3.79)   D) (2.51, 3.53)

12) A random sample of 40 students has a test score with $\bar{x} = 81.5$ and $s = 10.2$. Construct the confidence interval for the population mean, μ if $c = 0.90$.

    A) (51.8, 92.3)   B) (66.3, 89.1)   C) (78.8, 84.2)   D) (71.8, 93.5)

13) A random sample of 40 students has a mean annual earnings of $3120 and a standard deviation of $677. Construct the confidence interval for the population mean, μ if $c = 0.95$.

    A) ($210, $110)   B) ($2910, $3330)   C) ($1987, $2346)   D) ($4812, $5342)

14) A random sample of 56 fluorescent light bulbs has a mean life of 645 hours with a standard deviation of 31 hours. Construct a 95% confidence interval for the population mean.

    A) (712.0, 768.0)   B) (112.0, 118.9)   C) (636.9, 653.1)   D) (539.6, 551.2)

15) A group of 49 randomly selected students has a mean age of 22.4 years with a standard deviation of 3.8. Construct a 98% confidence interval for the population mean.

    A) (20.3, 24.5)   B) (18.8, 26.3)   C) (21.1, 23.7)   D) (19.8, 25.1)

16) A group of 40 bowlers showed that their average score was 192 with a standard deviation of 8. Find the 95% confidence interval of the mean score of all bowlers.

    A) (186.5, 197.5)   B) (188.5, 195.6)   C) (189.5, 194.5)   D) (187.3, 196.1)

17) In a random sample of 60 computers, the mean repair cost was $150 with a standard deviation of $36. Construct a 99% confidence interval for the population mean.

    A) ($138, $162)   B) ($537, $654)   C) ($238, $274)   D) ($18, $54)

18) In a random sample of 60 computers, the mean repair cost was $150 with a standard deviation of $36.

    a) Construct the 99% confidence interval for the population mean repair cost.
    b) If the level of confidence was lowered to 90%, what will be the effect on the confidence interval?

19) In a recent study of 42 eighth graders, the mean number of hours per week that they watched television was 19.6 with a standard deviation of 5.8 hours. Find the 98% confidence interval for the population mean.

    A) (18.3, 20.9)   B) (17.5, 21.7)   C) (14.1, 23.2)   D) (19.1, 20.4)

20) In a recent study of 99 eighth graders, the mean number of hours per week that they watched television was 18.1 with a standard deviation of 5.4 hours.

    a) Find the 95% confidence interval of the mean.
    b) If the standard deviation is doubled to 10.8, what will be the effect on the confidence interval?

21) In a sample of 10 randomly selected women, it was found that their mean height was 63.4 inches. From previous studies, it is assumed that the standard deviation, σ, is 2.4. Construct the 95% confidence interval for the population mean.

    A) (58.1, 67.3)   B) (59.7, 66.5)   C) (60.8, 65.4)   D) (61.9, 64.9)

22) In a sample of 10 randomly selected women, it was found that their mean height was 63.4 inches. From previous studies, it is assumed that the standard deviation, σ, is 2.4 inches.

a) Construct the 99% confidence interval for the population mean height of women.
b) If the sample size was doubled to 20 women, what will be the effect on the confidence interval?

23) The standard IQ test has a mean of 98 and a standard deviation of 16. We want to be 90% certain that we are within 4 IQ points of the true mean. Determine the required sample size.
    A) 7   B) 142   C) 44   D) 1

24) A nurse at a local hospital is interested in estimating the birth weight of infants. How large a sample must she select if she desires to be 90% confident that the true mean is within 3 ounces of the sample mean? The standard deviation of the birth weights is known to be 9 ounces.
    A) 25   B) 5   C) 24   D) 4

25) In order to set rates, an insurance company is trying to estimate the number of sick days that full time workers at an auto repair shop take per year. A previous study indicated that the standard deviation was 2.8 days. How large a sample must be selected if the company wants to be 95% confident that the true mean differs from the sample mean by no more than 1 day?
    A) 1024   B) 512   C) 141   D) 31

26) In order to efficiently bid on a contract, a contractor wants to be 95% confident that his error is less than two hours in estimating the average time it takes to install tile flooring. Previous contracts indicate that the standard deviation is 4.5 hours. How large a sample must be selected?
    A) 5   B) 20   C) 19   D) 4

27) In order to fairly set flat rates for auto mechanics, a shop foreman needs to estimate the average time it takes to replace a fuel pump in a car. How large a sample must he select if he wants to be 99% confident that the true average time is within 15 minutes of the sample average? Assume the standard deviation of all times is 30 minutes.
    A) 27   B) 5   C) 6   D) 26

28) In order to set rates, an insurance company is trying to estimate the number of sick days that full time workers at an auto repair shop take per year. A previous study indicated that the standard deviation was 2.1 days. a) How large a sample must be selected if the company wants to be 95% confident that the true mean differs from the sample mean by no more than 1 day? b) Repeat part (a) using a 98% confidence interval. Which level of confidence requires a larger sample size? Explain.

29) The numbers of advertisements seen or heard in one week for 30 randomly selected people in the United States are listed below. Construct a 95% confidence interval for the true mean number of advertisements.

598	494	441	595	728	690	684	486	735	808
481	298	135	846	764	317	649	732	582	677
734	588	590	540	673	727	545	486	702	703

30) The number of wins in a season for 32 randomly selected professional football teams are listed below. Construct a 90% confidence interval for the true mean number of wins in a season.

9 9 9 8 10 9 7 2

11 10 6 4 11 9 8 8

12 10 7 5 12 6 4 3

12 9 9 7 10 7 7 5

31) There were 800 math instructors at a mathematics convention. Forty instructors were randomly selected and given an IQ test. The scores produced a mean of 130 with a standard deviation of 10. Find a 95% confidence interval for the mean of the 800 instructors. Use the finite population correction factor.

6.2 Confidence Intervals for the Mean (Small Samples)

Solve the problem.

1) Find the critical value, t_c for c = 0.99 and n = 10.

    A) 2.262   B) 3.250   C) 2.2821   D) 1.833

2) Find the critical value, t_c, for c = 0.95 and n = 16.

    A) 2.947   B) 2.131   C) 2.602   D) 1.753

3) Find the critical value, t_c, for c = 0.90 and n = 15.

    A) 2.145   B) 1.345   C) 2.624   D) 1.761

4) Find the value of E, the margin of error, for c = 0.90, n = 16 and s = 2.2.

    A) 0.96   B) 0.74   C) 0.18   D) 0.24

5) Find the value of E, the margin of error, for c = 0.95, n = 10 and s = 3.2.

    A) 2.25   B) 0.72   C) 1.85   D) 2.29

6) Find the value of E, the margin of error, for c = 0.90, n = 15 and s = 5.1.

    A) 0.60   B) 2.39   C) 2.32   D) 1.77

7) In a random sample of 28 families, the average weekly food expense was $95.60 with a standard deviation of $22.50. Determine whether a normal distribution or a t–distribution should be used or whether neither of these can be used to construct a confidence interval. Assume the distribution of weekly food expenses is normally shaped.

    A) Use a t–distribution.

    B) Use a normal distribution.

    C) Neither a normal distribution nor a t–distribution can be used.

8) For a sample of 20 IQ scores the mean score is 105.8. The standard deviation, σ, is 15. Determine whether a normal distribution or a t–distribution should be used or whether neither of these can be used to construct a confidence interval.

   A) Use a t–distribution.

   B) Use a normal distribution.

   C) Neither a normal distribution nor a t–distribution can be used.

9) A random sample of 40 college students has a mean earnings of $3120 with a standard deviation of $677 over the summer months. Determine whether a normal distribution or a t–distribution should be used or whether neither of these can be used to construct a confidence interval.

   A) Use a t–distribution.

   B) Use a normal distribution.

   C) Neither a normal distribution nor a t–distribution can be used.

10) A random sample of 15 statistics textbooks has a mean price of $105 with a standard deviation of $30.25. Determine whether a normal distribution or a t–distribution should be used or whether neither of these can be used to construct a confidence interval. Assume the distribution of prices is skewed left.

   A) Use a normal distribution.

   B) Use a t–distribution.

   C) Neither a normal distribution nor a t–distribution can be used.

11) Construct a 95% confidence interval for the population mean, μ. Assume the population has a normal distribution. A sample of 20 college students had mean annual earnings of $3120 with a standard deviation of $677.

   A) ($2803, $3437)   B) ($2135, $2567)   C) ($1324, $1567)   D) ($2657, $2891)

12) Construct a 90% confidence interval for the population mean, μ. Assume the population has a normal distribution. A sample of 15 randomly selected students has a grade point average of 2.86 with a standard deviation of 0.78.

   A) (2.41, 3.42)   B) (2.28, 3.66)   C) (2.51, 3.21)   D) (2.37, 3.56)

13) Construct a 95% confidence interval for the population mean, μ. Assume the population has a normal distribution. A sample of 25 randomly selected students has a mean test score of 81.5 with a standard deviation of 10.2.

   A) (66.35, 69.89)   B) (56.12, 78.34)   C) (77.29, 85.71)   D) (87.12, 98.32)

14) Construct a 98% confidence interval for the population mean, μ. Assume the population has a normal distribution. A random sample of 20 college students has mean annual earnings of $3050 with a standard deviation of $677.

15) Construct a 95% confidence interval for the population mean, μ. Assume the population has a normal distribution. A random sample of 16 fluorescent light bulbs has a mean life of 645 hours with a standard deviation of 31 hours.

   A) (876.2, 981.5)   B) (321.7, 365.8)   C) (628.5, 661.5)   D) (531.2, 612.9)

16) Construct a 99% confidence interval for the population mean, μ. Assume the population has a normal distribution. A group of 19 randomly selected students has a mean age of 22.4 years with a standard deviation of 3.8 years.

   A) (19.9, 24.9)   B) (16.3, 26.9)   C) (18.7, 24.1)   D) (17.2, 23.6)

17) Construct a 98% confidence interval for the population mean, μ. Assume the population has a normal distribution. A study of 14 bowlers showed that their average score was 192 with a standard deviation of 8.

   A) (115.4, 158.8)   B) (328.3, 386.9)   C) (222.3, 256.1)   D) (186.3, 197.7)

18) Construct a 95% confidence interval for the population mean, μ. Assume the population has a normal distribution. In a random sample of 26 computers, the mean repair cost was $145 with a standard deviation of $33.

19) Construct a 90% confidence interval for the population mean, μ. Assume the population has a normal distribution. In a recent study of 22 eighth graders, the mean number of hours per week that they watched television was 19.6 with a standard deviation of 5.8 hours.

   A) (5.87, 7.98)   B) (19.62, 23.12)   C) (18.63, 20.89)   D) (17.47, 21.73)

20) a) Construct a 95% confidence interval for the population mean, μ. Assume the population has a normal distribution. In a random sample of 26 computers, the mean repair cost was $129 with a standard deviation of $37.
   b) Suppose you did some research on repair costs for computers and found that the standard deviation is $\sigma = 37$. Use the normal distribution to construct a 95% confidence interval for the population mean, μ. Compare the results.

21) A random sample of 10 parking meters in a beach community showed the following incomes for a day. Assume the incomes are normally distributed.

   $3.60 $4.50 $2.80 $6.30 $2.60 $5.20 $6.75 $4.25 $8.00 $3.00

   Find the 95% confidence interval for the true mean.

   A) ($4.81, $6.31)   B) ($1.35, $2.85)   C) ($2.11, $5.34)   D) ($3.39, $6.01)

22) The grade point averages for 10 randomly selected high school students are listed below. Assume the grade point averages are normally distributed.

   2.0 3.2 1.8 2.9 0.9 4.0 3.3 2.9 3.6 0.8

   Find a 98% confidence interval for the true mean.

   A) (0.67, 1.81)   B) (1.55, 3.53)   C) (3.11, 4.35)   D) (2.12, 3.14)

23) A local bank needs information concerning the checking account balances of its customers. A random sample of 15 accounts was checked. The mean balance was $686.75 with a standard deviation of $256.20. Find a 98% confidence interval for the true mean. Assume that the account balances are normally distributed.

   A) ($238.23, $326.41)   B) ($326.21, $437.90)   C) ($513.17, $860.33)   D) ($487.31, $563.80)

24) A manufacturer receives an order for fluorescent light bulbs. The order requires that the bulbs have a mean life span of 550 hours. The manufacturer selects a random sample of 25 fluorescent light bulbs and finds that they have a mean life span of 545 hours with a standard deviation of 15 hours. Test to see if the manufacturer is making acceptable light bulbs. Use a 95% confidence level. Assume the data are normally distributed.

25) A coffee machine is supposed to dispense 12 ounces of coffee in each cup. An inspector selects a random sample of 40 cups of coffee and finds they have an average amount of 12.2 ounces with a standard deviation of 0.3 ounce. Use a 95% confidence interval to test whether the machine is dispensing acceptable amounts of coffee.

6.3 Confidence Intervals for Population Proportions

Solve the problem.

1) When 450 college students were surveyed, 160 said they own their car. Find a point estimate for p, the population proportion of students who own their cars.

    A) 0.262   B) 0.356   C) 0.644   D) 0.552

2) A survey of 100 fatal accidents showed that 17 were alcohol related. Find a point estimate for p, the population proportion of accidents that were alcohol related.

    A) 0.17   B) 0.205   C) 0.145   D) 0.83

3) A survey of 700 non-fatal accidents showed that 111 involved the use of a cell phone. Find a point estimate for p, the population proportion of non-fatal accidents that involved the use of a cell phone.

    A) 0.841   B) 0.188   C) 0.159   D) 0.137

4) A survey of 250 homeless persons showed that 98 were veterans. Find a point estimate p, for the population proportion of homeless persons who are veterans.

    A) 0.608   B) 0.392   C) 0.645   D) 0.282

5) A survey of 2070 golfers showed that 347 of them are left-handed. Find a point estimate for p, the population proportion of golfers that are left-handed.

    A) 0.144   B) 0.832   C) 0.201   D) 0.168

6) When 500 college students were surveyed, 150 said they own their car. Construct a 95% confidence interval for the proportion of college students who say they own their cars.

7) A survey of 300 fatal accidents showed that 123 were alcohol related. Construct a 98% confidence interval for the proportion of fatal accidents that were alcohol related.

8) A survey of 600 non-fatal accidents showed that 259 involved the use of a cell phone. Construct a 99% confidence interval for the proportion of fatal accidents that involved the use of a cell phone.

9) A survey of 280 homeless persons showed that 63 were veterans. Construct a 90% confidence interval for the proportion of homeless persons who are veterans.

    A) (0.176, 0.274)   B) (0.183, 0.266)   C) (0.161, 0.289)   D) (0.167, 0.283)

10) A survey of 2450 golfers showed that 281 of them are left-handed. Construct a 98% confidence interval for the proportion of golfers that are left-handed.

    A) (0.683, 0.712)   B) (0.100, 0.130)   C) (0.369, 0.451)   D) (0.203, 0.293)

11) A researcher at a major hospital wishes to estimate the proportion of the adult population of the United States that has high blood pressure. How large a sample is needed in order to be 95% confident that the sample proportion will not differ from the true proportion by more than 5%?

    A) 271   B) 385   C) 769   D) 10

12) A pollster wishes to estimate the proportion of United States voters who favor capital punishment. How large a sample is needed in order to be 90% confident that the sample proportion will not differ from the true proportion by more than 4%?

    A) 846   B) 11   C) 423   D) 256

13) A private opinion poll is conducted for a politician to determine what proportion of the population favors decriminalizing marijuana possession. How large a sample is needed in order to be 95% confident that the sample proportion will not differ from the true proportion by more than 6%?

    A) 188   B) 534   C) 9   D) 267

14) A manufacturer of golf equipment wishes to estimate the number of left-handed golfers. How large a sample is needed in order to be 95% confident that the sample proportion will not differ from the true proportion by more than 3%? A previous study indicates that the proportion of left-handed golfers is 11%.

    A) 10   B) 295   C) 418   D) 470

15) A researcher wishes to estimate the number of households with two cars. How large a sample is needed in order to be 90% confident that the sample proportion will not differ from the true proportion by more than 2%? A previous study indicates that the proportion of households with two cars is 18%.

    A) 605   B) 1218   C) 2   D) 999

16) A state highway patrol official wishes to estimate the number of drivers that exceed the speed limit traveling a certain road.
a) How large a sample is needed in order to be 99% confident that the sample proportion will not differ from the true proportion by more than 4%?
b) Repeat part (a) assuming previous studies found that 70% of drivers on this road exceeded the speed limit.

17) In a survey of 2480 golfers, 15% said they were left-handed. The survey's margin of error was 3%. Find the confidence interval for p.

    A) 98.5%   B) 84.5%   C) 80%   D) 95%

18) The Federal Bureau of Labor Statistics surveys 50,000 people to determine the unemployment rate. If the reported unemployment rate must have an error no more than 0.2% and the rate is known to be 5.8%, what is the corresponding confidence level?

19) In a survey of 10 golfers, 2 were found to be left-handed. Is it practical to construct the 90% confidence interval for the population proportion, p? Explain.

20) The USA Today claims that 44% of adults who access the Internet read the international news online. You want to check the accuracy of their claim by surveying a random sample of 120 adults who access the Internet and asking them if they read the international news online. Fifty-two adults responded "yes." Use a 95% confidence interval to test the newspaper's claim.

6.4 Confidence Intervals for Variance and Standard Deviation

Solve the problem.

1) Find the critical values, X^2_R and X^2_L, for $c = 0.95$ and $n = 12$.

    A) 4.575 and 26.757   B) 3.816 and 21.920   C) 2.603 and 19.675   D) 3.053 and 24.725

2) Find the critical values, X^2_R and X^2_L, for $c = 0.90$ and $n = 15$.

    A) 4.660 and 29.131   B) 5.629 and 26.119   C) 4.075 and 31.319   D) 6.571 and 23.685

3) Find the critical values, X^2_R and X^2_L, for c = 0.98 and n = 20.

    A) 7.633 and 36.191   B) 6.844 and 27.204   C) 10.117 and 32.852   D) 8.907 and 38.582

4) Find the critical values, X^2_R and X^2_L, for c = 0.99 and n = 10.

    A) 2.088 and 21.666   B) 2.156 and 25.188   C) 1.735 and 23.587   D) 2.558 and 23.209

5) Construct a 95% confidence interval for the population standard deviation σ of a random sample of 15 men who have a mean weight of 165.2 pounds with a standard deviation of 13.9 pounds. Assume the population is normally distributed.

    A) (10.2, 21.9)   B) (2.7, 5.9)   C) (10.7, 20.3)   D) (103.6, 480.5)

6) Assume that the heights of men are normally distributed. A random sample of 16 men have a mean height of 67.5 inches and a standard deviation of 1.8 inches. Construct a 99% confidence interval for the population standard deviation, σ.

    A) (0.9, 2.4)   B) (1.2, 3.3)   C) (1.3, 3.4)   D) (1.3, 3.0)

7) Assume that the heights of women are normally distributed. A random sample of 20 women have a mean height of 62.5 inches and a standard deviation of 3.8 inches. Construct a 98% confidence interval for the population variance, σ^2.

    A) (8.0, 37.8)   B) (7.6, 35.9)   C) (2.8, 6.0)   D) (2.0, 9.5)

8) The heights (in inches) of 20 randomly selected adult males are listed below. Construct a 99% confidence interval for the variance, σ^2. Assume the population is normally distributed.

70 72 71 70 69 73 69 68 70 71
67 71 70 74 69 68 71 71 71 72

9) The grade point averages for 10 randomly selected students are listed below. Construct a 90% confidence interval for the population standard deviation, σ. Assume the data are normally distributed.

2.0 3.2 1.8 2.9 0.9 4.0 3.3 2.9 3.6 0.8

    A) (0.81, 1.83)   B) (1.10, 2.01)   C) (0.32, 0.85)   D) (0.53, 1.01)

10) The mean replacement time for a random sample of 12 microwave ovens is 8.6 years with a standard deviation of 5.1 years. Construct the 98% confidence interval for the population variance, σ^2. Assume the data are normally distributed

    A) (11.6, 93.7)   B) (3.4, 9.7)   C) (10.9, 80.1)   D) (2.3, 18.4)

11) A student randomly selects 10 CDs at a store. The mean is $13.75 with a standard deviation of $1.50. Construct a 95% confidence interval for the population standard deviation, σ. Assume the data are normally distributed.

    A) ($1.06, $7.51)   B) ($0.84, $2.24)   C) ($1.03, $2.74)   D) ($0.99, $2.50)

12) A student, working with data that are normally distributed, calculates the confidence interval for the standard deviation to be (0.193, 0.623). The data has a mean of 3.56 and a standard deviation of 0.30. Determine the probability that the confidence interval contains σ.

    A) 99%   B) 90%   C) 98%   D) 95%

13) A container of car oil is supposed to contain 1000 milliliters of oil. A quality control manager wants to be sure that the standard deviation of the oil containers is less than 20 milliliters. He randomly selects 10 cans of oil with a mean of 997 milliliters and a standard deviation of 32 milliliters. Use these sample results to construct a 95% confidence interval for the true value of σ. Does this confidence interval suggest that the variation in the oil containers is at an acceptable level?

Ch. 6 Confidence Intervals
Answer Key

6.1 Confidence Intervals for the Mean (Large Samples)

1) The sample mean $\bar{x} = 492$ is the best estimator of the unknown population mean μ.

2) The sample mean $\bar{x} = 3.09$ is the best point estimate of the unknown population mean μ.

3) Sample mean $\bar{x} = 9.60$ and the error of estimate $E = 0.65$.

4) A
5) C
6) C
7) C
8) A
9) C
10) C
11) A
12) C
13) B
14) C
15) C
16) C
17) A
18) a) ($138, $162)

b) A decrease in the level of confidence will decrease the width of the confidence interval.

19) B
20) a) (17.0, 19.2)

b) An increase in the standard deviation will widen the confidence interval.

21) D
22) a) (61.9, 64.9)

b) An increase in the sample size will decrease the width of the confidence interval.

23) C
24) A
25) D
26) B
27) A
28) a) 17

b) 24; A 98% confidence interval requires a larger sample than a 95% confidence interval because more information is needed from the population to be 98% confident.

29) (543.8, 658. 0)
30) (7.2, 8.8)
31) (127.0, 133.0)

6.2 Confidence Intervals for the Mean (Small Samples)

1) B
2) B
3) D
4) A
5) D
6) C
7) A
8) B
9) B
10) C
11) A

12) C

13) C

14) ($2666, $3434)

15) C

16) A

17) D

18) ($131.67, $158.33)

19) D

20) a) ($114.05, $143.95)

b) ($114.78, $143.22); The t–confidence interval is wider.

21) D

22) B

23) C

24) (538.81, 551.19). Because the interval contains the desired life span of 550 hours, they are making good light bulbs.

25) (12.1, 12.3) Because the interval does not contain the desired amount of 12 ounces, the machine is not working properly.

6.3 Confidence Intervals for Population Proportions

1) B

2) A

3) C

4) B

5) D

6) (0.260, 0.340)

7) (0.344, 0.476)

8) (0.380, 0.484)

9) B

10) B

11) B

12) C

13) D

14) C

15) D

16) a) 1037

b) 871

17) B

18) Approximately 90%.

19) It is not practical to find the confidence interval. It is necessary that $n\hat{p} > 5$ to insure that the distribution of $\hat{p}$ be normal. ($n\hat{p} = 2$)

20) (0.344, 0.522) Because the interval contains the reported percentage of 44%, the newspaper's claim is accurate.

6.4 Confidence Intervals for Variance and Standard Deviation

1) B

2) D

3) A

4) C

5) A

6) B

7) B

8) $s = 1.73$; (1.47, 8.31)

9) A

10) A

11) C

12) C

13) The 95% confidence interval is (22.01, 58.42). Because this interval does not contain 20, the standard deviation is not at an acceptable level.

Ch. 7 Hypothesis Testing with One Sample

7.1 Introduction to Hypothesis Testing

Solve the problem.

1) The mean age of bus drivers in Chicago is 51.5 years. Write the null and alternative hypotheses.

2) The mean IQ of statistics teachers is greater than 120. Write the null and alternative hypotheses.

3) The mean score for all NBA games during a particular season was less than 95 points per game. Write the null and alternative hypotheses.

4) A candidate for governor of a particular state claims to be favored by at least half of the voters. Write the null and alternative hypotheses.

5) The dean of a major university claims that the mean time for students to earn a Master's degree is at most 5.4 years. Write the null and alternative hypotheses.

6) The buyer of a local hiking club store recommends against buying the new digital altimeters because they vary more than the old altimeters, which had a standard deviation of one yard. Write the null and alternative hypotheses.

7) The mean age of bus drivers in Chicago is 52.1 years. State this claim mathematically. Write the null and alternative hypotheses. Identify which hypothesis is the claim.

8) The mean IQ of statistics teachers is greater than 140. State this claim mathematically. Write the null and alternative hypotheses. Identify which hypothesis is the claim.

9) The mean score for all NBA games during a particular season was less than 92 points per game. State this claim mathematically. Write the null and alternative hypotheses. Identify which hypothesis is the claim.

10) A candidate for governor of a particular state claims to be favored by at least half of the voters. State the claim mathematically. Write the null and alternative hypotheses. Identify which hypothesis is the claim.

11) The dean of a major university claims that the mean time for students to earn a Master's degree is at most 3.1 years. State this claim mathematically. Write the null and alternative hypotheses. Identify which hypothesis is the claim.

12) The buyer of a local hiking club store recommends against buying the new digital altimeters because they vary more than the old altimeters, which had a standard deviation of one yard. State this claim mathematically. Write the null and alternative hypotheses. Identify which hypothesis is the claim.

13) The mean age of bus drivers in Chicago is 55.3 years. Identify the type I and type II errors for the hypothesis test of this claim.

14) The mean IQ of statistics teachers is greater than 130. Identify the type I and type II errors for the hypothesis test of this claim.

15) The mean score for all NBA games during a particular season was less than 97 points per game. Identify the type I and type II errors for the hypothesis test of this claim.

16) A candidate for governor of a certain state claims to be favored by at least half of the voters. Identify the type I and type II errors for the hypothesis test of this claim.

17) Given H_0: p ≥ 80% and H_a: p < 80%, determine whether the hypothesis test is left–tailed, right–tailed, or two–tailed.

    A) right–tailed   B) two–tailed   C) left–tailed

18) Given H_0: μ ≤ 25 and H_a: μ > 25, determine whether the hypothesis test is left–tailed, right–tailed, or two–tailed.

    A) left–tailed   B) two–tailed   C) right–tailed

19) A researcher claims that 60% of voters favor gun control. Determine whether the hypothesis test for this claim is left–tailed, right–tailed, or two–tailed.

    A) left–tailed   B) two–tailed   C) right–tailed

20) A brewery claims that the mean amount of beer in their bottles is at least 12 ounces. Determine whether the hypothesis test for this claim is left–tailed, right–tailed, or two–tailed.

    A) left–tailed   B) right–tailed   C) two–tailed

21) A car maker claims that its new sub–compact car gets better than 49 miles per gallon on the highway. Determine whether the hypothesis test for this is left–tailed, right–tailed, or two–tailed.

    A) two–tailed   B) left–tailed   C) right–tailed

22) The owner of a professional basketball team claims that the mean attendance at games is over 18,000 and therefore the team needs a new arena. Determine whether the hypothesis test for this claim is left–tailed, right–tailed, or two–tailed.

    A) left–tailed   B) two–tailed   C) right–tailed

23) An elementary school claims that the standard deviation in reading scores of its fourth grade students is less than 4.55. Determine whether the hypothesis test for this claim is left–tailed, right–tailed, or two–tailed.

    A) two–tailed   B) right–tailed   C) left–tailed

24) The mean age of bus drivers in Chicago is 50.1 years. If a hypothesis test is performed, how should you interpret a decision that rejects the null hypothesis?

    A) There is sufficient evidence to support the claim μ = 50.1.

    B) There is not sufficient evidence to reject the claim μ = 50.1.

    C) There is sufficient evidence to reject the claim μ = 50.1.

    D) There is not sufficient evidence to support the claim μ = 50.1.

25) The mean age of bus drivers in Chicago is 48.9 years. If a hypothesis test is performed, how should you interpret a decision that fails to reject the null hypothesis?

    A) There is not sufficient evidence to reject the claim μ = 48.9.

    B) There is sufficient evidence to reject the claim μ = 48.9.

    C) There is not sufficient evidence to support the claim μ = 48.9.

    D) There is sufficient evidence to support the claim μ = 48.9.

26) The mean age of bus drivers in Chicago is greater than 52.1 years. If a hypothesis test is performed, how should you interpret a decision that rejects the null hypothesis?

    A) There is not sufficient evidence to reject the claim $\mu > 52.1$.

    B) There is sufficient evidence to support the claim $\mu > 52.1$.

    C) There is sufficient evidence to reject the claim $\mu > 52.1$.

    D) There is not sufficient evidence to support the claim $\mu > 52.1$.

27) The mean age of bus drivers in Chicago is greater than 53.4 years. If a hypothesis test is performed, how should you interpret a decision that fails to reject the null hypothesis?

    A) There is not sufficient evidence to reject the claim $\mu > 53.4$.

    B) There is not sufficient evidence to support the claim $\mu > 53.4$.

    C) There is sufficient evidence to support the claim $\mu > 53.4$.

    D) There is sufficient evidence to reject the claim $\mu > 53.4$.

28) The mean IQ of statistics teachers is greater than 110. If a hypothesis test is performed, how should you interpret a decision that rejects the null hypothesis?

    A) There is sufficient evidence to support the claim $\mu > 110$.

    B) There is not sufficient evidence to reject the claim $\mu > 110$.

    C) There is sufficient evidence to reject the claim $\mu > 110$.

    D) There is not sufficient evidence to support the claim $\mu > 110$.

29) The mean IQ of statistics teachers is greater than 140. If a hypothesis test is performed, how should you interpret a decision that fails to reject the null hypothesis?

    A) There is not sufficient evidence to support the claim $\mu > 140$.

    B) There is sufficient evidence to support the claim $\mu > 140$.

    C) There is sufficient evidence to reject the claim $\mu > 140$.

    D) There is not sufficient evidence to reject the claim $\mu > 140$.

30) The mean score for all NBA games during a particular season was less than 107 points per game. If a hypothesis test is performed, how should you interpret a decision that rejects the null hypothesis?

    A) There is sufficient evidence to reject the claim $\mu < 107$.

    B) There is sufficient evidence to support the claim $\mu < 107$.

    C) There is not sufficient evidence to reject the claim $\mu < 107$.

    D) There is not sufficient evidence to support the claim $\mu < 107$.

31) The mean score for all NBA games during a particular season was less than 93 points per game. If a hypothesis test is performed, how should you interpret a decision that fails to reject the null hypothesis?

    A) There is sufficient evidence to support the claim $\mu < 93$.

    B) There is not sufficient evidence to support the claim $\mu < 93$.

    C) There is not sufficient evidence to reject the claim $\mu < 93$.

    D) There is sufficient evidence to reject the claim $\mu < 93$.

32) A candidate for governor of a certain state claims to be favored by at least half of the voters. If a hypothesis test is performed, how should you interpret a decision that rejects the null hypothesis?

    A) There is not sufficient evidence to support the claim $p \geq 0.5$.

    B) There is sufficient evidence to reject the claim $p \geq 0.5$.

    C) There is not sufficient evidence to reject the claim $p \geq 0.5$.

    D) There is sufficient evidence to support the claim $p \geq 0.5$.

33) A candidate for governor of a certain state claims to be favored by at least half of the voters. If a hypothesis test is performed, how should you interpret a decision that fails to reject the null hypothesis?

    A) There is not sufficient evidence to reject the claim $p \geq 0.5$.

    B) There is sufficient evidence to support the claim $p \geq 0.5$.

    C) There is not sufficient evidence to support the claim $p \geq 0.5$.

    D) There is sufficient evidence to reject the claim $p \geq 0.5$.

34) The dean of a major university claims that the mean time for students to earn a Master's degree is at most 4.7 years. If a hypothesis test is performed, how should you interpret a decision that rejects the null hypothesis?

    A) There is sufficient evidence to support the claim $\mu \leq 4.7$.

    B) There is not sufficient evidence to support the claim $\mu \leq 4.7$.

    C) There is sufficient evidence to reject the claim $\mu \leq 4.7$.

    D) There is not sufficient evidence to reject the claim $\mu \leq 4.7$.

35) The dean of a major university claims that the mean time for students to earn a Master's degree is at most 5.2 years. If a hypothesis test is performed, how should you interpret a decision that fails to reject the null hypothesis?

    A) There is not sufficient evidence to reject the claim $\mu \leq 5.2$.

    B) There is sufficient evidence to support the claim $\mu \leq 5.2$.

    C) There is not sufficient evidence to support the claim $\mu \leq 5.2$.

    D) There is sufficient evidence to reject the claim $\mu \leq 5.2$.

36) Given H_0: $\mu \leq 12$, for which confidence interval should you reject H_0?

    A) (10, 13)   B) (13, 16)   C) (11.5, 12.5)

37) Given H_0: $p \geq 0.45$, for which confidence interval should you reject H_0?

    A) (0.42, 0.47)   B) (0.32, 0.40)   C) (0.40, 0.50)

38) Given H_0: $p = 0.85$ and $\alpha = 0.10$, which level of confidence should you use to test the claim?

    A) 90%   B) 80%   C) 95%   D) 99%

39) Given H_0: $\mu \geq 23.5$ and $\alpha = 0.05$, which level of confidence should you use to test the claim?

    A) 95%   B) 80%   C) 90%   D) 99%

7.2 Hypothesis Testing for the Mean (Large Samples)

Solve the problem.

    1) Find the critical value for a right–tailed test with $\alpha = 0.01$ and $n = 75$.

    A) 1.96   B) 2.33   C) 1.645   D) 2.575

2) Find the critical value for a two-tailed test with $\alpha = 0.01$ and n = 30.

    A) ±1.645   B) ±1.96   C) ±2.33   D) ±2.575

3) Find the critical value for a left-tailed test with $\alpha = 0.05$ and n = 48.

    A) −1.645   B) −1.96   C) −2.575   D) −2.33

4) Find the critical value for a two-tailed test with $\alpha = 0.10$ and n = 100.

    A) ±1.645   B) ±2.33   C) ±1.96   D) ±2.575

5) Find the critical value for a left-tailed test with $\alpha = 0.025$ and n = 50.

    A) −1.645   B) −2.33   C) −1.96   D) −2.575

6) Find the critical value for a two-tailed test with $\alpha = 0.08$ and n = 36.

    A) ±1.96   B) ±2.575   C) ±2.33   D) ±1.75

7) You wish to test the claim that $\mu > 12$ at a level of significance of $\alpha = 0.05$ and are given sample statistics n = 50, $\bar{x} = 12.3$, and s = 1.2. Compute the value of the standardized test statistic. Round your answer to two decimal places.

    A) 1.77   B) 0.98   C) 3.11   D) 2.31

8) You wish to test the claim that $\mu \neq 15$ at a level of significance of $\alpha = 0.05$ and are given sample statistics n = 35, $\bar{x} = 14.1$, and s = 2.7. Compute the value of the standardized test statistic. Round your answer to two decimal places.

    A) −2.86   B) −1.97   C) −3.12   D) −1.83

9) You wish to test the claim that $\mu \leq 47$ at a level of significance of $\alpha = 0.01$ and are given sample statistics n = 40, $\bar{x} = 48.8$, and s = 4.3. Compute the value of the standardized test statistic. Round your answer to two decimal places.

    A) 3.51   B) 1.96   C) 2.12   D) 2.65

10) You wish to test the claim that $\mu = 1590$ at a level of significance of $\alpha = 0.01$ and are given sample statistics n = 35, $\bar{x} = 1560$ and s = 82. Compute the value of the standardized test statistic. Round your answer to two decimal places.

    A) −3.82   B) −4.67   C) −5.18   D) −2.16

11) Suppose you want to test the claim that $\mu = 3.5$. Given a sample size of n = 50 and a level of significance of $\alpha = 0.01$, when should you reject H_0?

    A) Reject H_0 if the standardized test statistic is greater than 1.645 or less than −1.645

    B) Reject H_0 if the standardized test statistic is greater than 2.33 or less than −2.33.

    C) Reject H_0 if the standardized test statistic is greater than 2.575 or less than −2.575.

    D) Reject H_0 if the standardized test statistic is greater than 1.96 or less than −1.96

12) Suppose you want to test the claim that $\mu > 25.6$. Given a sample size of n = 42 and a level of significance of $\alpha = 0.01$, when should you reject H_0?

    A) Reject H_0 if the standardized test statistic is greater than 1.645.

    B) Reject H_0 if the standardized test statistic is greater than 1.28.

    C) Reject H_0 if the standardized test statistic is greater than 1.96.

    D) Reject H_0 if the standardized test statistic is greater than 2.33.

13) Suppose you want to test the claim that $\mu < 65.4$. Given a sample size of n = 35 and a level of significance of $\alpha = 0.10$, when should you reject H_0?

    A) Reject H_0 if the standardized test is less than –2.33.

    B) Reject H_0 if the standardized test statistic is less than –2.575.

    C) Reject H_0 if the standardized test statistic is less than –1.645.

    D) Reject H_0 if the standardized test statistic is less than –1.28.

14) Test the claim that $\mu > 35$, given that $\alpha = 0.05$ and the sample statistics are n = 50, $\bar{x} = 35.3$, and s = 1.2.

15) Test the claim that $\mu \neq 23$, given that $\alpha = 0.05$ and the sample statistics are n = 35, $\bar{x} = 22.1$ and s = 2.7.

16) Test the claim that $\mu \leq 21$, given that $\alpha = 0.01$ and the sample statistics are n = 40, $\bar{x} = 22.8$, and s = 4.3.

17) Test the claim that $\mu = 820$, given that $\alpha = 0.01$ and the sample statistics are n = 35, $\bar{x} = 790$, and s = 82.

18) A local brewery distributes beer in bottles labeled 24 ounces. A government agency thinks that the brewery is cheating its customers. The agency selects 50 of these bottles, measures their contents, and obtains a sample mean of 23.6 ounces with a standard deviation of 0.70 ounce. Use a 0.01 significance level to test the agency's claim that the brewery is cheating its customers.

19) A manufacturer claims that the mean lifetime of its fluorescent bulbs is 1050 hours. A homeowner selects 40 bulbs and finds the mean lifetime to be 1030 hours with a standard deviation of 80 hours. Test the manufacturer's claim. Use $\alpha = 0.05$.

20) A trucking firm suspects that the mean lifetime of a certain tire it uses is less than 39,000 miles. To check the claim, the firm randomly selects and tests 54 of these tires and gets a mean lifetime of 38,620 miles with a standard deviation of 1200 miles. At $\alpha = 0.05$, test the trucking firm's claim.

21) A local politician, running for reelection, claims that the mean prison time for car thieves is less than the required 4 years. A sample of 80 convicted car thieves was randomly selected, and the mean length of prison time was found to be 3 years and 6 months, with a standard deviation of 1 year and 3 months. At $\alpha = 0.05$, test the politician's claim.

22) A local group claims that the police issue at least 60 speeding tickets a day in their area. To prove their point, they randomly select one month. Their research yields the number of tickets issued for each day. The data are listed below. At $\alpha = 0.01$, test the group's claim.

    70 48 41 68 69 55 70 57 60 83
    32 60 72 58 88 48 59 60 56 65
    66 60 68 42 57 59 49 70 75 63
    44

23) Suppose you are using $\alpha = 0.05$ to test the claim that $\mu > 3$ using a P-value. You are given the sample statistics $n = 50$, $\bar{x} = 3.3$, and $s = 1.2$. Find the P-value.

    A) 0.0012   B) 0.0384   C) 0.1321   D) 0.0128

24) Suppose you are using $\alpha = 0.05$ to test the claim that $\mu \ne 34$ using a P-value. You are given the sample statistics $n = 35$, $\bar{x} = 33.1$, and $s = 2.7$. Find the P-value.

    A) 0.0448   B) 0.0244   C) 0.0591   D) 0.1003

25) Suppose you are using $\alpha = 0.01$ to test the claim that $\mu \le 40$ using a P-value. You are given the sample statistics $n = 40$, $\bar{x} = 41.8$, and $s = 4.3$. Find the P-value.

    A) 0.0211   B) 0.1030   C) 0.0040   D) 0.9960

26) Suppose you are using $\alpha = 0.01$ to test the claim that $\mu = 850$ using a P-value. You are given the sample statistics $n = 35$, $\bar{x} = 820$, and $s = 82$. Find the P-value.

    A) 0.0308   B) 0.0077   C) 0.0154   D) 0.3169

27) Given H_0: $\mu = 25$, H_a: $\mu \ne 25$, and $P = 0.029$. Do you reject or fail to reject H_0 at the 0.01 level of significance?

    A) reject H_0

    B) fail to reject H_0

    C) not sufficient information to decide

28) Given H_0: $\mu \ge 18$ and $P = 0.066$. Do you reject or fail to reject H_0 at the 0.05 level of significance?

    A) reject H_0

    B) fail to reject H_0

    C) not sufficient information to decide

29) Given H_a: $\mu > 85$ and $P = 0.006$. Do you reject or fail to reject H_0 at the 0.01 level of significance?

    A) reject H_0

    B) fail to reject H_0

    C) not sufficient information to decide

30) A fast food outlet claims that the mean waiting time in line is less than 4.5 minutes. A random sample of 60 customers has a mean of 4.4 minutes with a standard deviation of 0.6 minute. If $\alpha = 0.05$, test the fast food outlet's claim.

31) A fast food outlet claims that the mean waiting time in line is less than 3.5 minutes. A random sample of 60 customers has a mean of 3.6 minutes with a standard deviation of 0.6 minute. If $\alpha = 0.05$, test the fast food outlet's claim using critical values and rejection regions.

32) A fast food outlet claims that the mean waiting time in line is less than 3.5 minutes. A random sample of 60 customers has a mean of 3.6 minutes with a standard deviation of 0.6 minute. If $\alpha = 0.05$, test the fast food outlet's claim using confidence intervals.

33) A local school district claims that the number of school days missed by its teachers due to illness is below the national average of 5. A random sample of 40 teachers provided the data below. At $\alpha = 0.05$, test the district's claim using P-values.

```
0   3   6   3   3   5   4   1   3   5
7   3   1   2   3   3   2   4   1   6
2   5   2   8   3   1   2   5   4   1
1   1   2   1   5   7   5   4   9   3
```

34) A local school district claims that the number of school days missed by teachers due to illness is below the national average of 5 days. A random sample of 40 teachers provided the data below. At $\alpha = 0.05$, test the district's claim using critical values and rejection regions.

```
0   3   6   3   3   5   4   1   3   5
7   3   1   2   3   3   2   4   1   6
2   5   2   8   3   1   2   5   4   1
1   1   2   1   5   7   5   4   9   3
```

35) A local school district claims that the number of school days missed by teachers due to illness is below the national average of 5. A random sample of 40 teachers provided the data below. At $\alpha = 0.05$, test the district's claim using confidence intervals.

```
0   3   6   3   3   5   4   1   3   5
7   3   1   2   3   3   2   4   1   6
2   5   2   8   3   1   2   5   4   1
1   1   2   1   5   7   5   4   9   3
```

7.3 Hypothesis Testing for the Mean (Small Samples)

Solve the problem.

1) Find the critical values for a sample with $n = 15$ and $\alpha = 0.05$ if H_0: $\mu \leq 20$.

A) 1.345   B) 2.625   C) 1.761   D) 2.977

2) Find the standardized test statistic t for a sample with $n = 12$, $\bar{x} = 12.2$, $s = 2.2$, and $\alpha = 0.01$ if H_0: $\mu = 11$. Round your answer to three decimal places.

A) 1.991   B) 2.001   C) 1.890   D) 2.132

3) Find the standardized test statistic t for a sample with $n = 10$, $\bar{x} = 10.2$, $s = 1.3$, and $\alpha = 0.05$ if H_0: $\mu \geq 11.1$. Round your answer to three decimal places.

A) -2.189   B) -2.617   C) -3.010   D) -3.186

4) Find the standardized test statistic t for a sample with $n = 15$, $\bar{x} = 6.4$, $s = 0.8$, and $\alpha = 0.05$ if H_0: $\mu \leq 6.1$. Round your answer to three decimal places.

A) 1.631   B) 1.312   C) 1.728   D) 1.452

5) Find the standardized test statistic t for a sample with $n = 20$, $\bar{x} = 11.5$, $s = 2.0$, and $\alpha = 0.05$ if H_a: $\mu < 11.9$. Round your answer to three decimal places.

A) -1.233   B) -0.872   C) -0.894   D) -1.265

6) Find the standardized test statistic t for a sample with n = 25, $\bar{x}$ = 32, s = 3, and α = 0.005 if H_a: μ > 31. Round your answer to three decimal places.

A) 1.239   B) 1.667   C) 1.452   D) 1.997

7) Find the standardized test statistic t for a sample with n = 12, $\bar{x}$ = 23.5, s = 2.1, and α = 0.01 if H_a: μ ≠ 24. Round your answer to three decimal places.

A) –0.825   B) –0.037   C) –0.008   D) –0.381

8) Use a t-test to test the claim μ = 22 at α = 0.01, given the sample statistics n = 12, $\bar{x}$ = 23.2, and s = 2.2.

9) Use a t-test to test the claim μ ≥ 12.5 at α = 0.05, given the sample statistics n = 10, $\bar{x}$ = 11.6, and s = 1.3.

10) Use a t-test to test the claim μ ≤ 8.6 at α = 0.05, given the sample statistics n = 15, $\bar{x}$ = 8.9, and s = 0.8.

11) Use a t-test to test the claim μ < 12.8 at α = 0.10, given the sample statistics n = 20, $\bar{x}$ = 12.4, and s = 2.0.

12) Use a t-test to test the claim μ > 13 at α = 0.005, given the sample statistics n = 25, $\bar{x}$ = 14, and s = 3.

13) Use a t-test to test the claim μ = 19 at α = 0.01, given the sample statistics n = 12, $\bar{x}$ = 18.5, and s = 2.1.

14) The Metropolitan Bus Company claims that the mean waiting time for a bus during rush hour is less than 7 minutes. A random sample of 20 waiting times has a mean of 5.6 minutes with a standard deviation of 2.1 minutes. At α = 0.01, test the bus company's claim. Assume the distribution is normally distributed.

15) A local brewery distributes beer in bottles labeled 12 ounces. A government agency thinks that the brewery is cheating its customers. The agency selects 20 of these bottles, measures their contents, and obtains a sample mean of 11.7 ounces with a standard deviation of 0.7 ounce. Use a 0.01 significance level to test the agency's claim that the brewery is cheating its customers.

16) A local group claims that the police issue at least 60 speeding tickets a day in their area. To prove their point, they randomly select two weeks. Their research yields the number of tickets issued for each day. The data are listed below. At α = 0.01, test the group's claim.

70   48   41   68   69   55   70
57   60   83   32   60   72   58

17) A local group claims that the police issue at least 60 speeding tickets a day in their area. To prove their point, they randomly select two weeks. Their research yields the number of tickets issued for each day. The data are listed below. At α = 0.01, test the group's claim using P-values.

70   48   41   68   69   55   70
57   60   83   32   60   72   58

18) A local group claims that the police issue at least 60 speeding tickets a day in their area. To prove their point, they randomly select two weeks. Their research yields the number of tickets issued for each day. The data are listed below. At $\alpha = 0.01$, test the group's claim using confidence intervals.

70 48 41 68 69 55 70
57 60 83 32 60 72 58

19) A manufacturer claims that the mean lifetime of its fluorescent bulbs is 1000 hours. A homeowner selects 25 bulbs and finds the mean lifetime to be 990 hours with a standard deviation of 80 hours. Test the manufacturer's claim. Use $\alpha = 0.05$.

20) A manufacturer claims that the mean lifetime of its fluorescent bulbs is 1000 hours. A homeowner selects 25 bulbs and finds the mean lifetime to be 980 hours with a standard deviation of 80 hours. If $\alpha = 0.05$, test the manufacturer's claim using P-values.

21) A manufacturer claims that the mean lifetime of its fluorescent bulbs is 1000 hours. A homeowner selects 25 bulbs and finds the mean lifetime to be 980 hours with a standard deviation of 80 hours. If $\alpha = 0.05$, test the manufacturer's claim using confidence intervals.

22) A trucking firm suspects that the mean life of a certain tire it uses is less than 31,000 miles. To check the claim, the firm randomly selects and tests 18 of these tires and gets a mean lifetime of 30,350 miles with a standard deviation of 1200 miles. At $\alpha = 0.05$, test the trucking firm's claim.

23) A fast food outlet claims that the mean waiting time in line is less than 2.1 minutes. A random sample of 20 customers has a mean of 1.9 minutes with a standard deviation of 0.8 minute. If $\alpha = 0.05$, test the fast food outlet's claim using P-values.

24) A local school district claims that the number of school days missed by its teachers due to illness is below the national average of $\mu = 5$. A random sample of 28 teachers provided the data below. At $\alpha = 0.05$, test the district's claim using P-values.

0 3 6 3 3 5 4 1 3 5
7 3 1 2 3 3 2 4 1 6
2 5 2 8 3 1 2 5

7.4 Hypothesis Testing for Proportions

Solve the problem.

1) Determine whether the normal sampling distribution can be used. The claim is $p > 0.25$ and the sample size is $n = 18$.

A) Do not use the normal distribution.   B) Use the normal distribution.

2) Determine whether the normal sampling distribution can be used. The claim is $p \neq 0.300$ and the sample size is $n = 20$.

A) Do not use the normal distribution.   B) Use the normal distribution.

3) Determine the critical value, z_0, to test the claim about the population proportion $p \neq 0.325$ given $n = 42$ and $\hat{p} = 0.247$. Use $\alpha = 0.05$.

A) ±2.575   B) ±2.33   C) ±1.96   D) ±1.645

4) Determine the standardized test statistic, z, to test the claim about the population proportion $p < 0.850$ given $n = 60$ and $\hat{p} = 0.656$. Use $\alpha = 0.05$.

    A) -1.96   B) -1.85   C) -4.21   D) -1.76

5) Test the claim about the population proportion $p = 0.250$ given $n = 48$ and $\hat{p} = 0.231$. Use $\alpha = 0.01$.

6) Fifty-five percent of registered voters in a congressional district are registered Democrats. The Republican candidate takes a poll to assess his chances in a two-candidate race. He polls 1200 potential voters and finds that 621 plan to vote for the Democratic candidate. Does the Republican candidate have a chance to win? Use $\alpha = 0.05$.

7) An airline claims that the no-show rate for passengers is less than 5%. In a sample of 420 randomly selected reservations, 19 were no-shows. At $\alpha = 0.01$, test the airline's claim.

8) A recent study claimed that at least 15% of junior high students are overweight. In a sample of 160 students, 18 were found to be overweight. At $\alpha = 0.05$, test the claim.

9) A recent study claimed that at least 15% of junior high students are overweight. In a sample of 160 students, 18 were found to be overweight. If $\alpha = 0.05$, test the claim using P-values.

10) A recent study claimed that at least 15% of junior high students are overweight. In a sample of 160 students, 18 were found to be overweight. If $\alpha = 0.05$, test the claim using confidence intervals.

11) The engineering school at a major university claims that 20% of its graduates are women. In a graduating class of 210 students, 58 were women. Does this suggest that the school is believable? Use $\alpha = 0.05$.

12) A coin is tossed 1000 times and 570 heads appear. At $\alpha = 0.05$, test the claim that this is not a biased coin. Does this suggest the coin is fair?

13) A telephone company claims that 20% of its customers have at least two telephone lines. The company selects a random sample of 500 customers and finds that 88 have two or more telephone lines. At $\alpha = 0.05$, does the data support the claim? Use a P-value.

14) A telephone company claims that 20% of its customers have at least two telephone lines. The company selects a random sample of 500 customers and finds that 88 have two or more telephone lines. If $\alpha = 0.05$, test the company's claim using critical values and rejection regions.

15) A telephone company claims that 20% of its customers have at least two telephone lines. The company selects a random sample of 500 customers and finds that 88 have two or more telephone lines. If $\alpha = 0.05$, test the company's claim using confidence intervals.

16) A coin is tossed 1000 times and 530 heads appear. At $\alpha = 0.05$, test the claim that this is not a biased coin. Use a P-value. Does this suggest the coin is fair?

7.5 Hypothesis Testing for Variance and Standard Deviation

Solve the problem.

1) Find the critical X^2-values to test the claim $\sigma^2 = 4.3$ if $n = 12$ and $\alpha = 0.05$.

    A) 2.603, 26.757   B) 4.575, 19.675   C) 3.053, 24.725   D) 3.816, 21.920

2) Find the critical X^2 –value to test the claim $\sigma^2 \geq 1.8$ if $n = 15$ and $\alpha = 0.05$.

    A) 4.660   B) 6.571   C) 5.629   D) 4.075

3) Find the critical X^2 –value to test the claim $\sigma^2 \leq 3.2$ if $n = 20$ and $\alpha = 0.01$.

    A) 32.852   B) 36.191   C) 27.204   D) 30.144

4) Find the critical X^2 –value to test the claim $\sigma^2 > 1.9$ if $n = 18$ and $\alpha = 0.01$.

    A) 30.181   B) 33.409   C) 35.718   D) 27.587

5) Find the critical X^2 –value to test the claim $\sigma^2 < 5.6$ if $n = 28$ and $\alpha = 0.10$.

    A) 16.151   B) 18.114   C) 36.741   D) 14.573

6) Find the critical X^2 –values to test the claim $\sigma^2 \neq 6.8$ if $n = 10$ and $\alpha = 0.01$.

    A) 3.325, 16.919   B) 1.735, 23.589   C) 2.700, 19.023   D) 2.088, 21.666

7) Compute the standardized test statistic, X^2, to test the claim $\sigma^2 = 38.7$ if $n = 12$, $s^2 = 32.4$, and $\alpha = 0.05$.

    A) 12.961   B) 9.209   C) 0.492   D) 18.490

8) Compute the standardized test statistic, X^2, to test the claim $\sigma^2 \geq 12.6$ if $n = 15$, $s^2 = 10.5$, and $\alpha = 0.05$.

    A) 12.823   B) 11.667   C) 8.713   D) 23.891

9) Compute the standardized test statistic, X^2, to test the claim $\sigma^2 \leq 16$ if $n = 20$, $s^2 = 31$, and $\alpha = 0.01$.

    A) 36.813   B) 12.82   C) 33.41   D) 9.322

10) Compute the standardized test statistic, X^2, to test the claim $\sigma^2 > 15.2$ if $n = 18$, $s^2 = 21.6$, and $\alpha = 0.01$.

    A) 24.158   B) 28.175   C) 43.156   D) 33.233

11) Compute the standardized test statistic, X^2, to test the claim $\sigma^2 < 33.6$ if $n = 28$, $s^2 = 21$, and $\alpha = 0.10$.

    A) 21.478   B) 14.324   C) 16.875   D) 18.132

12) Compute the standardized test statistic, X^2 to test the claim $\sigma^2 \neq 40.8$ if $n = 10$, $s^2 = 45$, and $\alpha = 0.01$.

    A) 12.008   B) 4.919   C) 9.926   D) 3.276

13) Test the claim that $\sigma^2 = 30.1$ if $n = 12$, $s^2 = 25.2$ and $\alpha = 0.05$. Assume that the population is normally distributed.

14) Test the claim that $\sigma^2 \geq 9$ if $n = 15$, $s^2 = 7.5$, and $\alpha = 0.05$. Assume that the population is normally distributed.

15) Test the claim that $\sigma^2 \leq 6.4$ if $n = 20$, $s^2 = 12.4$, and $\alpha = 0.01$. Assume that the population is normally distributed.

16) Test the claim that $\sigma^2 > 9.5$ if $n = 18$, $s^2 = 13.5$, and $\alpha = 0.01$. Assume that the population is normally distributed.

17) Test the claim that $\sigma^2 < 33.6$ if $n = 28$, $s^2 = 21$, and $\alpha = 0.10$. Assume that the population is normally distributed.

18) Test the claim that $\sigma^2 \neq 40.8$ if $n = 10$, $s^2 = 45$, and $\alpha = 0.01$. Assume that the population is normally distributed.

19) Test the claim that $\sigma = 2.07$ if $n = 12$, $s = 1.9$, and $\alpha = 0.05$. Assume that the population is normally distributed.

Elementary Statistics 126

20) Test the claim that $\sigma \geq 8.04$ if n = 15, s = 7.32, and $\alpha = 0.05$. Assume that the population is normally distributed.

21) Test the claim that $\sigma \leq 1.79$ if n = 20, s = 2.49, and $\alpha = 0.01$. Assume that the population is normally distributed.

22) Test the claim that $\sigma > 8.28$ if n = 18, s = 9.84, and $\alpha = 0.01$. Assume that the population is normally distributed.

23) Test the claim that $\sigma < 21.33$ if n = 28, s = 16.83 and $\alpha = 0.10$. Assume that the population is normally distributed.

24) Test the claim that $\sigma \neq 2.61$ if n = 10, s = 2.74, and $\alpha = 0.01$. Assume that the population is normally distributed.

25) Listed below is the number of tickets issued by a local police department. Assuming that the data is normally distributed, test the claim that the standard deviation for the data is 15 tickets. Use $\alpha = 0.01$.

70 48 41 68 69 55 70
57 60 83 32 60 72 58

26) The heights (in inches) of 20 randomly selected adult males are listed below. Test the claim that the variance is less than 6.25. Use $\alpha = 0.05$. Assume the population is normally distributed.

70 72 71 70 69 73 69 68 70 71
67 71 70 74 69 68 71 71 71 72

27) The heights (in inches) of 20 randomly selected adult males are listed below. Test the claim that the variance is less than 6.25. Assume the population is normally distributed. Use $\alpha = 0.05$ and P–values.

70 72 71 70 69 73 69 68 70 71
67 71 70 74 69 68 71 71 71 72

28) The heights (in inches) of 20 randomly selected adult males are listed below. Test the claim that the variance is less than 6.25. Assume the population is normally distributed. Use $\alpha = 0.05$ and confidence intervals.

70 72 71 70 69 73 69 68 70 71
67 71 70 74 69 68 71 71 71 72

29) A trucking firm suspects that the variance for a certain tire is greater than 1,000,000. To check the claim, the firm puts 101 of these tires on its trucks and gets a standard deviation of 1200 miles. At $\alpha = 0.05$, test the trucking firm's claim.

30) A trucking firm suspects that the variance for a certain tire is greater than 1,000,000. To check the claim, the firm puts 101 of these tires on its trucks and gets a standard deviation of 1200 miles. If $\alpha = 0.05$, test the trucking firm's claim using P–values.

31) A trucking firm suspects that the variance for a certain tire is greater than 1,000,000. To check the claim, the firm puts 101 of these tires on its trucks and gets a standard deviation of 1200 miles. If $\alpha = 0.05$, test the trucking firm's claim using confidence intervals.

32) A local bank needs information concerning the standard deviation of the checking account balances of its customers. From previous information it was assumed to be $250. A random sample of 61 accounts was checked. The standard deviation was $286.20. At $\alpha = 0.01$, test the bank's assumption. Assume that the account balances are normally distributed.

33) In one area, monthly incomes of college graduates have a standard deviation of $650. It is believed that the standard deviation of monthly incomes of non-college graduates is higher. A sample of 71 non-college graduates are randomly selected and found to have a standard deviation of $950. Test the claim that non-college graduates have a higher standard deviation. Use $\alpha = 0.05$.

34) A statistics professor at an all-women's college determined that the standard deviation of women's heights is 2.5 inches. The professor then randomly selected 41 male students from a nearby all-male college and found the standard deviation to be 2.9 inches. Test the professor's claim that the standard deviation of male heights is greater than 2.5 inches. Use $\alpha = 0.01$.

7.1 Introduction to Hypothesis Testing

1) H_0: $\mu = 51.5$, H_a: $\mu \neq 51.5$

2) H_0: $\mu \leq 120$, H_a: $\mu > 120$

3) H_0: $\mu \geq 95$, H_a: $\mu < 95$

4) H_0: $\rho \geq 0.5$, H_a: $p < 0.5$

5) H_0: $\mu \leq 5.4$, H_a: $\mu > 5.4$

6) H_0: $\sigma \leq 1$, H_a: $\sigma > 1$

7) claim: $\mu = 52.1$; H_0: $\mu = 52.1$, H_a: $\mu \neq 52.1$; claim is H_0

8) claim: $\mu > 140$; H_0: $\mu \leq 140$, H_a: $\mu > 140$; claim is H_a

9) claim: $\mu < 92$; H_0: $\mu \geq 92$, H_a: $\mu < 92$; claim is H_a

10) claim: $\rho \geq 0.5$; H_0: $\rho \geq 0.5$, H_a: $p < 0.5$; claim is H_0

11) claim: $\mu \leq 3.1$; H_0: $\mu \leq 3.1$, H_a: $\mu > 3.1$; claim is H_0

12) claim: $\sigma > 1$; H_0: $\sigma \leq 1$, H_a: $\sigma > 1$; claim is H_a

13) type I: rejecting H_0: $\mu = 55.3$ when $\mu = 55.3$

   type II: failing to reject H_0: $\mu = 55.3$ when $\mu \neq 55.3$

14) type I: rejecting H_0: $\mu \leq 130$ when $\mu \leq 130$

   type II: failing to reject H_0: $\mu \leq 130>$ when $\mu > 130$

15) type I: rejecting H_0: $\mu \geq 97$ when $\mu \geq 97$

   type II: failing to reject H_0: $\mu \geq 97$ when $\mu < 97$

16) type I: rejecting H_0: $\rho \geq 0.5$ when $\rho \geq 0.5$

   type II: failing to reject H_0: $\rho \geq 0.5$ when $\rho < 0.5$

17) C

18) C

19) B

20) B

21) C

22) C

23) C

24) C

25) A

26) B

27) B

28) A

29) A

30) B

31) B

32) B

33) A

34) C

35) A

36) B

37) B

38) A

39) C

7.2 Hypothesis Testing for the Mean (Large Samples)

1) B

2) D

3) A

4) A

5) C

6) D

7) A

8) B

9) D

10) D

11) C

12) D

13) D

14) standardized test statistic ≈ 1.77; critical value = 1.645; reject H_0; There is enough evidence to support the claim.

15) standardized test statistic ≈ -1.97; critical value = ± 1.96; reject H_0; There is enough evidence to support the claim.

16) standardized test statistic ≈ 2.65; critical value = 2.33; fail to reject H_0; There is not enough evidence to reject the claim.

17) standardized test statistic ≈ -2.16, critical value = ± 2.575, fail to reject H_0; There is not enough evidence to reject the claim.

18) standardized test statistic ≈ -4.04; critical value $z_0 = -2.33$; reject H_0; The data support the agency's claim.

19) standardized test statistic ≈ -1.58; critical value $z_0 = \pm 1.96$; fail to reject H_0; There is not sufficient evidence to reject the manufacturer's claim.

20) standardized test statistic ≈ -2.33; critical value $z_0 = -1.645$; reject H_0; There is sufficient evidence to support the trucking firm's claim.

21) standardized test statistic ≈ -3.58; critical value $z_0 = -1.645$; reject H_0; There is sufficient evidence to support the politician's claim.

22) $\bar{x} = 60.4$, s = 12.2, standardized test statistic ≈ 0.18; critical value $z_0 = 2.33$; fail to reject H_0; There is not sufficient evidence to reject the claim.

23) B

24) A

25) C

26) A

27) B

28) B

29) A

30) Fail to reject H_0; There is not enough evidence to support the fast food outlet's claim that the mean waiting time is less than 4.5 minutes.

31) Standardized test statistic ≈ 1.29; critical value $z_0 = -1.645$; fail to reject H_0; There is not enough evidence to support the fast food outlet's claim.

32) Confidence interval (3.47, 3.73); 3.5 lies in the interval, fail to reject H_0; There is not enough evidence to support the fast food outlet's claim.

33) P-value = 0.000001, P < α, reject H_0; There is sufficient evidence to support the school district's claim.

34) Standardized test statistic ≈ -4.71; critical value $z_0 = -1.645$; reject H_0; There is sufficient evidence to support the district's claim.

35) Confidence interval (2.84, 3.96); 5 lies outside the interval, reject H_0; There is sufficient evidence to support the district's claim.

7.3 Hypothesis Testing for the Mean (Small Samples)

1) C

2) C

3) A

4) D

5) C

6) B

7) A

8) $t_0 = \pm 3.106$, standardized test statistic ≈ 1.890, fail to reject H_0; There is not sufficient evidence to reject the claim.

9) $t_0 = -1.833$, standardized test statistic ≈ -2.189, reject H_0; There is sufficient evidence to reject the claim

10) $t_0 = 1.761$, standardized test statistic ≈ 1.452, fail to reject H_0; There is not sufficient evidence to reject the claim

11) $t_0 = -1.328$, standardized test statistic ≈ -0.894, fail to reject H_0; There is not sufficient evidence to support the claim

12) $t_0 = 2.797$, standardized test statistic ≈ 1.667, fail to reject H_0; There is not sufficient evidence to support the claim

13) $t_0 = \pm 3.106$, standardized test statistic ≈ -0.825, fail to reject H_0; There is not sufficient evidence to support the claim

14) critical value $t_0 = -2.539$; standardized test statistic ≈ -2.981; reject H_0; There is sufficient evidence to support the Metropolitan Bus Company's claim.

15) critical value $t_0 = -2.539$; standardized test statistic ≈ -1.917; fail to reject H_0; There is not sufficient evidence to support the government agency's claim.

16) $\bar{x} = 60.21$, $s = 13.43$; critical value $t_0 = 2.650$; standardized test statistic ≈ 0.060; fail to reject H_0; There is not sufficient evidence to reject the claim.

17) Standardized test statistic ≈ 0.060; Therefore, at a degree of freedom of 13, P must be greater than 0.25. $P > \alpha$, fail to reject H_0; There is not sufficient evidence to reject the group's claim.

18) Confidence interval (50.70, 69.72); 60 lies in the interval, fail to reject H_0; There is not sufficient evidence to reject the group's claim.

19) critical value $t_0 = \pm 2.064$; standardized test statistic ≈ -0.625; fail to reject H_0; There is not sufficient evidence to reject the manufacturer's claim.

20) Standardized test statistic ≈ -1.25; Therefore, at a degree of freedom of 24, P must be between 0.10 and 0.25. $P > \alpha$, fail to reject H_0; There is not sufficient evidence to reject the manufacturer's claim.

21) Confidence interval (946.98, 1013.02); 1000 lies in the interval, fail to reject H_0; There is not sufficient evidence to reject the manufacturer's claim.

22) critical value $t_0 = -1.740$; standardized test statistic ± 2.298; reject H_0; There is sufficient evidence to support the trucking firm's claim.

23) Standardized test statistic ≈ -1.118; Therefore, at 19 degrees of freedom, P must lie between 0.10 and 0.25. Since $P > \alpha$, fail to reject H_0. There is not sufficient evidence to support the fast food outlet's claim.

24) standardized test statistic ≈ -4.536; Therefore, at a degree of freedom of 27, P must lie between 0.0001 and 0.005. $P < \alpha$, reject H_0. There is sufficient evidence to support the school district's claim.

7.4 Hypothesis Testing for Proportions

1) A

2) B

3) C

4) C

5) critical value $z_0 = \pm 2.575$; standardized test statistic ≈ 0.304; fail to reject H_0; There is not sufficient evidence to reject the claim.

6) critical value $z_0 = 1.645$; standardized test statistic ≈ 1.21; fail to reject H_0; There is not sufficient evidence to support the claim $p > 0.5$. The Republican candidate has no chance.

7) critical value $z_0 = -2.33$; standardized test statistic ≈ -0.45; fail to reject H_0; There is not sufficient evidence to support the airline's claim.

8) critical value $z_0 = -1.645$; standardized test statistic ≈ -1.33; fail to reject H_0; There is not sufficient evidence to reject the claim.

9) $\alpha = 0.05$; P–value = 0.0918; $P > \alpha$, fail to reject H_0; There is not sufficient evidence to reject the study's claim.

10) Confidence interval (0.071, 0.154); 15% lies in the interval, fail to reject H_0; There is not sufficient evidence to reject the study's claim.

11) critical value $z_0 = \pm 1.96$; standardized test statistic ≈ 2.76; reject H_0; There is enough evidence to reject the university's claim. The school is not believable.

12) critical value $z_0 = \pm 1.96$; standardized test statistic ≈ 4.43; reject H_0; There is enough evidence to reject the claim that this is not a biased coin. The coin is not fair.

13) $\alpha = 0.05$; P–value = 0.0901; $P > \alpha$; fail to reject H_0; There is not sufficient evidence to reject the telephone company's claim.

14) Standardized test statistic ≈ -1.34; critical value $z_0 = \pm 1.96$; fail to reject H_0; There is not sufficient evidence to reject the company's claim.

15) Confidence interval (0.143, 0.209); 20% lies in the interval, fail to reject H_0; There is not sufficient evidence to reject the company's claim.

16) $\alpha = 0.05$; P–value $= 0.0574$; $P > \alpha$; fail to reject H_0; There is not enough evidence to reject the claim that this is not a biased coin. The coin is fair.

7.5 Hypothesis Testing for Variance and Standard Deviation

1) D

2) B

3) B

4) B

5) B

6) B

7) B

8) B

9) A

10) A

11) C

12) C

13) critical values $X_L^2 = 3.816$ and $X_R^2 = 21.920$; standardized test statistic $X^2 = 9.209$; fail to reject H_0; There is not sufficient evidence to reject the claim.

14) critical value $X_0^2 = 6.571$; standardized test statistic $X^2 \approx 11.667$; fail to reject H_0; There is not sufficient evidence to reject the claim.

15) critical value $X_0^2 = 36.191$; standardized test statistic $X^2 \approx 36.813$; reject H_0; There is sufficient evidence to reject the claim.

16) critical value $X_0^2 = 33.409$; standardized test statistic $X^2 \approx 24.158$; fail to reject H_0; There is not sufficient evidence to reject the claim.

17) critical value $X_0^2 = 18.114$; standardized test statistic $X^2 \approx 16.875$; reject H_0; There is sufficient evidence to support the claim.

18) critical values $X_L^2 = 1.735$ and $X_R^2 = 23.589$; standardized test statistic $X^2 \approx 9.926$; fail to reject H_0; There is not sufficient evidence to support the claim.

19) critical values $X_L^2 = 3.816$ and $X_R^2 = 21.920$; standardized test statistic $X^2 \approx 9.267$; fail to reject H_0; There is not sufficient evidence to reject the claim.

20) critical value $X_0^2 = 6.571$; standardized test statistic $X^2 \approx 11.605$; fail to reject H_0; There is not sufficient evidence to reject the claim.

21) critical value $X_0^2 = 36.191$; standardized test statistic $X^2 \approx 36.766$; reject H_0; There is sufficient evidence to reject the claim.

22) critical value $X_0^2 = 33.409$; standardized test statistic $X^2 \approx 24.009$; fail to reject H_0; There is not sufficient evidence to support the claim.

23) critical value $X_0^2 = 18.114$; standardized test statistic $X^2 \approx 16.809$; reject H_0; There is sufficient evidence to support the claim.

24) critical values $X_L^2 = 1.735$ and $X_R^2 = 23.589$; standardized test statistic $X^2 \approx 9.919$; fail to reject H_0; There is not sufficient evidence to support the claim.

25) critical values $X_L^2 = 3.565$ and $X_R^2 = 29.819$; standardized test statistic $X^2 \approx 10.42$; fail to reject H_0; There is not sufficient evidence to reject the claim.

26) critical value $X_0^2 = 10.117$; standardized test statistic $X^2 \approx 9.048$; reject H_0; There is sufficient evidence to support the claim.

27) Standardized test statistic ≈ 9.048; Therefore, at a degree of freedom of 19, P must be between 0.025 and 0.05. $P < \alpha$, reject H_0; There is sufficient evidence to support the claim.

28) Confidence interval (1.89, 5.62); 6.25 lies outside the interval, reject H_0; There is sufficient evidence to support the claim.

29) critical value $X_0^2 = 124.342$; standardized test statistic $X^2 = 144$; reject H_0; There is sufficient evidence to support the claim.

30) Standardized test statistic ≈ 144; Therefore, at a degree of freedom of 100, P must be less than 0.005. $P < \alpha$, reject H_0; There is sufficient evidence to support the firm's claim.

31) Confidence interval (1,847,835, 1,940,125); 1,000,000 lies outside the interval, reject H_0; There is sufficient evidence to support the claim.

32) critical values $X_L^2 = 35.534$ and $X_R^2 = 91.952$; standardized test statistic $X^2 \approx 78.634$; fail to reject H_0; There is not sufficient evidence to reject the claim.

33) critical value $X_0^2 = 90.531$; standardized test statistics $X^2 = 149.527$; reject H_0; There is sufficient evidence to support the claim.

34) critical value $X_0^2 = 63.691$; standardized test statistic $X^2 = 53.824$; fail to reject H_0; There is not sufficient evidence to support the claim.

Ch. 8 Hypothesis Testing with Two Samples

8.1 Testing the Difference Between Means (Large Independent Samples)

Solve the problem.

1) Find the standardized test statistic to test the claim that $\mu_1 = \mu_2$. Two samples are randomly selected from each population. The sample statistics are given below.

$n_1 = 50$ $n_2 = 60$
$\overline{x}_1 = 32$ $\overline{x}_2 = 30$
$s_1 = 1.5$ $s_2 = 1.9$

    A) 8.1   B) 3.8   C) 4.2   D) 6.2

2) Find the standardized test statistic to test the claim that $\mu_1 = \mu_2$. Two samples are randomly selected from each population. The sample statistics are given below.

$n_1 = 40$ $n_2 = 35$
$\overline{x}_1 = 9$ $\overline{x}_2 = 10$
$s_1 = 2.5$ $s_2 = 2.8$

    A) −2.6   B) −1.6   C) −1.0   D) −0.8

3) Find the standardized test statistic to test the claim that $\mu_1 > \mu_2$. Two samples are randomly selected from each population. The sample statistics are given below.

$n_1 = 100$ $n_2 = 125$
$\overline{x}_1 = 450$ $\overline{x}_2 = 435$
$s_1 = 45$ $s_2 = 25$

    A) 2.98   B) 2.81   C) 0.91   D) 1.86

4) Find the standardized test statistic to test the claim that $\mu_1 < \mu_2$. Two samples are randomly selected from each population. The sample statistics are given below.

$n_1 = 35$ $n_2 = 42$
$\overline{x}_1 = 20.13$ $\overline{x}_2 = 22.68$
$s_1 = 2.9$ $s_2 = 2.8$

    A) −3.16   B) −1.66   C) −2.63   D) −3.90

5) Find the standardized test statistic to test the claim that $\mu_1 \neq \mu_2$. Two samples are randomly selected from each population. The sample statistics are given below.

$n_1 = 51$ $n_2 = 38$
$\overline{x}_1 = 5.7$ $\overline{x}_2 = 6.1$
$s_1 = 0.76$ $s_2 = 0.51$

    A) −2.97   B) −1.82   C) −2.32   D) −2.12

6) Suppose you want to test the claim that $\mu_1 \neq \mu_2$. Two samples are randomly selected from each population. The sample statistics are given below. At a level of significance of $\alpha = 0.05$, when should you reject H_0?

$n_1 = 50$ $n_2 = 60$
$\overline{x}_1 = 24$ $\overline{x}_2 = 22$
$s_1 = 1.5$ $s_2 = 1.9$

    A) Reject H_0 if the standardized test statistic is less than -1.645 or greater than 1.645.

    B) Reject H_0 if the standardized test statistic is less than -2.575 or greater than 2.575.

    C) Reject H_0 if the standardized test statistic is less than -2.33 or greater than 2.33.

    D) Reject H_0 if the standardized test statistic is less than -1.96 or greater than 1.96.

7) Suppose you want to test the claim that $\mu_1 = \mu_2$. Two samples are randomly selected from each population. If a hypothesis test is performed, how should you interpret a decision that rejects the null hypothesis?
    A) There is sufficient evidence to support the claim $\mu_1 = \mu_2$.

    B) There is not sufficient evidence to support the claim $\mu_1 = \mu_2$.

    C) There is sufficient evidence to reject the claim $\mu_1 = \mu_2$.

    D) There is not sufficient evidence to reject the claim $\mu_1 = \mu_2$.

8) Test the claim that $\mu_1 = \mu_2$. Two samples are randomly selected from each population. The sample statistics are given below. Use $\alpha = 0.05$.

$n_1 = 50$ $n_2 = 60$
$\overline{x}_1 = 18$ $\overline{x}_2 = 16$
$s_1 = 1.5$ $s_2 = 1.9$

9) Suppose you want to test the claim that $\mu_1 > \mu_2$. Two samples are randomly selected from each population. The sample statistics are given below. At a level of significance of $\alpha = 0.01$, when should you reject H_0?

$n_1 = 100$ $n_2 = 125$
$\overline{x}_1 = 665$ $\overline{x}_2 = 650$
$s_1 = 45$ $s_2 = 25$

    A) Reject H_0 if the standardized test statistic is greater than 2.33.

    B) Reject H_0 if the standardized test statistic is greater than 1.645.

    C) Reject H_0 if the standardized test statistic is greater than 1.96.

    D) Reject H_0 if the standardized test statistic is greater than 2.575.

10) Suppose you want to test the claim that $\mu_1 > \mu_2$. Two samples are randomly selected from each population. If a hypothesis test is performed, how should you interpret a decision that rejects the null hypothesis?
    A) There is sufficient evidence to reject the claim $\mu_1 > \mu_2$.

    B) There is not sufficient evidence to reject the claim $\mu_1 > \mu_2$.

    C) There is sufficient evidence to support the claim $\mu_1 > \mu_2$.

    D) There is not sufficient evidence to support the claim $\mu_1 > \mu_2$.

11) Test the claim that $\mu_1 > \mu_2$. Two samples are randomly selected from each population. The sample statistics are given below. Use $\alpha = 0.01$.

$n_1 = 100$ $n_2 = 125$
$\overline{x}_1 = 425$ $\overline{x}_2 = 410$
$s_1 = 45$ $s_2 = 25$

12) Suppose you want to test the claim that $\mu_1 < \mu_2$. Two samples are randomly selected from each population. The sample statistics are given below. At a level of significance of $\alpha = 0.05$, when should you reject H_0?

$n_1 = 35$ $n_2 = 42$
$\overline{x}_1 = 29.05$ $\overline{x}_2 = 31.6$
$s_1 = 2.9$ $s_2 = 2.8$

   A) Reject H_0 if the standardized test statistic is less than –1.645.

   B) Reject H_0 if the standardized test statistic is less than –2.33.

   C) Reject H_0 if the standardized test statistic is less than –2.575.

   D) Reject H_0 if the standardized test statistic is less than –1.96.

13) Suppose you want to test the claim that $\mu_1 < \mu_2$. Two samples are randomly selected from each population. If a hypothesis test is performed, how should you interpret a decision that fails to reject the null hypothesis?
   A) There is not sufficient evidence to reject the claim $\mu_1 < \mu_2$.

   B) There is sufficient evidence to support the claim $\mu_1 < \mu_2$.

   C) There is sufficient evidence to reject the claim $\mu_1 < \mu_2$.

   D) There is not sufficient evidence to support the claim $\mu_1 < \mu_2$.

14) Test the claim that $\mu_1 < \mu_2$. Two samples are randomly selected from each population. The sample statistics are given below. Use $\alpha = 0.05$.

$n_1 = 35$ $n_2 = 42$
$\overline{x}_1 = 21.18$ $\overline{x}_2 = 23.73$
$s_1 = 2.9$ $s_2 = 2.8$

   A) critical value $z_0 = -1.65$; standardized test statistic ≈ -3.90; reject H_0; There is sufficient evidence to support the claim.

15) Suppose you want to test the claim that $\mu_1 \neq \mu_2$. Two samples are randomly selected from each population. The sample statistics are given below. At a level of significance of $\alpha = 0.02$, when should you reject H_0?

$n_1 = 51$ $n_2 = 38$

$\overline{x_1} = 4.2$ $\overline{x_2} = 4.6$

$s_1 = 0.76$ $s_2 = 0.51$

    A) Reject H_0 if the standardized test statistic is less than –2.33 or greater than 2.33.

    B) Reject H_0 if the standardized test statistic is less than –2.575 or greater than 2.575.

    C) Reject H_0 if the standardized test statistic is less than –1.645 or greater than 1.645.

    D) Reject H_0 if the standardized test statistic is less than –1.96 or greater than 1.96.

16) Suppose you want to test the claim that $\mu_1 \neq \mu_2$. Two samples are randomly selected from each population. If a hypothesis test is performed, how should you interpret a decision that fails to reject the null hypothesis?

    A) There is sufficient evidence to reject the claim $\mu_1 \neq \mu_2$.

    B) There is sufficient evidence to support the claim $\mu_1 \neq \mu_2$.

    C) There is not sufficient evidence to reject the claim $\mu_1 \neq \mu_2$.

    D) There is not sufficient evidence to support the claim $\mu_1 \neq \mu_2$.

17) Test the claim that $\mu_1 \neq \mu_2$. Two samples are randomly selected from each population. The sample statistics are given below. Use $\alpha = 0.02$.

$n_1 = 51$ $n_2 = 38$

$\overline{x_1} = 3.6$ $\overline{x_2} = 4$

$s_1 = 0.76$ $s_2 = 0.51$

18) A study was conducted to determine if the salaries of elementary school teachers from two neighboring states were equal. A sample of 100 teachers from each state was randomly selected. The mean from the first state was $29,300 with a standard deviation of $2300. The mean from the second state was $30,700 with a standard deviation of $2100. Test the claim that the salaries from both states are equal. Use $\alpha = 0.05$.

19) At a local college, 65 female students were randomly selected and it was found that their mean monthly income was $628 with a standard deviation of $121.50. Seventy–five male students were also randomly selected and their mean monthly income was found to be $670 with a standard deviation of $168.70. Test the claim that male students have a higher monthly income than female students. Use $\alpha = 0.01$.

20) A medical researcher suspects that the pulse rate of smokers is higher than the pulse rate of non–smokers. Use the sample statistics below to test the researcher's suspicion. Use $\alpha = 0.05$.

Smokers   Nonsmokers

$n_1 = 100$ $n_2 = 100$

$\overline{x_1} = 84$ $\overline{x_2} = 81$

$s_1 = 4.8$ $s_2 = 5.3$

21) A statistics teacher believes that students in an evening statistics class score higher than the students in a day class. The results of a special exam are shown below. Can the teacher conclude that the evening students have a higher score? Use $\alpha = 0.01$.

Day Students   Evening Students
$n_1 = 36$ $n_2 = 41$
$\bar{x}_1 = 81$ $\bar{x}_2 = 84$
$s_1 = 5.8$ $s_2 = 6.3$

22) A statistics teacher wanted to see whether there was a significant difference in ages between day students and night students. A random sample of 35 students is selected from each group. The data are given below. Test the claim that there is no difference in age between the two groups. Use $\alpha = 0.05$.

Day Students

22   24   24   23   19   19   23   22   18   21   21   18
18   25   29   24   23   22   22   21   20   20   20   27
17   19   18   21   20   23   26   30   25   21   25

Evening Students

18   23   25   23   21   21   23   24   27   31   24   20
20   23   19   25   24   27   23   20   20   21   25   24
23   28   20   19   23   24   20   27   21   29   30

23) A local bank claims that the waiting time for its customers to be served is the lowest in the area. A competitor bank checks the waiting times at both banks. The sample statistics are listed below. Test the local bank's claim. Use $\alpha = 0.05$.

Local Bank   Competitor Bank
$n_1 = 45$ $n_2 = 50$
$\bar{x}_1 = 5.3$ minutes $\bar{x}_2 = 5.6$ minutes
$s_1 = 1.1$ minutes $s_2 = 1.0$ minute

24) Two samples are randomly selected from each population. The sample statistics are given below. Find the P-value used to test the claim that $\mu_1 = \mu_2$. Use $\alpha = 0.05$.

$n_1 = 40$ $n_2 = 35$
$\bar{x}_1 = 12$ $\bar{x}_2 = 13$
$s_1 = 2.5$ $s_2 = 2.8$

   A) 0.4020   B) 0.1138   C) 0.1052   D) 0.0018

25) Two samples are randomly selected from each population. The sample statistics are given below. Find the P-value used to test the claim that $\mu_1 > \mu_2$. Use $\alpha = 0.05$.

$n_1 = 100$ $n_2 = 125$
$\bar{x}_1 = 615$ $\bar{x}_2 = 600$
$s_1 = 40$ $s_2 = 24$

   A) 0.1015   B) 0.5105   C) 0.001   D) 0.0505

26) A local bank claims that the waiting time for its customers to be served is the lowest in the area. A competitor bank checks the waiting times at both banks. The sample statistics are listed below. Use P-values to test the local bank's claim. Use $\alpha = 0.05$.

Local Bank
$n_1 = 45$
$\overline{x}_1 = 5.3$ minutes
$s_1 = 1.1$ minutes

Competitor Bank
$n_2 = 50$
$\overline{x}_2 = 5.6$ minutes
$s_2 = 1.0$ minutes

27) A local bank claims that the waiting time for its customers to be served is the lowest in the area. A competitor bank checks the waiting times at both banks. The sample statistics are listed below. Use $\alpha = 0.05$ and a confidence interval to test the local bank's claim.

Local Bank
$n_1 = 45$
$\overline{x}_1 = 5.3$ minutes
$s_1 = 1.1$ minutes

Competitor Bank
$n_2 = 50$
$\overline{x}_2 = 5.6$ minutes
$s_2 = 1.0$ minute

28) Construct a 95% confidence interval for $\mu_1 - \mu_2$. Two samples are randomly selected from each population. The sample statistics are given below.

$n_1 = 50$ $n_2 = 60$
$\overline{x}_1 = 25$ $\overline{x}_2 = 23$
$s_1 = 1.5$ $s_2 = 1.9$

A) (1.364, 2.636)   B) (1.919, 3.142)   C) (1.572, 2.987)   D) (1.723, 3.012)

29) Construct a 95% confidence interval for $\mu_1 - \mu_2$. Two samples are randomly selected from each population. The sample statistics are given below.

$n_1 = 40$ $n_2 = 35$
$\overline{x}_1 = 12$ $\overline{x}_2 = 13$
$s_1 = 2.5$ $s_2 = 2.8$

A) (-1.673, 1.892)   B) (-2.001, -1.873)   C) (-2.209, 0.209)   D) (-1.968, 1.561)

30) For which confidence interval for the difference in the means $\mu_1 - \mu_2$, would you reject the null hypothesis?

A) (-1.968, 1.561)   B) (-2.001, -1.873)   C) (-1.673, 1.892)   D) (-2.209, 0.209)

31) A financial advisor wants to know whether there is a significant difference between the NYSE and NASDAQ markets in the annual dividend rates for preferred stocks. A random sample of 30 returns is selected from each market. The data are given below. Test the claim that there is no difference in the annual dividend rates for the two markets. Use $\alpha = 0.05$.

NASDAQ
2.00 1.02 2.11 2.56 2.15 0.93 0.91 1.67 1.88 2.13
2.44 1.97 2.00 1.81 2.25 1.72 1.75 1.05 0.90 2.34
0.51 1.00 2.25 0.85 1.50 2.33 1.59 2.25 0.23 1.63

NYSE
1.46 3.00 1.74 5.19 1.69 1.88 2.85 2.00 2.19 2.03
1.81 5.00 1.72 3.38 2.09 4.50 3.07 1.97 1.78 1.50
1.97 4.65 3.12 2.19 2.19 3.50 1.56 4.10 3.00 4.40

32) A researcher wishes to determine whether people with high blood pressure can lower their blood pressure by following a certain diet. A treatment group and a control group are selected. The sample statistics are given below. Construct a 90% confidence interval for the difference between the two population means, $\mu_1 - \mu_2$. Would you recommend using this diet plan? Explain your reasoning.

Treatment Group	Control Group
$n_1 = 100$	$n_2 = 100$
$\bar{x}_1 = 178$	$\bar{x}_2 = 193$
$s_1 = 35$	$s_2 = 37$

33) A recent study of 100 elementary school teachers in a southern state found that their mean salary was $24,100 with a standard deviation of $2100. A similar study of 100 elementary school teachers in a western state found that their mean salary was $34,500 with a standard deviation of $3200. Test the claim that the salaries of elementary school teachers in the western state is more than $10,000 greater than that of elementary teachers in the southern state. Use $\alpha = 0.05$.

34) At $\alpha = 0.05$, test a financial advisor's claim that the difference between the mean dividend rate for listings in the NYSE market and the mean dividend rate for listings in the NASDAQ market is more than 0.75. The sample statistics from randomly selected listings from each market are listed below.

NYSE	NASDAQ
$n_1 = 30$	$n_2 = 50$
$\bar{x}_1 = 2.75\%$	$\bar{x}_2 = 1.66\%$
$s_1 = 1.14\%$	$s_2 = 0.63\%$

35) Two groups of patients with colorectal cancer are treated with a different drug to reduce pain. A random sample of 140 patients are treated using the drug Irinotican and a random sample of 127 patients are treated using the drug Fluorouracil. The sample statistics are listed below. At $\alpha = 0.01$, test a pharmaceutical representative's claim that the difference between the mean number of pain-free months for patients using Fluorouracil and the mean number of pain-free months for patients using Irinotican is less than two months.

Fluorouracil   Irinotican
$n_1 = 127$ $n_2 = 140$
$\overline{x}_1 = 8.5$ months $\overline{x}_2 = 10.3$ months
$s_1 = 1.5$ months $s_2 = 1.2$ months

8.2 Testing the Difference Between Means (Small Independent Samples)

Solve the problem.

1) Find the critical values, t_0, to test the claim that $\mu_1 = \mu_2$. Two samples are randomly selected and come from populations that are normal. The sample statistics are given below. Assume that $\sigma_1^2 \neq \sigma_2^2$. Use $\alpha = 0.05$.

$n_1 = 25$ $n_2 = 30$
$\overline{x}_1 = 30$ $\overline{x}_2 = 28$
$s_1 = 1.5$ $s_2 = 1.9$

A) ±1.711   B) ±2.797   C) ±2.492   D) ±2.064

2) Find the critical values, t_0, to test the claim that $\mu_1 = \mu_2$. Two samples are randomly selected and come from populations that are normal. The sample statistics are given below. Assume that $\sigma_1^2 = \sigma_2^2$. Use $\alpha = 0.05$.

$n_1 = 14$ $n_2 = 12$
$\overline{x}_1 = 16$ $\overline{x}_2 = 17$
$s_1 = 2.5$ $s_2 = 2.8$

A) ±2.492   B) ±2.064   C) ±1.711   D) ±1.318

3) Find the critical value, t_0, to test the claim that $\mu_1 > \mu_2$. Two samples are randomly selected and come from populations that are normal. The sample statistics are given below. Assume that $\sigma_1^2 \neq \sigma_2^2$. Use $\alpha = 0.01$.

$n_1 = 18$ $n_2 = 13$
$\overline{x}_1 = 650$ $\overline{x}_2 = 635$
$s_1 = 40$ $s_2 = 25$

A) 1.699   B) 2.179   C) 2.681   D) 3.055

4) Find the critical value, t_0, to test the claim that $\mu_1 < \mu_2$. Two samples are randomly selected and come from populations that are normal. The sample statistics are given below. Assume that $\sigma_1^2 = \sigma_2^2$. Use $\alpha = 0.05$.

$n_1 = 15$ $\qquad$ $n_2 = 15$

$\overline{x}_1 = 28.08$ $\qquad$ $\overline{x}_2 = 30.63$

$s_1 = 2.9$ $\qquad$ $s_2 = 2.8$

A) 0.683 $\qquad\qquad$ B) –1.313 $\qquad\qquad$ C) 2.467 $\qquad\qquad$ D) –1.701

5) Find the critical value, t_0, to test the claim that $\mu_1 \neq \mu_2$. Two samples are randomly selected and come from populations that are normal. The sample statistics are given below. Assume that $\sigma_1^2 \neq \sigma_2^2$. Use $\alpha = 0.02$.

$n_1 = 11$ $\qquad$ $n_2 = 18$

$\overline{x}_1 = 5.3$ $\qquad$ $\overline{x}_2 = 5.7$

$s_1 = 0.76$ $\qquad$ $s_2 = 0.51$

A) ±0.684 $\qquad\qquad$ B) ±2.228 $\qquad\qquad$ C) ±2.764 $\qquad\qquad$ D) ±3.169

6) Find the standardized test statistic, t, to test the claim that $\mu_1 = \mu_2$. Two samples are randomly selected and come from populations that are normal. The sample statistics are given below. Assume that $\sigma_1^2 \neq \sigma_2^2$.

$n_1 = 25$ $\qquad$ $n_2 = 30$

$\overline{x}_1 = 24$ $\qquad$ $\overline{x}_2 = 22$

$s_1 = 1.5$ $\qquad$ $s_2 = 1.9$

A) 4.361 $\qquad\qquad$ B) 3.287 $\qquad\qquad$ C) 1.986 $\qquad\qquad$ D) 2.892

7) Find the standardized test statistic, t, to test the claim that $\mu_1 = \mu_2$. Two samples are randomly selected and come from populations that are normal. The sample statistics are given below. Assume that $\sigma_1^2 = \sigma_2^2$.

$n_1 = 14$ $\qquad$ $n_2 = 12$

$\overline{x}_1 = 21$ $\qquad$ $\overline{x}_2 = 22$

$s_1 = 2.5$ $\qquad$ $s_2 = 2.8$

A) –1.326 $\qquad\qquad$ B) –0.962 $\qquad\qquad$ C) –1.101 $\qquad\qquad$ D) –0.813

8) Find the standardized test statistic, t, to test the claim that $\mu_1 > \mu_2$. Two samples are randomly selected and come from populations that are normal. The sample statistics are given below. Assume that $\sigma_1^2 \neq \sigma_2^2$.

$n_1 = 18$ $\qquad$ $n_2 = 13$

$\overline{x}_1 = 490$ $\qquad$ $\overline{x}_2 = 475$

$s_1 = 40$ $\qquad$ $s_2 = 25$

A) 2.819 $\qquad\qquad$ B) 1.282 $\qquad\qquad$ C) 3.271 $\qquad\qquad$ D) 1.865

9) Find the standardized test statistic, t, to test the claim that $\mu_1 < \mu_2$. Two samples are randomly selected and come from populations that are normal. The sample statistics are given below. Assume that $\sigma_1^2 = \sigma_2^2$.

$n_1 = 15$ $n_2 = 15$
$\overline{x}_1 = 23.05$ $\overline{x}_2 = 25.6$
$s_1 = 2.9$ $s_2 = 2.8$

A) -2.450   B) -0.669   C) -1.667   D) -3.165

10) Find the standardized test statistic, t, to test the claim that $\mu_1 \neq \mu_2$. Two samples are randomly selected and come from populations that are normal. The sample statistics are given below. Assume that $\sigma_1^2 \neq \sigma_2^2$.

$n_1 = 11$ $n_2 = 18$
$\overline{x}_1 = 5.6$ $\overline{x}_2 = 6$
$s_1 = 0.76$ $s_2 = 0.51$

A) -2.123   B) -1.546   C) -1.326   D) -1.821

11) Suppose you want to test the claim that $\mu_1 = \mu_2$. Two samples are randomly selected from normal populations. The sample statistics are given below. Assume that $\sigma_1^2 \neq \sigma_2^2$. At a level of significance of $\alpha = 0.05$, when should you reject H_0?

$n_1 = 25$ $n_2 = 30$
$\overline{x}_1 = 17$ $\overline{x}_2 = 15$
$s_1 = 1.5$ $s_2 = 1.9$

A) Reject H_0 if the standardized test statistic is less than -1.711 or greater than 1.711.
B) Reject H_0 if the standardized test statistic is less than -2.492 or greater than 2.492.
C) Reject H_0 if the standardized test statistic is less than -2.789 or greater than 2.797.
D) Reject H_0 if the standardized test statistic is less than -2.064 or greater than 2.064

12) Suppose you want to test the claim that $\mu_1 = \mu_2$. Two samples are randomly selected from normal populations. The sample statistics are given below. Assume that $\sigma_1^2 = \sigma_2^2$. At a level of significance of $\alpha = 0.05$, when should you reject H_0?

$n_1 = 14$ $n_2 = 12$
$\overline{x}_1 = 19$ $\overline{x}_2 = 20$
$s_1 = 2.5$ $s_2 = 2.8$

A) Reject H_0 if the standardized test statistic is less than -1.318 or greater than 1.318.
B) Reject H_0 if the standardized test statistic is less than -1.711 or greater than 1.711.
C) Reject H_0 if the standardized test statistic is less than -2.064 or greater than 2.064.
D) Reject H_0 if the standardized test statistic is less than -2.492 or greater than 2.492

13) Suppose you want to test the claim that $\mu_1 > \mu_2$. Two samples are randomly selected from normal populations.

The sample statistics are given below. Assume that $\sigma_1^2 \neq \sigma_2^2$. At a level of significance of $\alpha = 0.01$, when should you reject H_0?

$n_1 = 18$ $n_2 = 13$

$\overline{x}_1 = 445$ $\overline{x}_2 = 430$

$s_1 = 40$ $s_2 = 25$

   A) Reject H_0 if the standardized test statistic is greater than 2.179.

   B) Reject H_0 if the standardized test statistic is greater than 3.055.

   C) Reject H_0 if the standardized test statistic is greater than 1.699.

   D) Reject H_0 if the standardized test statistic is greater than 2.681.

14) Suppose you want to test the claim that $\mu_1 < \mu_2$. Two samples are randomly selected from normal populations.

The sample statistics are given below. Assume that $\sigma_1^2 = \sigma_2^2$. At a level of significance of $\alpha = 0.05$, when should you reject H_0?

$n_1 = 15$ $n_2 = 15$

$\overline{x}_1 = 23.23$ $\overline{x}_2 = 25.78$

$s_1 = 2.9$ $s_2 = 2.8$

   A) Reject H_0 if the standardized test statistic is less than –0.683.

   B) Reject H_0 if the standardized test statistic is less than –1.313.

   C) Reject H_0 if the standardized test statistic is less than –1.701.

   D) Reject H_0 if the standardized test statistic is less than –2.467.

15) Suppose you want to test the claim that $\mu_1 \neq \mu_2$. Two samples are randomly selected from normal populations.

The sample statistics are given below. Assume that $\sigma_1^2 \neq \sigma_2^2$. At a level of significance of $\alpha = 0.02$, when should you reject H_0?

$n_1 = 11$ $n_2 = 18$

$\overline{x}_1 = 4.2$ $\overline{x}_2 = 4.6$

$s_1 = 0.76$ $s_2 = 0.51$

   A) Reject H_0 if the standardized test statistic is less than –0.684 or greater than 0.684.

   B) Reject H_0 if the standardized test statistic is less than –2.764 or greater than 2.764.

   C) Reject H_0 if the standardized test statistic is less than –3.169 or greater than 3.169.

   D) Reject H_0 if the standardized test statistic is less than –2.228 or greater than 2.228.

16) Test the claim that $\mu_1 = \mu_2$. Two samples are randomly selected from normal populations. The sample statistics are given below. Assume that $\sigma_1^2 \neq \sigma_2^2$. Use $\alpha = 0.05$.

$n_1 = 25$ $n_2 = 30$
$\overline{x}_1 = 24$ $\overline{x}_2 = 22$
$s_1 = 1.5$ $s_2 = 1.9$

17) Test the claim that $\mu_1 = \mu_2$. Two samples are randomly selected from normal populations. The sample statistics are given below. Assume that $\sigma_1^2 = \sigma_2^2$. Use $\alpha = 0.05$.

$n_1 = 14$ $n_2 = 12$
$\overline{x}_1 = 6$ $\overline{x}_2 = 7$
$s_1 = 2.5$ $s_2 = 2.8$

18) Test the claim that $\mu_1 > \mu_2$. Two samples are randomly selected from normal populations. The sample statistics are given below. Assume that $\sigma_1^2 \neq \sigma_2^2$. Use $\alpha = 0.01$.

$n_1 = 18$ $n_2 = 13$
$\overline{x}_1 = 605$ $\overline{x}_2 = 590$
$s_1 = 40$ $s_2 = 25$

19) Test the claim that $\mu_1 < \mu_2$. Two samples are randomly selected from normal populations. The sample statistics are given below. Assume that $\sigma_1^2 = \sigma_2^2$. Use $\alpha = 0.05$.

$n_1 = 15$ $n_2 = 15$
$\overline{x}_1 = 27.98$ $\overline{x}_2 = 30.53$
$s_1 = 2.9$ $s_2 = 2.8$

20) Test the claim that $\mu_1 \neq \mu_2$. Two samples are randomly selected from normal populations. The sample statistics are given below. Assume that $\sigma_1^2 \neq \sigma_2^2$. Use $\alpha = 0.02$.

$n_1 = 11$ $n_2 = 18$
$\overline{x}_1 = 7.4$ $\overline{x}_2 = 7.8$
$s_1 = 0.76$ $s_2 = 0.51$

21) Construct a 95% confidence interval for $\mu_1 - \mu_2$. Two samples are randomly selected from normal populations. The sample statistics are given below. Assume that $\sigma_1^2 = \sigma_2^2$.

$n_1 = 10 \qquad n_2 = 12$
$\bar{x}_1 = 25 \qquad \bar{x}_2 = 23$
$s_1 = 1.5 \qquad s_2 = 1.9$

A) (1.335, 3.012)   B) (1.554, 3.651)   C) (0.453, 3.547)   D) (1.413, 3.124)

22) Construct a 95% confidence interval for $\mu_1 - \mu_2$. Two samples are randomly selected from normal populations. The sample statistics are given below. Assume that $\sigma_1^2 = \sigma_2^2$.

$n_1 = 11 \qquad n_2 = 18$
$\bar{x}_1 = 4.8 \qquad \bar{x}_2 = 5.2$
$s_1 = 0.76 \qquad s_2 = 0.51$

A) (–4.152, 3.981)   B) (–1.762, 1.762)   C) (–0.883, 0.083)   D) (–2.762, 2.762)

23) Construct a 95% confidence interval for $\mu_1 - \mu_2$. Two samples are randomly selected from normal populations. The sample statistics are given below. Assume that $\sigma_1^2 = \sigma_2^2$.

$n_1 = 8 \qquad n_2 = 7$
$\bar{x}_1 = 4.1 \qquad \bar{x}_2 = 5.5$
$s_1 = 0.76 \qquad s_2 = 2.51$

A) (2.112, 2.113)   B) (–3.406, 0.606)   C) (–1.132, 1.543)   D) (–1.679, 1.987)

24) A local bank claims that the waiting time for its customers to be served is the lowest in the area. A competitor's bank checks the waiting times at both banks. The sample statistics are listed below. Test the local bank's claim:
(a) assuming that $\sigma_1^2 = \sigma_2^2$, and (b) assuming that $\sigma_1^2 \neq \sigma_2^2$. Use $\alpha = 0.05$.

Local Bank   Competitor Bank
$n_1 = 15$ $n_2 = 16$
$\bar{x}_1 = 5.3$ minutes $\bar{x}_2 = 5.6$ minutes
$s_1 = 1.1$ minutes $s_2 = 1.0$ minutes

25) A study was conducted to determine if the salaries of elementary school teachers from two neighboring districts were equal. A sample of 15 teachers from each district was randomly selected. The mean from the first district was $28,900 with a standard deviation of $2300. The mean from the second district was $30,300 with a standard deviation of $2100. Test the claim that the salaries from both districts are equal. Assume that $\sigma_1^2 = \sigma_2^2$. Use $\alpha = 0.05$.

26) A sports analyst claims that the mean batting average for teams in the American League is not equal to the mean batting average for teams in the National League because a pitcher does not bat in the American League. The data listed below are from randomly selected teams in both leagues. At $\alpha = 0.05$, test the sports analyst's claim. Assume the population variances are equal.

American League
0.279   0.274   0.271   0.268
0.265   0.254   0.240

National League
0.284   0.267   0.266   0.263
0.261   0.259   0.256

27) A sports analyst claims that the mean batting average for teams in the American League is not equal to the mean batting average for teams in the National League because a pitcher does not bat in the American League. The data listed below are from randomly selected teams in both leagues. Construct a 95% confidence interval for the difference in the means $\mu_1 - \mu_2$. Assume the population variances are equal.

American League
0.279   0.274   0.271   0.268
0.265   0.254   0.240

National League
0.284   0.267   0.266   0.263
0.261   0.259   0.256

28) A women's advocacy group claims that women golfers receive significantly less prize money than their male counterparts when they win first place in a professional tournament. The data listed below are the first place prize monies from randomly selected male and female tournament winners. At $\alpha = 0.01$, test the group's claim. Assume the population variances are not equal.

Female Golfers
180,000   150,000   240,000   195,000   202,500
120,000   165,000   225,000   150,000   315,000

Male Golfers
864,000   810,000   1,170,000   810,000   630,000
1,050,000 945,000   1,008,000   900,000   756,000
630,000   900,000

29) A women's advocacy group claims that women golfers receive significantly less prize money than their male counterparts when they win first place in a professional tournament. The data listed below are the first place prize monies from randomly selected male and female tournament winners. Construct a 99% confidence interval for the difference in the means $\mu_1 - \mu_2$. Assume the population variances are not equal.

Female Golfers
180,000   150,000   240,000   195,000   202,500
120,000   165,000   225,000   150,000   315,000

Male Golfers
864,000   810,000   1,170,000   810,000   630,000
1,050,000 945,000   1,008,000   900,000   756,000
630,000   900,000

30) A study was conducted to determine if the salaries of elementary school teachers from two neighboring districts were equal. A sample of 15 teachers from each district was randomly selected. The mean from the first district was $28,900 with a standard deviation of $2300. The mean from the second district was $30,300 with a standard deviation of $2100. Construct a 95% confidence interval for $\mu_1 - \mu_2$. Assume that $\sigma_1^2 = \sigma_2^2$.

    A) (−2871, 567)   B) (−3047, 247)   C) (−4081, 597)   D) (−2054, 238)

8.3 Testing the Difference Between Means (Dependent Samples)

Solve the problem.

1) Classify the two given samples as independent or dependent.

    Sample 1: Pre-training weights of 24 people
    Sample 2: Post-training weights of 24 people

    A) independent   B) dependent

2) Classify the two given samples as independent or dependent.

    Sample 1: The weights in pounds of 19 newborn females
    Sample 2: The weights in pounds of 19 newborn males

    A) dependent   B) independent

3) Classify the two given samples as independent or dependent.

    Sample 1: The scores of 27 students who took the ACT
    Sample 2: The scores of 27 different students who took the SAT

    A) dependent   B) independent

4) As part of a marketing experiment, a department store regularly mailed discount coupons to 25 of its credit card holders. Their total credit card purchases over the next three months were compared to their prior credit card purchases during the previous three months. Determine whether the samples are dependent or independent.

    A) dependent   B) independent

5) As part of a marketing experiment, a department store regularly mailed discount coupons to 25 of its credit card holders. Their total credit card purchases over the next three months were compared to the credit card purchases over the next three months for 25 credit card holders who were not sent discount coupons. Determine whether the samples are dependent or independent.

    A) independent   B) dependent

6) As part of a Master's thesis project, a mathematics teacher is interested in the effects of two different teaching methods on mathematics achievement. She randomly chooses one class of students to learn an algebraic concept using traditional methods and another class of students to learn the same algebraic concept using manipulatives. The teacher then compares their test scores. Determine whether the samples are dependent or independent.

    A) independent   B) dependent

7) As part of a Master's thesis project, a mathematics teacher is interested in the effects of two different teaching methods on mathematics achievement. She randomly chooses a class of students to learn one algebraic concept using traditional methods. Then on another day, the same students learn a similar algebraic concept using manipulatives. The teacher then compares their test scores. Determine whether the samples are dependent or independent.

A) dependent   B) independent

8) Data sets A and B are dependent. Find $\overline{d}$.

A	13	11	30	26	14
B	11	7	8	18	5

A) 33.1   B) 25.2   C) 9.0   D) –5.1

9) Data sets A and B are dependent. Find $\overline{d}$.

A	3.3	4.3	6.2	3.2	3.3
B	5.7	4.6	4.5	4.4	5.8

A) –0.76   B) –0.94   C) 0.89   D) 0.58

10) Data sets A and B are dependent. Find s_d.

A	15	13	32	28	16
B	13	9	10	20	7

A) 5.6   B) 8.9   C) 7.8   D) 6.8

11) Data sets A and B are dependent. Find s_d.

A	2.4	3.4	5.3	2.3	2.4
B	4.8	3.7	3.6	3.5	4.9

A) 1.21   B) 1.32   C) 1.73   D) 1.89

12) Data sets A and B are dependent. Find the critical value, t_0, to test the claim that $\mu_d = 0$. Use $\alpha = 0.05$.

A	40	38	57	53	41
B	38	34	35	45	32

A) 2.132   B) 3.747   C) ±4.604   D) ±2.776

13) Data sets A and B are dependent. Find the critical value, t_0, to test the claim that $\mu_d = 0$. Use $\alpha = 0.01$.

A	5.1	6.1	8.0	5.0	5.1
B	7.5	6.4	6.3	6.2	7.6

A) 0.741   B) ±4.604   C) 2.132   D) ±3.747

14) Data sets A and B are dependent. Find the critical value, t_0, to test the claim that $\mu_d = 0$. Use $\alpha = 0.02$.

A	5.3	6.5	8.4	5.4	5.5
B	2.7	1.6	2.5	1.4	2.8

A) 0.741   B) ±4.604   C) 2.132   D) ±3.747

15) Construct a 95% confidence interval for data sets A and B. Data sets A and B are dependent.

A	30	28	47	43	31
B	28	24	25	35	22

    A) (–0.683, 18.700)   B) (–1.324, 8.981)   C) (–15.341, 15.431)   D) (–0.113, 12.761)

16) Construct a 99% confidence interval for data sets A and B. Data sets A and B are dependent.

A	5.8	6.8	8.7	5.7	5.8
B	8.2	7.1	7.0	6.9	8.3

    A) (–25.123, 5.761)   B) (–15.123, 15.123)   C) (–4.502, 2.622)   D) (–21.342, 18.982)

17) Data sets A and B are dependent. Test the claim that the paired sample data is from a population with a mean difference of 0. Use $\alpha = 0.05$.

A	37	35	54	50	38
B	35	31	32	42	29

18) Data sets A and B are dependent. Test the claim that the paired sample data is from a population with a mean difference of 0. Use $\alpha = 0.01$.

A	4.5	5.5	7.4	4.4	4.5
B	6.9	5.8	5.7	5.6	7.0

19) Test the claim that $\mu_d = 0$ using the sample statistics below. Assume that the populations are normally distributed. Use $\alpha = 0.05$.

Sample statistics: n = 12, $\overline{d} = 7.4$, $s_d = 1.7$

20) Test the claim that $\mu_d > 0$ using the sample statistics below. Assume that the populations are normally distributed. Use $\alpha = 0.01$.

Sample statistics: n = 15, $\overline{d} = 4.4$, $s_d = 0.2$

21) Test the claim that $\mu_d < 0$ using the sample statistics below. Assume that the populations are normally distributed. Use $\alpha = 0.10$.

Sample statistics: n = 18, $\overline{d} = -1.9$, $s_d = 0.4$

22) Test the claim that $\mu_d \neq 0$ using the sample statistics below. Assume that the populations are normally distributed. Use $\alpha = 0.02$.

Sample statistics: n = 13, $\overline{d} = 2.4$, $s_d = 5.1$

23) Nine students took the SAT. Their scores are listed below. Later on, they took a test preparation course and retook the SAT. Their new scores are listed below. Test the claim that the test preparation had no effect on their scores. Use $\alpha = 0.05$. Assume that the distribution is normally distributed.

Student	1	2	3	4	5	6	7	8	9
Scores before course	720	860	850	880	860	710	850	1200	950
Scores after course	740	860	840	920	890	720	840	1240	970

24) A weight-lifting coach claims that weight-lifters can increase their strength by taking a certain supplement. To test the theory, the coach randomly selects 9 athletes and gives them a strength test using a bench press. The results are listed below. Thirty days later, after regular training using the supplement, they are tested again. The new results are listed below. Test the claim that the supplement is effective in increasing the athletes' strength. Use $\alpha = 0.05$. Assume that the distribution is normally distributed.

Athlete	1	2	3	4	5	6	7	8	9
Before	215	240	188	212	275	260	225	200	185
After	225	245	188	210	282	275	230	195	190

25) A pharmaceutical company wishes to test a new drug with the expectation of lowering cholesterol levels. Ten subjects are randomly selected and pretested. The results are listed below. The subjects were placed on the drug for a period of 6 months, after which their cholesterol levels were tested again. The results are listed below. (All units are milligrams per deciliter.) Test the company's claim that the drug lowers cholesterol levels. Use $\alpha = 0.01$. Assume that the distribution is normally distributed.

Subject	1	2	3	4	5	6	7	8	9	10
Before	195	225	202	195	175	250	235	268	190	240
After	180	220	210	175	170	250	205	250	190	225

26) In a study of effectiveness of physical exercise on weight loss, 20 people were randomly selected to participate in a program for 30 days. Test the claim that exercise had no bearing on weight loss. Use $\alpha = 0.02$. Assume that the distribution is normally distributed.

Weight before Program (in pounds)	178	210	156	188	193	225	190	165	168	200
Weight after program (in pounds)	182	205	156	190	183	220	195	155	165	200

Weight before Program (in pounds) Con't	186	172	166	184	225	145	208	214	148	174
Weight after program (in pounds) Con't	180	173	165	186	240	138	203	203	142	174

27) Nine students took the SAT. Their scores are listed below. Later on, they took a test preparation course and retook the SAT. Their new scores are listed below. Construct a 95% confidence interval for μ_d. Assume that the distribution is normally distributed.

Student	1	2	3	4	5	6	7	8	9
Scores before course	720	860	850	880	860	710	850	1200	950
Scores after course	740	860	840	920	890	720	840	1240	970

A) (1.651, 30.590)   B) (–30.503, –0.617)   C) (–20.341, 4.852)   D) (–10.321, 15.436)

28) A local school district is concerned about the number of school days missed by its teachers due to illness. A random sample of 10 teachers is selected. The number of days absent in one year is listed below. An incentive program is offered in an attempt to decrease the number of days absent. The number of days absent in one year after the incentive program is listed below. Test the claim that the incentive program cuts down on the number of days missed by teachers. Use $\alpha = 0.05$. Assume that the distribution is normally distributed.

Teacher	A	B	C	D	E	F	G	H	I	J
Days absent before incentive	3	8	7	2	9	4	2	0	7	5
Days absent after incentive	1	7	7	0	8	2	0	1	5	5

29) A physician claims that a person's diastolic blood pressure can be lowered if, instead of taking a drug, the person listens to a relaxation tape each evening. Ten subjects are randomly selected and pretested. Their blood pressures, measured in millimeters of mercury, are listed below. The 10 patients are given the tapes and told to listen to them each evening for one month. At the end of the month, their blood pressures are taken again. The data are listed below. Test the physician's claim. Use $\alpha = 0.01$.

Patient	1	2	3	4	5	6	7	8	9	10
Before	85	96	92	83	80	91	79	98	93	96
After	82	90	92	75	74	80	82	88	89	80

8.4 Testing the Difference Between Proportions

Solve the problem.

1) Find the weighted estimate, $\overline{p}$ to test the claim that $p_1 = p_2$. Use $\alpha = 0.05$. The sample statistics listed below are from independent samples.

Sample statistics: $n_1 = 50$, $x_1 = 35$, and $n_2 = 60$, $x_2 = 40$

A) 0.238   B) 0.682   C) 0.328   D) 1.367

2) Find the weighted estimate, $\overline{p}$ to test the claim that $p_1 > p_2$. Use $\alpha = 0.01$. The sample statistics listed below are from independent samples.

Sample statistics: $n_1 = 100$, $x_1 = 38$, and $n_2 = 140$, $x_2 = 50$

A) 0.633   B) 0.367   C) 0.523   D) 0.179

3) Find the weighted estimate, $\overline{p}$, to test the claim that $p_1 < p_2$. Use $\alpha = 0.10$. The sample statistics listed below are from independent samples.

Sample statistics: $n_1 = 550$, $x_1 = 121$, and $n_2 = 690$, $x_2 = 195$

A) 1.116   B) 0.255   C) 0.338   D) 0.730

4) Find the weighted estimate, $\overline{p}$ to test the claim that $p_1 \neq p_2$. Use $\alpha = 0.02$. The sample statistics listed below are from independent samples.

Sample statistics: $n_1 = 1000$, $x_1 = 250$, and $n_2 = 1200$, $x_2 = 195$

A) 0.789   B) 0.110   C) 0.202   D) 0.138

5) Find the standardized test statistic, z to test the claim that $p_1 = p_2$. The sample statistics listed below are from independent samples.

Sample statistics: $n_1 = 50$, $x_1 = 35$, and $n_2 = 60$, $x_2 = 40$

   A) 0.982   B) 0.374   C) 2.361   D) 1.328

6) Find the standardized test statistic estimate, z, to test the claim that $p_1 > p_2$. The sample statistics listed below are from independent samples.

Sample statistics: $n_1 = 100$, $x_1 = 38$, and $n_2 = 140$, $x_2 = 50$

   A) 0.362   B) 1.324   C) 2.116   D) 0.638

7) Find the standardized test statistic, z, to test the claim that $p_1 < p_2$. The sample statistics listed below are from independent samples.

Sample statistics: $n_1 = 550$, $x_1 = 121$, and $n_2 = 690$, $x_2 = 195$

   A) –2.132   B) –2.513   C) –0.985   D) 1.116

8) Find the standardized test statistic, z, to test the claim that $p_1 \neq p_2$. The sample statistics listed below are from independent samples.

Sample statistics: $n_1 = 1000$, $x_1 = 250$, and $n_2 = 1200$, $x_2 = 195$

   A) 2.798   B) 3.212   C) 5.087   D) 4.761

9) Construct a 95% confidence interval for $p_1 - p_2$. The sample statistics listed below are from independent samples.

Sample statistics: $n_1 = 50$, $x_1 = 35$, and $n_2 = 60$, $x_2 = 40$

   A) (–2.391, 3.112)   B) (–0.141, 0.208)   C) (–0.871, 0.872)   D) (–1.341, 1.781)

10) Construct a 98% confidence interval for $p_1 - p_2$. The sample statistics listed below are from independent samples.

Sample statistics: $n_1 = 1000$, $x_1 = 250$, and $n_2 = 1200$, $x_2 = 195$

   A) (–0.621, 0.781)   B) (0.047, 0.128)   C) (1.516, 3.021)   D) (0.581, 1.819)

11) Test the claim that $p_1 = p_2$. Use $\alpha = 0.05$. The sample statistics listed below are from independent samples.

Sample statistics: $n_1 = 50$, $x_1 = 35$, and $n_2 = 60$, $x_2 = 40$

12) Test the claim that $p_1 > p_2$. Use $\alpha = 0.01$. The sample statistics listed below are from independent samples.

Sample statistics: $n_1 = 100$, $x_1 = 38$, and $n_2 = 140$, $x_2 = 50$

13) Test the claim that $p_1 < p_2$. Use $\alpha = 0.10$. The sample statistics listed below are from independent samples.

Sample statistics: $n_1 = 550$, $x_1 = 121$, and $n_2 = 690$, $x_2 = 195$

14) Test the claim that $p_1 \neq p_2$. Use $\alpha = 0.02$. The sample statistics listed below are from independent samples.

Sample statistics: $n_1 = 1000$, $x_1 = 250$, and $n_2 = 1200$, $x_2 = 195$.

15) In a recent survey of gun control laws, a random sample of 1000 women showed that 65% were in favor of stricter gun control laws. In a random sample of 1000 men, 60% favored stricter gun control laws. Test the claim that the percentage of men and women favoring stricter gun control laws is the same. Use $\alpha = 0.05$.

16) In a recent survey of gun control laws, a random sample of 1000 women showed that 65% were in favor of stricter gun control laws. In a random sample of 1000 men, 60% favored stricter gun control laws. Construct a 95% confidence interval for $p_1 - p_2$.

   A) (0.587, 0.912)   B) (0.008, 0.092)   C) (–2.153, 1.679)   D) (–1.423, 1.432)

17) A recent survey showed that in a sample of 100 elementary school teachers, 15 smoked. In a sample of 180 high school teachers, 36 smoked. Is the proportion of high school teachers who smoke greater than the proportion of elementary teachers who smoke? Use $\alpha = 0.01$.

18) Construct a 95% confidence interval for $p_1 - p_2$ for a survey that finds 30% of 240 males and 41% of 200 females are opposed to the death penalty.

   A) (–1.532, 1.342)   B) (–0.200, –0.021)   C) (–0.561, 0.651)   D) (–1.324, 1.512)

19) In a survey of 500 doctors that practice specialized medicine, 20% felt that the government should control health care. In a sample of 800 doctors that were general practitioners, 30% felt that the government should control health care. Test the claim that there is a difference in the proportions. Use $\alpha = 0.10$.

20) A nutritionist believes that obesity is more prevalent among American adults than it was in the past. He discovers that in a study conducted in the year 1994, 380 of the1630 randomly chosen adults were classified as obese. However, in a more recent study, he finds 726 out of 2350 randomly chosen adults were classified as obese. At $\alpha = 0.05$, do these studies provide evidence to support the nutritionist's claim that the proportion of obese adults has significantly increased since 1994?

21) A nutritionist believes that obesity is more prevalent among American adults than it was in the past. He discovers that in a study conducted in the year 1994, 380 of the1630 randomly chosen adults were classified as obese. However, in a more recent study, he finds 726 out of 2350 randomly chosen adults were classified as obese. Construct a 95% confidence interval for the difference in proportions $p_1 - p_2$.

22) To test the effectiveness of a new drug designed to relieve pain, 200 patients were randomly selected and divided into two equal groups. One group of 100 patients was given a pill containing the drug while the other group of 100 was given a placebo. What can we conclude about the effectiveness of the drug if 62 of those actually taking the drug felt a beneficial effect while 41 of the patients taking the placebo felt a beneficial effect? Use $\alpha = 0.05$.

23) A random sample of 100 students at a high school was asked whether they would ask their father or mother for help with a homework assignment in science. A second sample of 100 different students was asked the same question for an assignment in history. If 43 students in the first sample and 47 students in the second sample replied that they turned to their mother rather than their father for help, test the claim whether the difference between the proportions is due to chance. Use $\alpha = 0.02$.

24) A random sample of 100 students at a high school was asked whether they would ask their father or mother for help with a homework assignment in science. A second sample of 100 different students was asked the same question for an assignment in history. Forty-three students in the first sample and 47 students in the second sample replied that they turned to their mother rather than their father for help. Construct a 98% confidence interval for $p_1 - p_2$.

    A) (–1.324, 1.521)   B) (–0.591, 0.762)   C) (–1.113, 1.311)   D) (–0.204, 0.124)

25) In the initial test of the Salk vaccine for polio, 400,000 children were selected and divided into two groups of 200,000. One group was vaccinated with the Salk vaccine while the second group was vaccinated with a placebo. Of those vaccinated with the Salk vaccine, 33 later developed polio. Of those receiving the placebo, 115 later developed polio. Test the claim that the Salk vaccine is effective in lowering the polio rate. Use $\alpha = 0.01$.

26) A well-known study of 22,000 male physicians was conducted to determine if taking aspirin daily reduces the chances of a heart attack. Half of the physicians were given a regular dose of aspirin while the other half was given placebos. Six years later, among those who took aspirin, 104 suffered heart attacks while among those who took placebos, 189 suffered heart attacks. Does it appear that the aspirin can reduce the number of heart attacks among the sample group that took aspirin? Use $\alpha = 0.01$.

27) A youth prevention organization is examining the effect of parental smoking on the decision of their teenagers to smoke. A survey of 1150 teenagers, ages 11 to 17 years who smoked in the last 30 days, was conducted. The random sample consisted of 500 teenagers who had at least one parent that smoked and 650 who had parents that did not smoke. The results are shown in the figure. At $\alpha = 0.01$, can you support the organization's claim that the proportion of teens who decide to smoke is greater when one or both of their parents smoke?

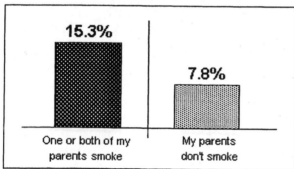

Effect of Parental Smoking
Percentage of 11-17-year-olds who smoked a cigarette at least once in the past 30 days who reported that:

15.3% — One or both of my parents smoke
7.8% — My parents don't smoke

Source: Philip Morris USA Youth Smoking Prevention. Teenage Attitudes and Behavior Study. 2002.

28) A youth prevention organization is examining the effect of peer pressure on the decision of teenagers to smoke. A survey of 97 teenagers, ages 11 to 17 years who smoked in the last 30 days, was conducted. The random sample consisted of 25 teenagers who said all/most of their friends smoke, 40 who said some of their friends smoke, and 32 who said none of their friends smoke. The results are shown in the figure. At $\alpha = 0.01$, can you support the organization's claim that the proportion of teens who decide to smoke is lower when none of their friends smoke?

How Friends Affect Youth Smoking
Percentage of 11-17-year-olds who smoked a cigarette at least once in the past 30 days.

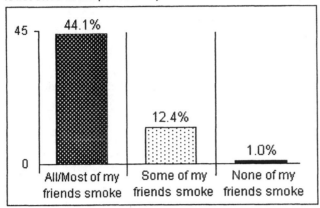

Source: Philip Morris USA Youth Smoking Prevention. Teenage Attitudes and Behavior Study. 2002.

8.1 Testing the Difference Between Means (Large Independent Samples)

1) D
2) B
3) A
4) D
5) A
6) D
7) C
8) critical value $z_0 = \pm 1.96$; standardized test statistic ≈ 6.17; reject H_0; There is sufficient evidence to reject the claim.
9) A
10) C
11) critical value $z_0 = 2.33$; standardized test statistic ≈ 2.99; reject H_0; There is sufficient evidence to support the claim.
12) A
13) D
14) A
15) A
16) D
17) critical value $z_0 = \pm 2.33$; standardized test statistic ≈ -2.97; reject H_0; There is sufficient evidence to support the claim.
18) critical values $z_0 = \pm 1.96$; standardized test statistic $z \approx -4.50$; reject H_0; There is sufficient evidence to reject the claim.
19) critical value $z_0 = 2.33$; standardized test statistic ≈ 1.71; fail to reject H_0; There is not sufficient evidence to support the claim.
20) critical value $z_0 = 1.645$; standardized test statistic $z \approx 4.20$; reject H_0; There is sufficient evidence to support the claim.
21) critical value $z_0 = -2.33$; standardized test statistic $z \approx -2.18$; fail to reject H_0; There is not sufficient evidence to support the claim.
22) day students $\overline{x_1} = 22$, $s_1 = 3.13$; evening students $\overline{x_2} = 23.29$, $s_2 = 3.27$; critical values $z_0 = \pm 1.96$; standardized test statistic $z = -1.69$; fail to reject H_0; There is not sufficient evidence to reject the claim.
23) critical value $z_0 = -1.645$; standardized test statistic $z \approx -1.39$; fail to reject H_0; There is not sufficient evidence to support the claim.
24) C
25) C
26) P–value = 0.0823; $\alpha = 0.05$, $P > \alpha$; fail to reject H_0; There is not sufficient evidence to support the claim.
27) Confidence interval (–0.656, 0.056); 0 lies in the interval, fail to reject H_0; There is not sufficient evidence to support the claim.
28) A
29) C
30) B
31) NASDAQ: $\overline{x_1} = 1.66$, $s_1 = 0.63$; NYSE: $\overline{x_2} = 2.72$, $s_2 = 1.14$; standardized test statistic ≈ -4.46; critical value $z_0 = \pm 1.96$; reject H_0; There is enough evidence to reject the claim.
32) confidence interval: $-23.38 < \mu_1 - \mu_2 < -6.623$; Since the interval does not contain zero, we can reject the claim of $\mu_1 = \mu_2$. Since the interval is negative, it appears that the diet lowers blood pressure.
33) critical value $z_0 = 1.645$; standardized test statistic $z \approx 1.05$; fail to reject H_0; There is not sufficient evidence to support the claim.
34) Standardized test statistic ≈ 1.30; critical value $z_0 = 1.645$; fail to reject H_0; There is not sufficient evidence to support the claim

35) Standardized test statistic $\approx$ -1.20; critical value $z_0 = $ -2.326; fail to reject H_0; There is not sufficient evidence to support the claim.

8.2 Testing the Difference Between Means (Small Independent Samples)

1) D
2) B
3) C
4) D
5) C
6) A
7) B
8) B
9) A
10) B
11) D
12) C
13) D
14) C
15) B
16) critical value $t_0 = \pm 2.064$; standardized test statistic $\approx$ 4.361; reject H_0; There is sufficient evidence to reject the claim.
17) critical value $t_0 = \pm 2.064$; standardized test statistic $\approx$ -0.962; fail to reject H_0; There is not sufficient evidence to reject the claim.
18) critical value $t_0 = $ 2.681; standardized test statistic $\approx$ 1.282; fail to reject H_0; There is not sufficient evidence to support the claim.
19) critical value $t_0 = $ -1.701; standardized test statistic = -2.420; reject H_0; There is sufficient evidence to support the claim.
20) critical value $t_0 = \pm 2.764$; standardized test statistic $\approx$ -1.546; fail to reject H_0; There is not sufficient evidence to support the claim.

21) C
22) C
23) B
24) (a) critical value $t_0 = $ -1.699; standardized test statistic $\approx$ -0.795; fail to reject H_0; There is not sufficient evidence to support the claim.
(b) critical value $t_0 = $ -1.761; standardized test statistic $\approx$ -0.793; fail to reject H_0; There is not sufficient evidence to support the claim.
25) critical value $t_0 = \pm 2.048$; standardized test statistic $t \approx$ -1.741; fail to reject H_0; There is not sufficient evidence to reject the claim.
26) Standardized test statistic $\approx$ -0.167; critical value $t_0 = \pm 2.179$; fail to reject H_0; There is not sufficient evidence to support the claim.
27) (-0.014, 0.012)
28) Standardized test statistic $\approx$ -13.663; critical value $t_0 = $ -2.821; reject H_0; There is sufficient evidence to support the claim.
29) (-839,897, -517,103)
30) B

8.3 Testing the Difference Between Means (Dependent Samples)

1) B
2) B
3) B
4) A
5) A
6) A
7) A
8) C

9) B

10) C

11) C

12) D

13) B

14) D

15) A

16) C

17) critical values $t_0 = \pm 2.776$; standardized test statistic $t \approx 2.580$; fail to reject H_0; There is not sufficient evidence to reject the claim.

18) critical values $t_0 = \pm 4.604$; standardized test statistic $t \approx -1.215$; fail to reject H_0; There is not sufficient evidence to reject the claim.

19) critical values $t_0 = \pm 2.201$; standardized test statistic $t \approx 15.079$; reject H_0; There is sufficient evidence to reject the claim.

20) critical value $t_0 = 2.624$; standardized test statistic $t \approx 85.206$; reject H_0; There is sufficient evidence to support the claim.

21) critical value $t_0 = -1.333$; standardized test statistic $t \approx -20.153$; reject H_0; There is sufficient evidence to support the claim.

22) critical values $t_0 = \pm 2.681$; standardized test statistic $t \approx 1.697$; fail to reject H_0; There is not sufficient evidence to support the claim.

23) claim: $\mu_d = 0$; critical values $t_0 = \pm 2.306$; standardized test statistic $t \approx -2.401$; reject H_0; There is sufficient evidence to reject the claim.

24) claim: $\mu_d < 0$; critical value $t_0 = -1.860$; standardized test statistic $t \approx -2.177$; reject H_0; There is sufficient evidence to support the claim.

25) claim: $\mu_d > 0$; critical value $t_0 = 2.821$; standardized test statistic $t \approx 2.752$; fail to reject H_0; There is not sufficient evidence to support the claim.

26) claim: $\mu_d = 0$; critical values $t_0 = \pm 2.539$; standardized test statistic $t \approx 1.451$; fail to reject H_0; There is not sufficient evidence to reject the claim.

27) B

28) claim: $\mu_d > 0$; critical values $t_0 = 1.833$; standardized test statistic $t \approx 3.161$; reject H_0; There is sufficient evidence to support the claim.

29) claim: $\mu_d > 0$; critical value $t_0 = 2.821$; standardized test statistic $t \approx 3.490$; reject H_0; There is sufficient evidence to support the claim.

8.4 Testing the Difference Between Proportions

1) B

2) B

3) B

4) C

5) B

6) A

7) B

8) C

9) B

10) B

11) critical values $z_0 = \pm 1.96$; standardized test statistic $t \approx 0.374$; fail to reject H_0; There is not sufficient evidence to reject the claim.

12) critical values $z_0 = \pm 2.33$; standardized test statistic $t \approx 0.362$; fail to reject H_0; There is not sufficient evidence to support the claim.

13) critical value $z_0 = -1.28$; standardized test statistic $t \approx -2.513$; reject H_0; There is sufficient evidence to support the claim.

14) critical values $z_0 = \pm 2.33$; standardized test statistic $t \approx 5.087$; reject H_0; There is sufficient evidence to support the claim.

15) claim: $p_1 = p_2$; critical value $z_0 = 1.96$; standardized test statistic $t \approx 2.309$; reject the null hypothesis; There is sufficient evidence to reject the claim.

16) B

17) claim: $p_1 < p_2$; critical value $z_0 = -2.33$; standardized test statistic $t \approx -1.039$; fail to reject H_0; There is not sufficient evidence to support the claim.

18) B

19) claim: $p_1 \neq p_2$; critical values $z_0 = \pm 1.645$; standardized test statistic ≈ -3.991; reject H_0; There is sufficient evidence to support the claim.

20) Standardized test statistic ≈ 5.250; critical value $z_0 = 1.645$; reject H_0; There is sufficient evidence to support the claim.

21) (–0.104, –0.048)

22) claim: $p_1 = p_2$; critical values $z_0 = \pm 1.96$; standardized test statistic $t \approx 2.971$; reject H_0; The new drug is effective.

23) claim: $p_1 = p_2$; critical values $z_0 = \pm 2.33$; standardized test statistic $t \approx -0.569$; fail to reject H_0; There is not sufficient evidence to reject the claim.

24) D

25) claim: $p_1 < p_2$; critical value $z_0 = -2.33$; standardized test statistic $t \approx -6.742$; reject H_0; There is sufficient evidence to support the claim.

26) claim: $p_1 < p_2$; critical value $z_0 = -2.33$; standardized test statistic $t \approx -4.999$; reject H_0; There is sufficient evidence to support the claim.

27) Standardized test statistic ≈ 4.030; critical value $z_0 = 2.326$; reject H_0; There is sufficient evidence to support the claim.

28) Standardized test statistic ≈ -3.326; critical value $z_0 = -2.326$; reject H_0; There is sufficient evidence to support the claim.

Ch. 9 Correlation and Regression

9.1 Correlation

Solve the problem.

1) Given the length of a human's femur, x, and the length of a human's humerus, y, would you expect a positive correlation, a negative correlation, or no correlation?

   A) negative correlation   B) no correlation   C) positive correlation

2) Given the supply of a commodity, x, and the price of a commodity, y, would you expect a positive correlation, a negative correlation, or no correlation?

   A) no correlation   B) negative correlation   C) positive correlation

3) Given the size of a human's brain, x, and their score on an IQ test, y, would you expect a positive correlation, a negative correlation, or no correlation?

   A) negative correlation   B) positive correlation   C) no correlation

4) The data below are the gestation periods, in months, of randomly selected animals and their corresponding life spans, in years. Construct a scatter plot for the data. Determine whether there is a positive linear correlation, a negative linear correlation, or no linear correlation.

Gestation, x	8	2.1	1.3	1	11.5	5.3	3.8	24.3
Life span, y	30	12	6	3	25	12	10	40

5) Construct a scatter plot for the given data. Determine whether there is a positive linear correlation, negative linear correlation, or no linear correlation.

x	-5	-3	4	1	-1	-2	0	2	3	-4
y	11	6	-6	-1	3	4	1	-4	-5	8

6) Construct a scatter plot for the given data. Determine whether there is a positive linear correlation, negative linear correlation, or no linear correlation.

x	-5	-3	4	1	-1	-2	0	2	3	-4
y	11	-6	8	-3	-2	1	5	-5	6	7

7) The data below are the final exam scores of 10 randomly selected statistics students and the number of hours they studied for the exam. Construct a scatter plot for the data.

Hours, x	3	5	2	8	2	4	4	5	6	3
Scores, y	65	80	60	88	66	78	85	90	90	71

8) The data below are the temperatures on randomly chosen days during a summer class and the number of absences on those days. Construct a scatter plot for the data.

Temperature, x	72	85	91	90	88	98	75	100	80
Number of absences, y	3	7	10	10	8	15	4	15	5

9) The data below are the ages and systolic blood pressures (measured in millimeters of mercury) of 9 randomly selected adults. Construct a scatter plot for the data.

Age, x	38	41	45	48	51	53	57	61	65
Pressure, y	116	120	123	131	142	145	148	150	152

10) The data below are the number of absences and the final grades of 9 randomly selected students from a statistics class. Construct a scatter plot for the data.

Number of absences, x	0	3	6	4	9	2	15	8	5
Final grade, y	98	86	80	82	71	92	55	76	82

11) A manager wishes to determine the relationship between the number of miles (in hundreds of miles) the manager's sales representatives travel per month and the amount of sales (in thousands of dollars) per month. Construct a scatter plot for the data.

Miles traveled, x	2	3	10	7	8	15	3	1	11
Sales, y	31	33	78	62	65	61	48	55	120

12) In order for applicants to work for the foreign–service department, they must take a test in the language of the country where they plan to work. The data below show the relationship between the number of years that applicants have studied a particular language and the grades they received on the proficiency exam. Construct a scatter plot for the data.

Number of years, x	3	4	4	5	3	6	2	7	3
Grades on test, y	61	68	75	82	73	90	58	93	72

13) In an area of the Midwest, records were kept on the relationship between the rainfall (in inches) and the yield of wheat (bushels per acre). Construct a scatter plot for the data.

Rain fall (in inches), x	10.5	8.8	13.4	12.5	18.8	10.3	7.0	15.6	16.0
Yield (bushels per acre), y	50.5	46.2	58.8	59.0	82.4	49.2	31.9	76.0	78.8

14) Explain the difference between $\sum x^2$ and $\left(\sum x\right)^2$.

15) If Data A has a correlation coefficient of r = –0.991, and Data B has a correlation coefficient of r = 0.991, which correlation is correct?

  A) Data A and Data B have the same strength in linear correlation.

  B) Data A has a weaker linear correlation than Data B.

  C) Data A has a stronger linear correlation than Data B.

16) Which of the following values could not represent a correlation coefficient?

  A) 0   B) 1.032   C) –1   D) 0.927

17) Calculate the correlation coefficient, r, for the data below.

x	-8	-6	1	-2	-4	-5	-3	-1	0	-7
y	-15	-13	4	-4	-7	-11	-6	-2	1	-13

A) 0.990　　　　　　　B) 0.819　　　　　　　C) 0.881　　　　　　D) 0.792

18) Calculate the correlation coefficient, r, for the data below.

x	-3	-1	6	3	1	0	2	4	5	-2
y	5	0	-12	-7	-3	-2	-5	-10	-11	2

A) -0.995　　　　　　B) -0.885　　　　　　C) -0.778　　　　　D) -0.671

19) Calculate the correlation coefficient, r, for the data below.

x	-13	-11	-4	-7	-9	-10	-8	-6	-5	-12
y	12	-5	9	-2	-1	2	6	-4	7	8

A) -0.581　　　　　　B) -0.104　　　　　　C) -0.132　　　　　D) -0.549

20) The data below are the gestation periods, in months, of randomly selected animals and their corresponding life spans, in years. Calculate the correlation coefficient r.

Gestation, x	8	2.1	1.3	1	11.5	5.3	3.8	24.3
Life span, y	30	12	6	3	25	12	10	40

21) The data below are the average monthly temperatures, in °F, and the monthly natural gas consumption, in ccf, for a household in northwestern Pennsylvania. Calculate the correlation coefficient, r.

Temperature	47	35	21	27	39	48	61	65	70
Consumption	34	169	248	134	137	100	19	34	12

22) The data below are the final exam scores of 10 randomly selected statistics students and the number of hours they studied for the exam. Calculate the correlation coefficient r.

Hours, x	5	7	4	10	4	6	6	7	8	5
Scores, y	60	75	55	83	61	73	80	85	85	66

A) 0.847　　　　　　　B) 0.654　　　　　　C) 0.991　　　　　D) 0.761

23) The data below are the temperatures on randomly chosen days during a summer class and the number of absences on those days. Calculate the correlation coefficient, r.

Temperature, x	76	89	95	94	92	102	79	104	84
Number of absences, y	10	14	17	17	15	22	11	22	12

A) 0.819　　　　　　　B) 0.881　　　　　　C) 0.980　　　　　D) 0.890

24) The data below are the ages and systolic blood pressures (measured in millimeters of mercury) of 9 randomly selected adults. Calculate the correlation coefficient, r.

Age, x	41	44	48	51	54	56	60	64	68
Pressure, y	111	115	118	126	137	140	143	145	147

A) 0.908   B) 0.998   C) 0.890   D) 0.960

25) The data below are the number of absences and the final grades of 9 randomly selected students from a statistics class. Calculate the correlation coefficient, r.

Number of absences, x	4	7	10	8	13	6	19	12	9
Final Grade, y	96	84	78	80	69	90	53	74	80

A) –0.918   B) –0.899   C) –0.888   D) –0.991

26) A manager wishes to determine the relationship between the number of miles (in hundreds of miles) the manager's sales representatives travel per month and the amount of sales (in thousands of dollars) per month. Calculate the correlation coefficient, r.

Miles traveled, x	2	3	10	7	8	15	3	1	11
Sales, y	22	24	69	53	56	52	39	46	111

A) 0.632   B) 0.791   C) 0.717   D) 0.561

27) In order for applicants to work for the foreign-service department, they must take a test in the language of the country where they plan to work. The data below shows the relationship between the number of years that applicants have studied a particular language and the grades they received on the proficiency exam. Calculate the correlation coefficient, r.

Number of years, x	5	6	6	7	5	8	4	9	5
Grades on test, y	58	65	72	79	70	87	55	90	69

A) 0.911   B) 0.934   C) 0.902   D) 0.891

28) In an area of the Midwest, records were kept on the relationship between the rainfall (in inches) and the yield of wheat (bushels per acre). Calculate the correlation coefficient, r.

Rain fall (in inches), x	12.7	11	15.6	14.7	21	12.5	9.2	17.8	18.2
Yield (bushels per acre), y	52.5	48.2	60.8	61	84.4	51.2	33.9	78	80.8

A) 0.900   B) 0.981   C) 0.998   D) 0.899

29) An agricultural business wants to determine if the rainfall in inches can be used to predict the yield per acre on a wheat farm. Identify the explanatory variable and the response variable.

30) A college counselor wants to determine if the number of hours spent studying for a test can be used to predict the grades on a test. Identify the explanatory variable and the response variable.

31) Given a sample with $r = 0.823$, $n = 10$, and $\alpha = 0.05$, determine the standardized test statistic t necessary to test the claim $\rho = 0$. Round answers to three decimal places.

A) 4.098   B) 2.891   C) 3.816   D) 1.782

32) Given a sample with r = −0.541, n = 20, and α = 0.01, determine the standardized test statistic t necessary to test the claim ρ = 0. Round answers to three decimal places.

    A) −5.132   B) −2.729   C) −3.251   D) −4.671

33) Given a sample with r = 0.321, n = 30, and α = 0.10, determine the standardized test statistic t necessary to test the claim ρ = 0. Round answers to three decimal places.

    A) 3.198   B) 2.561   C) 1.793   D) 2.354

34) Given a sample with r = −0.765, n = 22, and α = 0.02, determine the standardized test statistic t necessary to test the claim ρ = 0. Round answers to three decimal places.

    A) −3.783   B) −4.392   C) −2.653   D) −5.312

35) Given a sample with r = 0.823, n = 10, and α = 0.05, determine the critical values t_0 necessary to test the claim ρ = 0.

    A) ± 1.383   B) ± 1.833   C) ± 2.306   D) ± 2.821

36) Given a sample with r = −0.541, n = 20, and α = 0.01, determine the critical values t_0 necessary to test the claim ρ = 0.

    A) ± 1.729   B) ± 2.093   C) ± 2.540   D) ± 2.878

37) Given a sample with r = 0.321, n = 30, and α = 0.10, determine the critical values t_0 necessary to test the claim ρ = 0.

    A) ± 1.701   B) ± 1.311   C) ± 0.683   D) ± 2.462

38) Given a sample with r = −0.765, n = 22, and α = 0.02, determine the critical values t_0 necessary to test the claim ρ = 0.

    A) ± 2.528   B) ± 2.080   C) ± 1.721   D) ± 2.831

39) Given a sample with r = 0.823 and n = 10, test the significance of the correlation r using α = 0.05 and the claim ρ = 0.

40) Given a sample with r = −0.541, n = 20, test the significance of the correlation r using α = 0.01 and the claim ρ = 0.

41) Given a sample with r = 0.321 and n = 30, test the significance of the correlation r using α = 0.10 and the claim ρ = 0.

42) Given a sample with r = −0.765 and n = 22, test the significance of the correlation r using α = 0.02 and the claim ρ = 0.

43) For the data below, test the significance of the correlation coefficient using α = 0.05 and the claim ρ = 0.

x	−9	−7	0	−3	−5	−6	−4	−2	−1	−8
y	−2	0	17	9	6	2	7	11	14	0

44) For the data below, test the significance of the correlation coefficient using α = 0.01 and the claim ρ = 0.

x	−2	0	7	4	2	1	3	5	6	−1
y	5	0	−12	−7	−3	−2	−5	−10	−11	2

45) For the data below, test the significance of the correlation coefficient using $\alpha = 0.10$ and the claim $\rho = 0$.

x	-4	-2	5	2	0	-1	1	3	4	-3
y	5	-12	2	-9	-8	-5	-1	-11	0	1

46) The data below are the gestation periods, in months, of randomly selected animals and their corresponding life spans, in years. Test the significance of the correlation coefficient using $\alpha = 0.01$ and the claim $\rho > 0$.

Gestation, x	8	2.1	1.3	1	11.5	5.3	3.8	24.3
Life span, y	30	12	6	3	25	12	10	40

47) The data below are the final exam scores of 10 randomly selected statistics students and the number of hours they studied for the exam. Test the significance of the correlation coefficient using $\alpha = 0.05$ and the claim $\rho = 0$.

Hours, x	8	10	7	13	7	9	9	10	11	8
Scores, y	66	81	61	89	67	79	86	91	91	72

48) The data below are the temperatures on randomly chosen days during a summer class and the number of absences on those days. Test the significance of the correlation coefficient using $\alpha = 0.02$, and the claim $\rho = 0$.

Temperature, x	76	89	95	94	92	102	79	104	84
Number of absences, y	0	4	7	7	5	12	1	12	2

49) The data below are the ages and systolic blood pressures (measured in millimeters of mercury) of 9 randomly selected adults. Test the significance of the correlation coefficient using $\alpha = 0.05$ and the claim $\rho = 0$.

Age, x	37	40	44	47	50	52	56	60	64
Pressure, y	113	117	120	128	139	142	145	147	149

50) The data below are the number of absences and the final grades of 9 randomly selected students from a statistics class. Test the significance of the correlation coefficient using $\alpha = 0.05$ and the claim $\rho = 0$.

Number of absences, x	5	8	11	9	14	7	20	13	10
Final Grade, y	91	79	73	75	64	85	48	69	75

51) A manager wishes to determine the relationship between the number of miles (in hundreds of miles) the manager's sales representatives travel per month and the amount of sales (in thousands of dollars) per month. Test the significance of the correlation coefficient using $\alpha = 0.01$ and the claim $\rho = 0$.

Miles traveled, x	2	3	10	7	8	15	3	1	11
Sales, y	25	27	72	56	59	55	42	49	114

52) In order for applicants to work for the foreign-service department, they must take a test in the language of the country where they plan to work. The data below shows the relationship between the number of years that applicants have studied a particular language and the grades they received on the proficiency exam. Test the significance of the correlation coefficient using $\alpha = 0.10$ and the claim $\rho = 0$.

Number of years, x	7	8	8	9	7	10	6	11	7
Grades on test, y	64	71	78	85	76	93	61	96	75

Elementary Statistics 166

53) In an area of the Midwest, records were kept on the relationship between the rainfall (in inches) and the yield of wheat (bushels per acre). Test the significance of the correlation coefficient using α = 0.01 and the claim ρ = 0.

Rain fall (in inches), x	10.4	8.7	13.3	12.4	18.7	10.2	6.9	15.5	15.9
Yield (bushels per acre), y	53.5	49.2	61.8	62	85.4	52.2	34.9	79	81.8

54) The data below are the average monthly temperatures, in °F, and the monthly natural gas consumption, in ccf, for a household in northwestern Pennsylvania. Test the significance of the correlation coefficient using α = 0.05 and the claim ρ < 0.

Temperature	47	35	21	27	39	48	61	65	70
Consumption	34	169	248	134	137	100	19	34	12

55) Calculate the coefficient of correlation, r, letting Row 1 represent the x–values and Row 2 represent the y–values. Now calculate the coefficient of correlation, r, letting Row 2 represent the x–values and Row 1 represent the y–values. What effect does switching the explanatory and response variables have on the correlation coefficient?

Row 1	–6	–4	3	0	–2	–3	–1	1	2	–5
Row 2	0	18	19	11	8	4	9	13	16	18

9.2 Linear Regression

Solve the problem.

1) Given the equation of a regression line is $\hat{y} = -1.04x + 50.3$, determine whether there is a positive linear correlation or a negative linear correlation.

   A) negative linear correlation   B) positive linear correlation

2) Given the equation of a regression line is $\hat{y} = 0.00014x + 2.53$, determine whether there is a positive linear correlation or a negative linear correlation.

   A) negative linear correlation   B) positive linear correlation

3) Find the equation of the regression line for the given data.

x	–5	–3	4	1	–1	–2	0	2	3	–4
y	–10	–8	9	1	–2	–6	–1	3	6	–8

   A) $\hat{y} = 2.097x + 0.552$ B) $\hat{y} = 2.097x - 0.552$ C) $\hat{y} = 0.522x - 2.097$ D) $\hat{y} = -0.552x + 2.097$

4) Find the equation of the regression line for the given data.

x	–5	–3	4	1	–1	–2	0	2	3	–4
y	11	6	–6	–1	3	4	1	–4	–5	8

   A) $\hat{y} = 0.758x + 1.885$ B) $\hat{y} = -0.758x - 1.885$ C) $\hat{y} = 1.885x - 0.758$ D) $\hat{y} = -1.885x + 0.758$

5) Find the equation of the regression line for the given data.

x	-5	-3	4	1	-1	-2	0	2	3	-4
y	11	-6	8	-3	-2	1	5	-5	6	7

A) $\hat{y} = -2.097x + 0.206$ B) $\hat{y} = 2.097x - 0.206$ C) $\hat{y} = -0.206x + 2.097$ D) $\hat{y} = 0.206x - 2.097$

6) The data below are the gestation periods, in months, of randomly selected animals and their corresponding life spans, in years. Find the equation of the regression line for the given data.

Gestation, x	8	2.1	1.3	1	11.5	5.3	3.8	24.3
Life span, y	30	12	6	3	25	12	10	40

7) The data below are the final exam scores of 10 randomly selected statistics students and the number of hours they studied for the exam. Find the equation of the regression line for the given data.

Hours, x	3	5	2	8	2	4	4	5	6	3
Scores, y	65	80	60	88	66	78	85	90	90	71

A) $\hat{y} = 5.044x + 56.11$ B) $\hat{y} = -5.044x + 56.11$ C) $\hat{y} = -56.11x - 5.044$ D) $\hat{y} = 56.11x - 5.044$

8) The data below are the temperatures on randomly chosen days during a summer class and the number of absences on those days. Find the equation of the regression line for the given data.

Temperature, x	72	85	91	90	88	98	75	100	80
Number of absences, y	3	7	10	10	8	15	4	15	5

A) $\hat{y} = 0.449x + 30.27$ B) $\hat{y} = 30.27x - 0.449$ C) $\hat{y} = 30.27x + 0.449$ D) $\hat{y} = 0.449x - 30.27$

9) The data below are ages and systolic blood pressures (measured in millimeters of mercury) of 9 randomly selected adults. Find the equation of the regression line for the given data.

Age, x	38	41	45	48	51	53	57	61	65
Pressure, y	116	120	123	131	142	145	148	150	152

A) $\hat{y} = 60.46x + 1.488$ B) $\hat{y} = 60.46x - 1.488$ C) $\hat{y} = 1.448x - 60.46$ D) $\hat{y} = 1.488x + 60.46$

10) The data below are the number of absences and the final grades of 9 randomly selected students from a statistics class. Find the equation of the regression line for the given data.

Number of absences, x	0	3	6	4	9	2	15	8	5
Final grade, y	98	86	80	82	71	92	55	76	82

A) $\hat{y} = 96.14x - 2.75$ B) $\hat{y} = -96.14x + 2.75$ C) $\hat{y} = -2.75x - 96.14$ D) $\hat{y} = -2.75x + 96.14$

Elementary Statistics 168

11) A manager wishes to determine the relationship between the number of miles (in hundreds of miles) the manager's sales representatives travel per month and the amount of sales (in thousands of dollars) per month. Find the equation of the regression line for the given data.

Miles traveled, x	2	3	10	7	8	15	3	1	11
Sales, y	31	33	78	62	65	61	48	55	120

A) $\hat{y} = 37.92x + 3.53$ B) $\hat{y} = 3.53x + 37.92$ C) $\hat{y} = 3.53x - 37.92$ D) $\hat{y} = 37.92x - 3.53$

12) In order for applicants to work for the foreign–service department, they must take a test in the language of the country where they plan to work. The data below shows the relationship between the number of years that applicants have studied a particular language and the grades they received on the proficiency exam. Find the equation of the regression line for the given data.

Number of years, x	3	4	4	5	3	6	2	7	3
Grades on test, y	61	68	75	82	73	90	58	93	72

A) $\hat{y} = 6.91x - 46.26$ B) $\hat{y} = 6.91x + 46.26$ C) $\hat{y} = 46.26x - 6.91$ D) $\hat{y} = 46.26x + 6.91$

13) In an area of the Midwest, records were kept on the relationship between the rainfall (in inches) and the yield of wheat (bushels per acre). Find the equation of the regression line for the given data.

Rain fall (in inches), x	10.5	8.8	13.4	12.5	18.8	10.3	7.0	15.6	16.0
Yield (bushels per acre), y	50.5	46.2	58.8	59.0	82.4	49.2	31.9	76.0	78.8

A) $\hat{y} = 4.379x + 4.267$ B) $\hat{y} = 4.267x - 4.379$ C) $\hat{y} = -4.379x + 4.267$ D) $\hat{y} = 4.267x + 4.379$

14) The data below are the average monthly temperatures, in °F, and the monthly natural gas consumption, in ccf, for a household in northwestern Pennsylvania. Find the equation of the regression line for the given data.

Temperature	47	35	21	27	39	48	61	65	70
Consumption	34	169	248	134	137	100	19	34	12

15) Given the equation of a regression line is $\hat{y} = 4x - 10$, what is the best predicted value for y given x = 6? Assume that the variables x and y have a significant correlation.

A) 34   B) 0   C) 56   D) 14

16) Given the equation of a regression line is $\hat{y} = -5.5x - 9.9$, what is the best predicted value for y given x = -3.8? Assume that the variables x and y have a significant correlation.

A) -11.00   B) 11.00   C) 30.80   D) -30.80

17) Given the equation of a regression line is $\hat{y} = 3.5x - 5.4$, what is the best predicted value for y given x = -1.2? Assume that the variables x and y have a significant correlation.

A) 12.3   B) -12.3   C) -6.9   D) -9.6

18) Use the regression equation to predict the value of y for x = 0.7. Assume that the variables x and y have a significant correlation.

x	-5	-3	4	1	-1	-2	0	2	3	-4
y	-10	-8	9	1	-2	-6	-1	3	6	-8

A) 2.483   B) 1.711   C) 0.916   D) 2.020

19) Use the regression equation to predict the value of y for x = –0.7. Assume that the variables x and y have a significant correlation.

x	-5	-3	4	1	-1	-2	0	2	3	-4
y	11	6	-6	-1	3	4	1	-4	-5	8

A) –2.416   B) –0.561   C) 1.354   D) 2.078

20) The data below are the gestation periods, in months, of randomly selected animals and their corresponding life spans, in years. Use the regression equation to predict the life span, y, for a gestation period of 6 months, x. Assume the variables x and y have a significant correlation.

Gestation, x	8	2.1	1.3	1	11.5	5.3	3.8	24.3
Life span, y	30	12	6	3	25	12	10	40

21) The data below are the final exam scores of 10 randomly selected statistics students and the number of hours they studied for the exam. What is the best predicted value for y given x = 7? Assume that the variables x and y have a significant correlation.

Hours, x	3	5	2	8	2	4	4	5	6	3
Scores, y	65	80	60	88	66	78	85	90	90	71

A) 91   B) 90   C) 92   D) 89

22) The data below are the temperatures on randomly chosen days during a summer class and the number of absences on those days. What is the best predicted value for y given x = 102? Assume that the variables x and y have a significant correlation.

Temperature, x	72	85	91	90	88	98	75	100	80
Number of absences, y	3	7	10	10	8	15	4	15	5

A) 18   B) 19   C) 17   D) 16

23) The data below are the ages and systolic blood pressures (measured in millimeters of mercury) of 9 randomly selected adults. What is the best predicted value for y given x = 38? Assume that the variables x and y have a significant correlation.

Age, x	38	41	45	48	51	53	57	61	65
ressure, y	116	120	123	131	142	145	148	150	152

A) 113   B) 119   C) 115   D) 117

24) The data below are the number of absences and the final grades of 9 randomly selected students from a statistics class. What is the best predicted value for y given x = 15? Assume that the variables x and y have a significant correlation.

Number of absences, x	0	3	6	4	9	2	15	8	5
Final grade, y	98	86	80	82	71	92	55	76	82

A) 54   B) 55   C) 57   D) 56

25) In order for applicants to work for the foreign–service department, they must take a test in the language of the country where they plan to work. The data below show the relationship between the number of years that applicants have studied a particular language and the grades they received on the proficiency exam. What is the best predicted value for y given x = 5.5? Assume that the variables x and y have a significant correlation.

Number of years, x	3	4	4	5	3	6	2	7	3
Grades on test, y	61	68	75	82	73	90	58	93	72

A) 84   B) 86   C) 82   D) 80

26) In an area of the Midwest, records were kept on the relationship between the rainfall (in inches) and the yield of wheat (bushels per acre). Which is the best predicted value for y given x = 9.0? Assume that the variables x and y have a significant correlation.

Rain fall (in inches), x	10.5	8.8	13.4	12.5	18.8	10.3	7.0	15.6	16.0
Yield (bushels per acre), y	50.5	46.2	58.8	59.0	82.4	49.2	31.9	76.0	78.8

A) 44.2   B) 44.0   C) 43.7   D) 43.5

27) The data below are the average monthly temperatures, in °F, and the monthly natural gas consumption, in ccf, for a household in northwestern Pennsylvania. What is the best-predicted value for the gas consumption, y, given x = 50°F? Assume that the variables x and y have a significant correlation.

Temperature	47	35	21	27	39	48	61	65	70
Consumption	34	169	248	134	137	100	19	34	12

28) Find the equation of the regression line by letting Row 1 represent the x–values and Row 2 represent the y–values. Now find the equation of the regression line letting Row 2 represent the x–values and Row 1 represent the y–values. What effect does switching the explanatory and response variables have on the regression line?

Row 1	–5	–3	4	1	–1	–2	0	2	3	–4
Row 2	–10	–8	9	1	–2	–6	–1	3	6	–8

29) A calculus instructor is interested in finding the strength of a relationship between the final exam grades of students enrolled in Calculus I and Calculus II at his college. The data (in percentages) are listed below.

Calculus I	88	78	62	75	95	91	83	86	98
Calculus II	81	80	55	78	90	90	81	80	100

a) Graph a scatter plot of the data.
b) Find an equation of the regression line.
c) Determine if there is a significant correlation between the data. Use $\alpha = 0.01$.
d) Predict a Calculus II exam score for a student who receives an 80 in Calculus I. Is your answer a valid prediction?

9.3 Measure of Regression and Prediction Intervals

Solve the problem.

1) Calculate the coefficient of determination, given that the linear correlation coefficient, r, is 0.837. What does this tell you about the explained variation and the unexplained variation of the data about the regression line?

2) Calculate the coefficient of determination, given that the linear correlation coefficient, r, is –0.625. What does this tell you about the explained variation and the unexplained variation of the data about the regression line?

3) Calculate the coefficient of determination, given that the linear correlation coefficient, r, is 1. What does this tell you about the explained variation and the unexplained variation of the data about the regression line?

4) Find the standard error of estimate, s_e, for the data below, given that $\hat{y} = 2x + 1$.

x	1	2	3	4
y	3	5	7	9

A) 2   B) 0   C) 1   D) 3

5) Find the standard error of estimate, s_e, for the data below, given that $\hat{y} = -2.5x$.

x	-1	-2	-3	-4
y	2	6	7	10

A) 0.675   B) 0.532   C) 0.866   D) 0.349

6) Find the standard error of estimate, s_e, for the data below, given that $\hat{y} = 2.097x - 0.552$.

x	-5	-3	4	1	-1	-2	0	2	3	-4
y	-10	-8	9	1	-2	-6	-1	3	6	-8

A) 0.976   B) 0.980   C) –0.990   D) 0.990

7) Find the standard error of estimate, s_e, for the data below, given that $\hat{y} = -1.885x + 0.758$.

x	-5	-3	4	1	-1	-2	0	2	3	-4
y	11	6	-6	-1	3	4	1	-4	-5	8

A) 0.981   B) 0.312   C) 0.613   D) 0.011

8) Find the standard error of estimate, s_e, for the data below, given that $\hat{y} = -0.206x + 2.097$.

x	-5	-3	4	1	-1	-2	0	2	3	-4
y	11	-6	8	-3	-2	1	5	-5	6	7

A) 8.214   B) 3.203   C) 6.306   D) 5.918

9) The data below are the gestation periods, in months, of randomly selected animals and their corresponding life spans, in years. Find the standard error of estimate, s_e, given that $\hat{y} = 1.523x + 6.343$.

Gestation, x	8	2.1	1.3	1	11.5	5.3	3.8	24.3
Life span, y	30	12	6	3	25	12	10	40

10) The data below are the final exam scores of 10 randomly selected statistics students and the number of hours they studied for the exam. Find the standard error of estimate, s_e, given that $\hat{y} = 5.044x + 56.11$.

Hours, x	3	5	2	8	2	4	4	5	6	3
Scores, y	65	80	60	88	66	78	85	90	90	71

A) 9.875   B) 7.913   C) 8.912   D) 6.305

11) The data below are the temperatures on randomly chosen days during a summer class and the number of absences on those days. Find the standard error of estimate, s_e, given that $\hat{y} = 0.449x - 30.27$.

Temperature, x	72	85	91	90	88	98	75	100	80
Number of absences, y	3	7	10	10	8	15	4	15	5

A) 0.934   B) 1.162   C) 0.815   D) 1.007

12) The data below are the ages and systolic blood pressures (measured in millimeters of mercury) of 9 randomly selected adults. Find the standard error of estimate, s_e, given that $\hat{y} = 1.488x + 60.46$.

Age, x	38	41	45	48	51	53	57	61	65
Pressure, y	116	120	123	131	142	145	148	150	152

A) 5.572   B) 4.199   C) 6.981   D) 3.099

13) The data below are the number of absences and the final grades of 9 randomly selected students from a statistics class. Find the standard error of estimate, s_e, given that $\hat{y} = -2.75X + 96.14$.

Number of absences, x	0	3	6	4	9	2	15	8	5
Final grade, y	98	86	80	82	71	92	55	76	82

A) 4.531   B) 3.876   C) 2.160   D) 1.798

14) A manager wishes to determine the relationship between the number of miles (in hundreds of miles) the manager's sales representatives travel per month and the amount of sales (in thousands of dollars) per month. Find the standard error of estimate, s_e, given that $\hat{y} = 3.53x + 37.92$.

Miles traveled, x	2	3	10	7	8	15	3	1	11
Sales, y	31	33	78	62	65	61	48	55	120

A) 15.951   B) 10.569   C) 22.062   D) 5.122

15) In order for applicants to work for the foreign–service department, they must take a test in the language of the country where they plan to work. The data below shows the relationship between the number of years that applicants have studied a particular language and the grades they received on the proficiency exam. Find the standard of estimate, s_e, given that $\hat{y} = 6.91x + 46.26$.

Number of years, x	3	4	4	5	3	6	2	7	3
Grades on test, y	61	68	75	82	73	90	58	93	72

A) 3.412   B) 4.578   C) 6.713   D) 5.192

16) In an area of the Midwest, records were kept on the relationship between the rainfall (in inches) and the yield of wheat (bushels per acre). Find the standard error of estimate, s_e, given that $\hat{y} = 4.379x + 4.267$.

Rain fall (in inches), x	10.5	8.8	13.4	12.5	18.8	10.3	7.0	15.6	16.0
Yield (bushels per acre), y	50.5	46.2	58.8	59.0	82.4	49.2	31.9	76.0	78.8

A) 1.332   B) 3.529   C) 2.813   D) 4.759

17) The data below are the average monthly temperatures, in °F, and the monthly natural gas consumption, in ccf, for a household in northwestern Pennsylvania. Find the standard error of estimate, s_e, given that $\hat{y} = -4.310x + 296.352$.

Temperature	47	35	21	27	39	48	61	65	70
Consumption	34	169	248	134	137	100	19	34	12

18) Construct a 95% prediction interval for y given x = 2.5, $\hat{y} = 2x + 1$ and $s_e = 0$.

x	1	2	3	4
y	3	5	7	9

19) Construct a 95% prediction interval for y given x = 2.5, $\hat{y} = -2.5x$ and $s_e = 0.866$.

x	-1	-2	-3	-4
y	2	6	7	10

A) $-16.156 < y < 3.656$ B) $-8.244 < y < -4.256$ C) $-12.594 < y < 0.094$ D) $-14.829 < y < 2.329$

20) Construct a 95% prediction interval for y given x = –3.5, $\hat{y}$ = 2.097x – 0.552 and s_e = 0.976.

x	–5	–3	4	1	–1	–2	0	2	3	–4
y	–10	–8	9	1	–2	–6	–1	3	6	–8

A) –10.367 < y < –5.417   B) –4.598 < y < –1.986   C) –12.142 < y < –6.475   D) –3.187 < y < –2.154

21) The data below are the gestation periods, in months, of randomly selected animals and their corresponding life spans, in years. Construct a 95% prediction interval for y, the life span, given x = 10 months, $\hat{y}$ = 1.523x + 6.343, and s_e = 5.618.

Gestation, x	8	2.1	1.3	1	11.5	5.3	3.8	24.3
Life span, y	30	12	6	3	25	12	10	40

22) The data below are the scores of 10 randomly selected students from a statistics class and the number of hours they studied for the exam. Construct a 95% prediction interval for y, the score on the final exam, given x = 7 hours, $\hat{y}$ = 5.044x + 56.11 and s_e = 6.305.

Hours, x	3	5	2	8	2	4	4	5	6	3
Scores, y	65	80	60	88	66	78	85	90	90	71

A) 79.16 < y < 112.34   B) 74.54 < y < 108.30   C) 77.21 < y < 110.45   D) 55.43 < y < 78.19

23) The data below are the temperatures on randomly chosen days during a summer class and the number of absences on those days. Construct a 95% prediction interval for y, the number of days absent, given x = 95 degrees, $\hat{y}$ = 0.449x – 30.27 and s_e = 0.934.

Temperature, x	72	85	91	90	88	98	75	100	80
Number of absences, y	3	7	10	10	8	15	4	15	5

A) 4.321 < y < 6.913   B) 9.957 < y < 14.813   C) 3.176 < y < 5.341   D) 6.345 < y < 8.912

24) In order for applicants to work for the foreign–service department, they must take a test in the language of the country where they plan to work. The data below shows the relationship between the number of years that applicants have studied a particular language and the grades they received on the proficiency exam. Construct a 95% prediction interval for y given x = 2.5, $\hat{y}$ = 6.91x + 46.26, and s_e = 4.578.

Number of years, x	3	4	4	5	3	6	2	7	3
Grades on test, y	61	68	75	82	73	90	58	93	72

A) 47.32 < y < 72.13   B) 60.23 < y < 91.42   C) 55.12 < y < 87.34   D) 51.50 < y < 75.57

25) In an area of the Midwest, records were kept on the relationship between the rainfall (in inches) and the yield of wheat (bushels per acre). Construct a 95% prediction interval for y, the yield, given x = 11 inches, $\hat{y} = 4.379x + 4.267$ and $s_e = 3.529$.

Rainfall (in inches), x	10.5	8.8	13.4	12.5	18.8	10.3	7.0	15.6	16.0
Yield (bushels per acre), y	50.5	46.2	58.8	59.0	82.4	49.2	31.9	76.0	78.8

A) $39.86 < y < 65.98$ B) $43.56 < y < 61.32$ C) $41.68 < y < 63.21$ D) $40.54 < y < 64.15$

26) The data below are the average monthly temperatures, in °F, and the monthly natural gas consumption, in ccf, for a household in northwestern Pennsylvania. Construct a 90% prediction interval for y, the monthly gas consumption, given x = 50°F.

Temperature	47	35	21	27	39	48	61	65	70
Consumption	34	169	248	134	137	100	19	34	12

27) A private organization conducted a survey in 9 regions of the country to determine the average weekly spending in dollars per person on tobacco products and alcoholic beverages. The data are listed below.

Region	1	2	3	4	5	6	7	8	9
Alcohol spending, x	$12.80	$13.20	$9.50	$10.30	$9.80	$11.70	$10.00	$8.90	$11.60
Tobacco spending, y	$8.50	$7.60	$6.90	$6.80	$6.80	$5.70	$6.50	$4.90	$7.00

a) Construct a scatter plot of the data letting x represent spending on alcohol and y represent spending on tobacco.
b) Find the regression line.
c) Find the coefficient of determination. What can you conclude?
d) Find the standard error of estimate, s_e.
e) Construct a 95% prediction interval for the weekly spending on tobacco when the amount spent on alcohol is $9.50.

9.4 Multiple Regression

Solve the problem.

1) A multiple regression equation is $\hat{y} = -35,000 + 130x_1 + 20,000x_2$, where x_1 is a person's age, x_2 is the person's grade point average in college, and y is the person's income. Predict the income for a person who is 29 years old and had a college grade point average of 3.2.

A) $32,770   B) $102,770   C) $545,416   D) $67,770

2) A researcher found a significant relationship between a student's IQ, x_1, grade point average, x_2, and the score, y, on the verbal section of the SAT test. The relationship can be represented by the multiple regression equation $\hat{y} = 250 + 1.5x_1 + 80x_2$. Predict the SAT verbal score of a student whose IQ is 127 and grade point average is 2.3.

A) 375   B) 525   C) 575   D) 625

3) A researcher found a significant relationship between a person's age, x_1, the number of hours a person works per week, x_2, and the number of accidents, y, the person has per year. The relationship can be represented by the multiple regression equation $\hat{y} = -3.2 + 0.012x_1 + 0.23x_2$. Predict the number of accidents per year (to the nearest whole number) for a person whose age is 42 and who works 50 hours per week.

A) 10   B) 8   C) 9   D) 11

4) A researcher at a local law university wishes to see whether a student's grade point average and age are related to a student's score on the state bar exam. Six students are randomly selected. The data are given below.

Student	GPA	Age	Score
1	3.5	23	530
2	2.8	28	550
3	3.9	22	690
4	3.4	27	620
5	2.3	21	430
6	3.3	26	580

a) Find a multiple regression equation for the data.
b) What is the standard error of estimate?
c) What is the coefficient of determination?
d) Interpret the results in (c).
e) Predict the state bar exam score for a 25–year–old student with a grade point average of 3.0.
f) Calculate the adjusted coefficient of determination, r^2adj.

5) A medical researcher wishes to see whether there is a relationship between a person's age, cholesterol level, and systolic blood pressure. Eight people are randomly selected. The data are listed below.

Person	Age	Cholesterol level	Blood Pressure
1	38	220	116
2	41	225	120
3	45	200	123
4	48	190	131
5	51	250	142
6	53	215	145
7	57	200	148
8	61	170	150

a) Find a multiple regression equation for the data.
b) What is the standard error of estimate?
c) What is the coefficient of determination?
d) Interpret the results in (c).
e) If a person 50 years old with a cholesterol reading of 220 is selected, what is that person's predicted blood pressure reading?
f) Calculate the adjusted coefficient of determination, r^2adj.

Ch. 9 Correlation and Regression
Answer Key

9.1 Correlation

1) C
2) B
3) C
4)

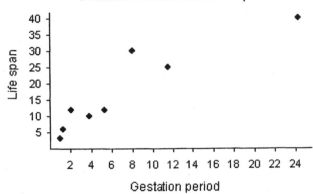

There appears to be a positive linear correlation.

5)

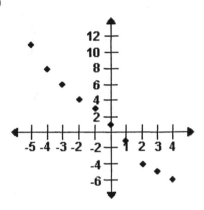

There appears to be a negative linear correlation.

6)

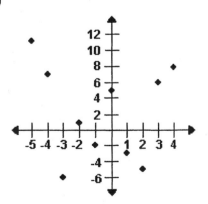

There appears to be no linear correlation.

7)

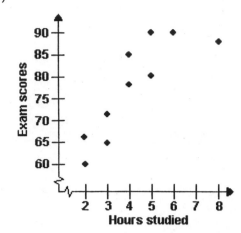

8)

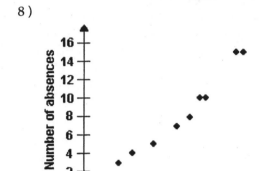

9)

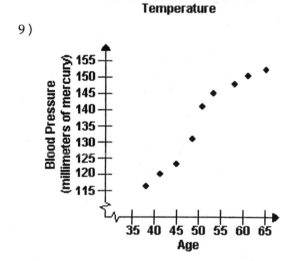

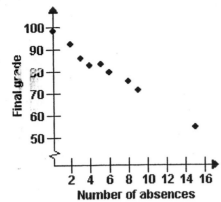

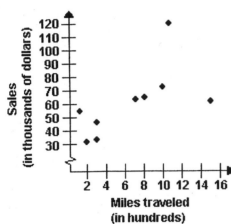

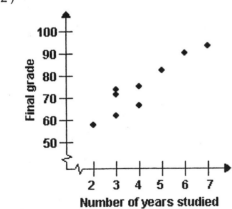

13)

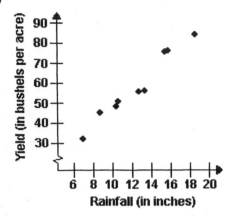

14) $\sum x^2$ means square each x-value and then add the squares, and $\left(\sum x\right)^2$ means add the x-values and then square the sum.

15) A

16) B

17) A

18) A

19) B

20) 0.916

21) −0.909

22) A

23) C

24) D

25) D

26) A

27) B

28) B

29) explanatory variable: rainfall in inches; response variable: yield per acre

30) explanatory variable: hours studying; response variable: grades on the test

31) A

32) B

33) C

34) D

35) C

36) D

37) A

38) A

39) critical value $t_0 = \pm 2.306$; standardized test statistic $t \approx 4.098$; reject H_0; There is sufficient evidence to conclude that a significant correlation exists.

40) critical value $t_0 = \pm 2.878$; standardized test statistic $t \approx -2.729$; fail to reject H_0; There is not sufficient evidence to conclude that a significant correlation exists.

41) critical value $t_0 = \pm 1.701$; standardized test statistic $t \approx 1.793$; reject H_0; There is sufficient evidence to conclude that a significant correlation exists.

42) critical value $t_0 = \pm 2.528$; standardized test statistic $t \approx -5.312$; reject H_0; There is sufficient evidence to conclude that a significant correlation exists.

43) critical value $t_0 = \pm 2.306$; standardized test statistic $t \approx 19.85$; reject H_0; There is sufficient evidence to conclude that a significant correlation exists.

44) critical value $t_0 = \pm 3.355$; standardized test statistic $t \approx -28.18$; reject H_0; There is sufficient evidence to conclude that a significant correlation exists.

45) critical value $t_0 = \pm 1.860$; standardized test statistic $t \approx 0.296$; fail to reject H_0; There is not sufficient evidence to conclude that a significant correlation exists.

46) standardized test statistic $t \approx 5.593$; critical value $t_0 = 3.143$; reject H_0; There is sufficient evidence to conclude that a significant positive correlation exists.

47) critical value $t_0 = \pm 2.306$; standardized test statistic $t \approx 4.51$; reject H_0; There is sufficient evidence to conclude that a significant correlation exists.

48) critical value $t_0 = \pm 2.998$; standardized test statistic $t \approx 13.03$; reject H_0; There is sufficient evidence to conclude that a significant correlation exists.

49) critical value $t_0 = \pm 2.365$; standardized test statistic $t \approx 9.07$; reject H_0; There is sufficient evidence to conclude that a significant correlation exists.

50) critical value $t_0 = \pm 2.365$; standardized test statistic $t \approx -19.59$; reject H_0; There is sufficient evidence to conclude that a significant correlation exists.

51) critical value $t_0 = \pm 3.499$; standardized test statistic $t \approx 2.16$; fail to reject H_0; There is not sufficient evidence to conclude that a significant correlation exists.

52) critical value $t_0 = \pm 1.895$; standardized test statistic $t \approx 6.92$; reject H_0; There is sufficient evidence to conclude that a significant correlation exists.

53) critical value $t_0 = \pm 3.499$; standardized test statistic $t \approx 13.38$; reject H_0; There is sufficient evidence to conclude that a significant correlation exists.

54) standardized test statistic $t \approx -5.770$; critical value $t_0 = -1.895$; reject H_0; There is sufficient evidence to conclude that a significant negative correlation exists.

55) The correlation coefficient remains unchanged.

9.2 Linear Regression

1) A
2) B
3) B
4) D
5) C
6) $\hat{y} = 1.523x + 6.343$

7) A
8) D
9) D
10) D
11) B
12) B
13) A
14) $\hat{y} = -4.310x + 296.352$

15) D
16) B
17) D
18) C
19) D
20) About 15 years.

21) A
22) D
23) D
24) B
25) A
26) C
27) About 81 ccf.
28) The regression lines are not necessarily the same.

29) a) See graph below.

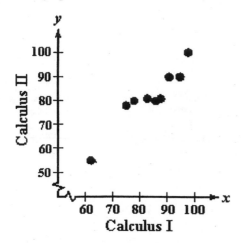

b) $\hat{y} = 1.044x - 5.990$

c) critical value $t_0 = \pm 3.499$; test statistic $t = 7.64$; reject H_0; There is sufficient evidence to conclude that a significant correlation exists.

d) When $x = 80$, $y = 78$. This is a valid prediction as there is a significant correlation between the data.

9.3 Measure of Regression and Prediction Intervals

1) The coefficient of determination, r^2, $= 0.701$. That is, 70.1% of the variation is explained and 29.9% of the variation is unexplained.

2) The coefficient of determination, r^2, $= 0.391$. That is, 39.1% of the variation is explained and 60.9% of the variation is unexplained.

3) The coefficient of determination, r^2, $= 1$. That is, 100% of the variation is explained and there is no variation that is unexplained.

4) B

5) C

6) A

7) C

8) C

9) 5.618

10) D

11) A

12) B

13) D

14) C

15) B

16) B

17) 35.899

18) Since $s_e = 0$, there is no interval for $x = 2.5$.

19) D

20) A

21) $6.99 < y < 36.161$

22) B

23) B

24) D

25) B

26) $8.91 < y < 152.794$

27) a)

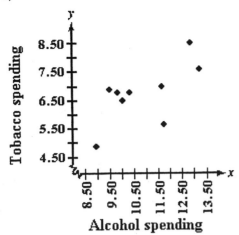

Tobacco spending

8.50
7.50
6.50
5.50
4.50

8.50 9.50 10.50 11.50 12.50 13.50

Alcohol spending

b) $\hat{y} = 0.449x + 1.87$

c) $r^2 = 0.437$. This means that about 43.7% of the variation can be explained. About 56.3% of the variation is unexplained and is due to chance or other variables.

d) $s_e = 0.8247$

e) $3.983 < y < 8.279$

9.4 Multiple Regression

1) A

2) D

3) C

4) a) $\hat{y} = -37.5 + 134.7x_1 + 7.1x_2$

b) $s_e = 48.4$

c) $r^2 = 0.82$.

d) The multiple regression model explains 82% of the variation in y.

e) 544

f) $r^2_{adj.} = 0.70$

5) a) $\hat{y} = 14.2 + 1.87x_1 + 0.13x_2$

b) $s_e = 2.02$

c) $r^2 = 0.984$.

d) The multiple regression equation explains 98.4% of the variation in y.

e) 136

f) $r^2_{adj.} = 0.978$

Ch. 10 Chi–Square Tests and the F–Distribution

10.1 Goodness of Fit

Solve the problem.

1) Many track runners believe that they have a better chance of winning if they start in the inside lane that is closest to the field. For the data below, the lane closest to the field is Lane 1, the next lane is Lane 2, and so on until the outermost lane, Lane 6. The data lists the number of wins for track runners in the different starting positions. Calculate the chi–square test statistic χ^2 to test the claim that the probabilities of winning are the same in the different positions. The results are based on 240 wins.

Starting Position	1	2	3	4	5	6
Number of Wins	44	32	50	45	36	33

   A) 12.592   B) 6.750   C) 15.541   D) 9.326

2) Many track runners believe that they have a better chance of winning if they start in the inside lane that is closest to the field. For the data below, the lane closest to the field is Lane 1, the next lane is Lane 2, and so on until the outermost lane, Lane 6. The data lists the number of wins for track runners in the different starting positions. Find the critical value χ_0^2 to test the claim that the probabilities of winning are the same in the different positions. Use $\alpha = 0.05$. The results are based on 240 wins.

Starting Position	1	2	3	4	5	6
Number of Wins	45	33	44	50	32	36

   A) 15.086   B) 9.236   C) 12.833   D) 11.070

3) Many track runners believe that they have a better chance of winning if they start in the inside lane that is closest to the field. For the data below, the lane closest to the field is Lane 1, the next lane is Lane 2, and so on until the outermost lane, Lane 6. The data lists the number of wins for track runners in the different starting positions. Test the claim that the probabilities of winning are the same in the different positions. Use $\alpha = 0.05$. The results are based on 240 wins.

Starting Position	1	2	3	4	5	6
Number of Wins	50	33	32	36	45	44

4) A coffeehouse wishes to see if customers have any preference among 5 different brands of coffee. A sample of 200 customers provided the data below. Calculate the chi–square test statistic χ^2 to test the claim that the probabilities show no preference.

Brand	1	2	3	4	5
Customers	65	30	32	55	18

   A) 45.91   B) 48.91   C) 55.63   D) 37.45

5) A coffeehouse wishes to see if customers have any preference among 5 different brands of coffee. A sample of 200 customers provided the data below. Find the critical value χ_0^2 to test the claim that the probabilities show no preference. Use $\alpha = 0.01$.

Brand	1	2	3	4	5
Customers	18	65	32	55	30

   A) 11.143   B) 14.860   C) 9.488   D) 13.277

6) A new coffeehouse wishes to see whether customers have any preference among 5 different brands of coffee. A sample of 200 customers provided the data below. Test the claim that the probabilities show no preference. Use $\alpha = 0.01$.

Brand	1	2	3	4	5
Customers	55	32	65	30	18

7) A teacher figures that final grades in the statistics department are distributed as: A, 25%; B, 25%; C, 40%; D, 5%; F, 5%. At the end of a randomly selected semester, the following number of grades were recorded. Calculate the chi–square test statistic χ^2 to determine if the grade distribution for the department is different than expected.

Grade	A	B	C	D	F
Number	42	36	60	14	8

A) 4.82   B) 6.87   C) 5.25   D) 3.41

8) A teacher figures that final grades in the statistics department are distributed as: A, 25%; B, 25%; C, 40%; D, 5%; F, 5%. At the end of a randomly selected semester, the following number of grades were recorded. Find the critical value χ_0^2 to determine if the grade distribution for the department is different than expected. Use $\alpha = 0.01$.

Grade	A	B	C	D	F
Number	42	36	60	14	8

A) 13.277   B) 9.488   C) 11.143   D) 7.779

9) A teacher figures that final grades in the statistics department are distributed as: A, 25%; B, 25%; C, 40%; D, 5%; F, 5%. At the end of a randomly selected semester, the following number of grades were recorded. Determine if the grade distribution for the department is different than expected. Use $\alpha = 0.01$.

Grade	A	B	C	D	F
Number	42	36	60	14	8

10) Each side of a standard six–sided die should appear approximately $\frac{1}{6}$ of the time when the die is rolled. A player suspects that a certain die is loaded. The suspected die is rolled 90 times. The results are shown below. Calculate the chi–square test statistic χ^2 to test the player's claim.

Number	1	2	3	4	5	6
Frequency	15	12	17	19	11	16

A) 3.067   B) 5.013   C) 4.312   D) 2.143

11) Each side of a standard six–sided die should appear approximately $\frac{1}{6}$ of the time when the die is rolled. A player suspects that a certain die is loaded. The suspected die is rolled 90 times. The results are shown below. Find the critical value χ_0^2 to test the player's claim. Use $\alpha = 0.10$.

Number	1	2	3	4	5	6
Frequency	15	19	16	12	11	17

A) 12.833   B) 11.071   C) 1.610   D) 9.236

12) Each side of a standard six–sided die should appear approximately $\frac{1}{6}$ of the time when the die is rolled. A player suspects that a certain die is loaded. The suspected die is rolled 90 times. The results are shown below. Test the player's claim. Use $\alpha = 0.10$.

Number	1	2	3	4	5	6
Frequency	16	11	12	19	15	17

13) A random sample of 160 car crashes are selected and categorized by age. The results are listed below. The age distribution of drivers for the given categories is 18% for the under 26 group, 39% for the 26–45 group, 31% for the 45–65 group, and 12% for the group over 65. Calculate the chi-square test statistic χ^2 to test the claim that all ages have crash rates proportional to their driving rates.

Age	Under 26	26 – 45	46 – 65	Over 65
Drivers	66	39	25	30

A) 95.431   B) 75.101   C) 101.324   D) 85.123

14) A random sample of 160 car crashes are selected and categorized by age. The results are listed below. The age distribution of drivers for the given categories is 18% for the under 26 group, 39% for the 26–45 group, 31% for the 45–65 group, and 12% for the group over 65. Find the critical value χ_0^2 to test the claim that all ages have crash rates proportional to their driving rates. Use $\alpha = 0.05$.

Age	Under 26	26 – 45	46 – 65	Over 65
Drivers	66	39	25	30

A) 9.348   B) 11.143   C) 6.251   D) 7.815

15) A random sample of 160 car crashes are selected and categorized by age. The results are listed below. The age distribution of drivers for the given categories is 18% for the under 26 group, 39% for the 26–45 group, 31% for the 46–65 group, and 12% for the group over 65. Test the claim that all ages have crash rates proportional to their driving rates. Use $\alpha = 0.05$.

Age	Under 26	26 – 45	46 – 65	Over 65
Drivers	66	39	25	30

16) A sociologist believes that the levels of educational attainment of homeless persons are not uniformly distributed. To test this claim, you randomly survey 100 homeless persons and record the educational attainment of each. The results are shown in the following table. Calculate the chi-square test statistic χ^2 to test the sociologist's claim.

Response	Frequency, f
Less than high school	38
High school graduate/G.E.D.	34
More than high school	28

17) A sociologist believes that the levels of educational attainment of homeless persons are not uniformly distributed. To test this claim, you randomly survey 100 homeless persons and record the educational attainment of each. The results are shown in the following table. Find the critical value χ_0^2 to test the sociologist's claim. Use $\alpha = 0.10$.

Response	Frequency, f
Less than high school	38
High school graduate/G.E.D.	34
More than high school	28

18) A sociologist believes that the levels of educational attainment of homeless persons are not uniformly distributed. To test this claim, you randomly survey 100 homeless persons and record the educational attainment of each. The results are shown in the following table. At $\alpha = 0.10$, is there evidence to support the sociologist's claim that the distribution is not uniform?

Response	Frequency, f
Less than high school	38
High school graduate/G.E.D.	34
More than high school	28

19) The frequency distribution shows the ages for a sample of 100 employees. Find the expected frequencies for each class to determine if the employee ages are normally distributed.

Class boundaries	Frequency, f
29.5 – 39.5	14
39.5 – 49.5	29
49.5 – 59.5	31
59.5 – 69.5	18
69.5 – 79.5	8

20) The frequency distribution shows the ages for a sample of 100 employees. Are the ages of employees normally distributed? Use $\alpha = 0.05$.

Class boundaries	Frequency, f
29.5 – 39.5	14
39.5 – 49.5	29
49.5 – 59.5	31
59.5 – 69.5	18
69.5 – 79.5	8

Elementary Statistics 188

21) The frequency distribution shows the heights, in feet, for a sample of 200 trees in the Allegheny National Forest. Find the expected frequencies for each class to determine if the heights of the trees are normally distributed.

Class boundaries	Frequency, f
15.5 – 21.5	7
21.5 – 25.5	8
25.5 – 30.5	59
30.5 – 36.5	14
36.5 – 40.5	53
40.5 – 46.5	38
46.5 – 50.5	21

22) The frequency distribution shows the heights, in feet, for a sample of 200 trees in the Allegheny National Forest. Are the heights of the trees normally distributed? Use $\alpha = 0.05$.

Class boundaries	Frequency, f
15.5 – 21.5	7
21.5 – 25.5	8
25.5 – 30.5	59
30.5 – 36.5	14
36.5 – 40.5	53
40.5 – 46.5	38
46.5 – 50.5	21

10.2 Independence

Solve the problem.

1) The contingency table below shows the results of a random sample of 200 state representatives that was conducted to see whether their opinions on a bill are related to their party affiliation. Use $\alpha = 0.05$.

	Opinion		
Party	Approve	Disapprove	No Opinion
Republican	42	20	14
Democrat	50	24	18
Independent	10	16	6

Find the critical value χ_0^2, to test the claim of independence.

A) 7.779   B) 11.143   C) 13.277   D) 9.488

2) The contingency table below shows the results of a random sample of 400 state representatives that was conducted to see whether their opinions on a bill are related to their party affiliation.

	Opinion		
Party	Approve	Disapprove	No Opinion
Republican	84	40	28
Democrat	100	48	36
Independent	20	32	12

Find the expected frequency for the cell $E_{2,2}$.

A) 45.6   B) 55.2   C) 93.84   D) 34.96

3) The contingency table below shows the results of a random sample of 200 state representatives that was conducted to see whether their opinions on a bill are related to their party affiliation.

	Opinion		
Party	Approve	Disapprove	No Opinion
Republican	42	20	14
Democrat	50	24	18
Independent	10	16	6

Find the chi–square test statistic, χ^2, to test the claim of independence.

A) 9.483   B) 11.765   C) 8.031   D) 7.662

4) The contingency table below shows the results of a random sample of 200 state representatives that was conducted to see whether their opinions on a bill are related to their party affiliation.

	Opinion		
Party	Approve	Disapprove	No Opinion
Republican	42	20	14
Democrat	50	24	18
Independent	10	16	6

Test the claim of independence.

5) A researcher wants to determine whether the number of minutes adults spend online per day is related to gender. A random sample of 315 adults was selected and the results are shown below. Find the critical value χ_0^2 to determine if there is enough evidence to conclude that the number of minutes spent online per day is related to gender.

	Minutes spent online per day			
Gender	0 – 30	30 – 60	60 – 90	90 – over
Male	25	35	75	45
Female	30	45	45	15

A) 7.815   B) 6.251   C) 9.348   D) 11.345

6) A researcher wants to determine whether the number of minutes adults spend online per day is related to gender. A random sample of 315 adults was selected and the results are shown below. Find the expected frequency for the cell $E_{2,2}$ to determine if there is enough evidence to conclude that the number of minutes spent online per day is related to gender.

	Minutes spent online per day			
Gender	0 – 30	30 – 60	60 – 90	90 – over
Male	23	33	76	48
Female	31	44	46	14

A) 33   B) 69.7   C) 52.3   D) 44

7) A researcher wants to determine whether the number of minutes adults spend online per day is related to gender. A random sample of 315 adults was selected and the results are shown below. Calculate the chi-square statistic χ^2 to determine if there is enough evidence to conclude that the number of minutes spent online per day is related to gender.

Gender	Minutes spent online per day			
	0 – 30	30 – 60	60 – 90	90 – over
Male	25	35	75	45
Female	30	45	45	15

    A) 19.874   B) 21.231   C) 20.912   D) 18.146

8) A researcher wants to determine whether the number of minutes adults spend online per day is related to gender. A random sample of 315 adults was selected and the results are shown below. Is there enough evidence to conclude that the number of minutes spent online per day is related to gender? Use $\alpha = 0.05$.

Gender	Minutes spent online per day			
	0 – 30	30 – 60	60 – 90	90 – over
Male	25	35	75	45
Female	30	45	45	15

9) A medical researcher is interested in determining if there is a relationship between adults over 50 who walk regularly and low, moderate, and high blood pressure. A random sample of 236 adults over 50 is selected and the results are given below. Find the critical value χ_0^2 to test the claim that walking and low, moderate, and high blood pressure are not related. Use $\alpha = 0.01$.

Blood Pressure	Low	Moderate	High
Walkers	35	62	25
Non-walkers	21	65	28

    A) 0.584   B) 9.348   C) 9.210   D) 6.251

10) A medical researcher is interested in determining if there is a relationship between adults over 50 who walk regularly and low, moderate, and high blood pressure. A random sample of 236 adults over 50 is selected and the results are given below. Find the expected frequency $E_{2,2}$ to test the claim that walking and low, moderate, and high blood pressure are not related.

Blood Pressure	Low	Moderate	High
Walkers	34	65	23
Non-walkers	28	66	20

    A) 63.3   B) 20.8   C) 29.9   D) 67.7

11) A medical researcher is interested in determining if there is a relationship between adults over 50 who walk regularly and low, moderate, and high blood pressure. A random sample of 236 adults over 50 is selected and the results are given below. Calculate the chi-square test statistic χ^2 to test the claim that walking and low, moderate, and high blood pressure are not related.

Blood Pressure	Low	Moderate	High
Walkers	35	62	25
Non-walkers	21	65	28

    A) 6.003   B) 3.473   C) 16.183   D) 18.112

12) A medical researcher is interested in determining if there is a relationship between adults over 50 who walk regularly and low, moderate, and high blood pressure. A random sample of 236 adults over 50 is selected and the results are given below. Test the claim that walking and low, moderate, and high blood pressure are not related. Use $\alpha = 0.01$.

Blood Pressure	Low	Moderate	High
Walkers	35	62	25
Non–walkers	21	65	28

13) A sports researcher is interested in determining if there is a relationship between the number of home team and visiting team wins and different sports. A random sample of 526 games is selected and the results are given below. Find the critical value χ_0^2 to test the claim that the number of home team and visiting team wins is independent of the sport. Use $\alpha = 0.01$.

	Football	Basketball	Soccer	Baseball
Home team wins	39	156	25	83
Visiting team wins	31	98	19	75

A) 12.838 B) 7.815 C) 11.345 D) 9.348

14) A sports researcher is interested in determining if there is a relationship between the number of home team and visiting team wins and different sports. A random sample of 526 games is selected and the results are given below. Find the expected frequency for $E_{2,2}$ to test the claim that the number of home team and visiting team wins are independent of the sport.

	Football	Basketball	Soccer	Baseball
Home team wins	39	156	23	85
Visiting team wins	30	98	18	77

A) 107.7 B) 146.3 C) 23.6 D) 17.4

15) A sports researcher is interested in determining if there is a relationship between the number of home team and visiting team wins and different sports. A random sample of 526 games is selected and the results are given below. Calculate the chi–square test statistic χ^2 to test the claim that the number of home team and visiting team wins is independent of the sport.

	Football	Basketball	Soccer	Baseball
Home team wins	39	156	25	83
Visiting team wins	31	98	19	75

A) 2.919 B) 5.391 C) 4.192 D) 3.290

16) A sports researcher is interested in determining if there is a relationship between the number of home team and visiting team wins and different sports. A random sample of 526 games is selected and the results are given below. Test the claim that the number of home team and visiting team wins is independent of the sport. Use $\alpha = 0.01$.

	Football	Basketball	Soccer	Baseball
Home team wins	39	156	25	83
Visiting team wins	31	98	19	75

17) The data below shows the age and favorite type of music of 779 randomly selected people. Test the claim that age and preferred music type are independent. Use $\alpha = 0.05$.

Age	Country	Rock	Pop	Classical
15 – 21	21	45	90	33
21 – 30	68	55	42	48
30 – 40	65	47	31	57
40 – 50	60	39	25	53

18) A random sample of 400 men and 400 women was randomly selected and asked whether they planned to vote in the next election. The results are listed below. Perform a homogeneity of proportions test to test the claim that the proportion of men who plan to vote in the next election is the same as the proportion of women who plan to vote. Use $\alpha = 0.05$.

	Men	Women
Plan to vote	230	255
Do not plan to vote	170	145

19) A random sample of 100 students from 5 different colleges was randomly selected, and the number who smoke was recorded. The results are listed below. Perform a homogeneity of proportions test to test the claim that the proportion of students who smoke is the same in all 5 colleges. Use $\alpha = 0.01$.

	Colleges				
	1	2	3	4	5
Smoker	18	25	12	33	22
Nonsmoker	82	75	88	67	78

10.3 Comparing Two Variances

Solve the problem.

1) Find the critical value F_0 for a two-tailed test using $\alpha = 0.05$, d.f.$_N = 5$, and d.f.$_D = 10$.

A) 6.62   B) 4.24   C) 4.07   D) 4.47

2) Find the critical value F_0 for a one-tailed test using $\alpha = 0.01$, d.f.$_N = 3$, and d.f.$_D = 20$.

A) 5.82   B) 25.58   C) 3.09   D) 4.94

3) Find the critical value F_0 for a one-tailed test using $\alpha = 0.05$, d.f.$_N = 6$, and d.f.$_D = 16$.

A) 3.94   B) 2.74   C) 2.19   D) 2.66

4) Find the critical value F_0 for a two-tailed test using $\alpha = 0.02$, d.f.$_N = 5$, and d.f.$_D = 10$.

A) 5.99   B) 5.64   C) 5.39   D) 10.05

5) Find the critical value F_0 to test the claim that $\sigma_1^2 = \sigma_2^2$. Two samples are randomly selected from populations that are normal. The sample statistics are given below. Use $\alpha = 0.05$.

$n_1 = 25 \qquad n_2 = 30$

$s_1^2 = 3.61 \qquad s_2^2 = 2.25$

A) 2.14   B) 2.09   C) 2.15   D) 2.21

6) Find the critical value F_0 to test the claim that $\sigma_1^2 = \sigma_2^2$. Two samples are randomly selected from populations that are normal. The sample statistics are given below. Use $\alpha = 0.02$.

$n_1 = 13 \qquad n_2 = 12$

$s_1^2 = 7.84 \qquad s_2^2 = 6.25$

A) 3.43   B) 4.40   C) 4.25   D) 2.79

7) Find the critical value F_0 to test the claim that $\sigma_1^2 > \sigma_2^2$. Two samples are randomly selected from populations that are normal. The sample statistics are given below. Use $\alpha = 0.01$.

$n_1 = 16 \qquad n_2 = 13$

$s_1^2 = 1600 \qquad s_2^2 = 625$

A) 4.01   B) 3.67   C) 2.62   D) 3.18

8) Find the critical value F_0 to test the claim that $\sigma_1^2 \leq \sigma_2^2$. Two samples are randomly selected from populations that are normal. The sample statistics are given below. Use $\alpha = 0.05$.

$n_1 = 16 \qquad n_2 = 15$

$s_1^2 = 8.41 \qquad s_2^2 = 7.84$

A) 2.40   B) 2.46   C) 2.95   D) 3.66

9) Find the critical value F_0 to test the claim that $\sigma_1^2 \neq \sigma_2^2$. Two samples are randomly selected from populations that are normal. The sample statistics are given below. Use $\alpha = 0.02$.

$n_1 = 11$ $n_2 = 18$

$s_1^2 = 0.578$ $s_2^2 = 0.260$

A) 3.59   B) 2.92   C) 2.45   D) 4.56

10) Calculate the test statistic F to test the claim that $\sigma_1^2 = \sigma_2^2$. Two samples are randomly selected from populations that are normal. The sample statistics are given below.

$n_1 = 25$ $n_2 = 30$

$s_1^2 = 6.859$ $s_2^2 = 4.275$

A) 1.267   B) 2.573   C) 0.623   D) 1.604

11) Calculate the test statistic F to test the claim that $\sigma_1^2 = \sigma_2^2$. Two samples are randomly selected from populations that are normal. The sample statistics are given below.

$n_1 = 13$ $n_2 = 12$

$s_1^2 = 20.384$ $s_2^2 = 16.25$

A) 0.797   B) 1.573   C) 1.254   D) 1.120

12) Calculate the test statistic F to test the claim that $\sigma_1^2 \geq \sigma_2^2$. Two samples are randomly selected from populations that are normal. The sample statistics are given below.

$n_1 = 13$ $n_2 = 12$

$s_1^2 = 12.376$ $s_2^2 = 9.867$

A) 1.254   B) 1.120   C) 1.573   D) 0.797

13) Calculate the test statistic F to test the claim that $\sigma_1^2 > \sigma_2^2$. Two samples are randomly selected from

populations that are normal. The sample statistics are given below.

$n_1 = 16$ $n_2 = 13$

$s_1^2 = 4800$ $s_2^2 = 1875$

   A) 6.554   B) 0.391   C) 1.600   D) 2.560

14) Calculate the test statistic F to test the claim that $\sigma_1^2 \leq \sigma_2^2$. Two samples are randomly selected from

populations that are normal. The sample statistics are given below.

$n_1 = 16$ $n_2 = 15$

$s_1^2 = 25.23$ $s_2^2 = 23.52$

   A) 0.932   B) 1.151   C) 1.036   D) 1.073

15) Calculate the test statistic F to test the claim that $\sigma_1^2 \neq \sigma_2^2$. Two samples are randomly selected from

populations that are normal. The sample statistics are given below.

$n_1 = 11$ $n_2 = 18$

$s_1^2 = 1.734>$ $s_2^2 = 0.78$

   A) 4.933   B) 2.223   C) 1.490   D) 0.450

16) Test the claim that $\sigma_1^2 = \sigma_2^2$. Two samples are randomly selected from populations that are normal. The

sample statistics are given below. Use $\alpha = 0.05$.

$n_1 = 25$ $n_2 = 30$

$s_1^2 = 13.357$ $s_2^2 = 8.325$

17) Test the claim that $\sigma_1^2 = \sigma_2^2$. Two samples are randomly selected from populations that are normal. The

sample statistics are given below. Use $\alpha = 0.02$.

$n_1 = 13$ $n_2 = 12$

$s_1^2 = 18.816$ $s_2^2 = 15$

Elementary Statistics 196

18) Test the claim that $\sigma_1^2 > \sigma_2^2$. Two samples are randomly selected from populations that are normal. The sample statistics are given below. Use $\alpha = 0.01$.

$n_1 = 16$ $\qquad$ $n_2 = 13$

$s_1^2 = 11{,}200$ $\qquad$ $s_2^2 = 4375$

19) Test the claim that $\sigma_1^2 \leq \sigma_2^2$. Two samples are randomly selected from populations that are normal. The sample statistics are given below. Use $\alpha = 0.05$.

$n_1 = 16$ $\qquad$ $n_2 = 15$

$s_1^2 = 27.753$ $\qquad$ $s_2^2 = 25.872$

20) Test the claim that $\sigma_1^2 \neq \sigma_2^2$. Two samples are randomly selected from populations that are normal. The sample statistics are given below. Use $\alpha = 0.02$.

$n_1 = 11$ $\qquad$ $n_2 = 18$

$s_1^2 = 4.046$ $\qquad$ $s_2^2 = 1.82$

21) Suppose you want to test the claim that $\mu_1 = \mu_2$. Two independent samples are randomly selected from populations that are normally distributed. The sample statistics are given below. Perform an F–test to determine which formula to use for the standardized test statistic, t. Use $\alpha = 0.02$.

$n_1 = 11$ $\qquad$ $n_2 = 18$
$s_1 = 0.76$ $\qquad$ $s_2 = 0.51$

A) $t = \dfrac{(\bar{x}_1 - \bar{x}_2) - (\mu_1 - \mu_2)}{\sqrt{\dfrac{s_1^2}{n_1} + \dfrac{s_2^2}{n_2}}}$

B) $t = \dfrac{(\bar{x}_1 - \bar{x}_2) - (\mu_1 - \mu_2)}{\sqrt{\dfrac{(n_1 - 1) s_1^2 + (n_2 - 1) s_2^2}{n_1 + n_2 - 2}} \cdot \sqrt{\dfrac{1}{n_1} + \dfrac{1}{n_2}}}$

22) Suppose you want to test the claim that $\mu_1 = \mu_2$. Two independent samples are randomly selected from populations that are normally distributed. The sample statistics are given below. Perform an F–test to determine which formula to use for the standardized test statistic, t. Use $\alpha = 0.01$.

$n_1 = 18 \qquad n_2 = 13$
$s_1 = 40 \qquad s_2 = 25$

A) $t = \dfrac{(\bar{x}_1 - \bar{x}_2) - (\mu_1 - \mu_2)}{\sqrt{\dfrac{s_1^2}{n_1} + \dfrac{s_2^2}{n_2}}}$

B) $t = \dfrac{(\bar{x}_1 - \bar{x}_2) - (\mu_1 - \mu_2)}{\sqrt{\dfrac{(n_1 - 1) s_1^2 + (n_2 - 1) s_2^2}{n_1 + n_2 - 2}} \cdot \sqrt{\dfrac{1}{n_1} + \dfrac{1}{n_2}}}$

23) Suppose you want to test the claim that $\mu_1 = \mu_2$. Two independent samples are randomly selected from populations that are normally distributed. The sample statistics are given below. Perform an F–test to determine which formula to use for the standardized test statistic, t. Use $\alpha = 0.05$.

$n_1 = 25 \qquad n_2 = 30$
$s_1 = 1.5 \qquad s_2 = 1.9$

A) $t = \dfrac{(\bar{x}_1 - \bar{x}_2) - (\mu_1 - \mu_2)}{\sqrt{\dfrac{(n_1 - 1) s_1^2 + (n_2 - 1) s_2^2}{n_1 + n_2 - 2}} \cdot \sqrt{\dfrac{1}{n_1} + \dfrac{1}{n_2}}}$

B) $t = \dfrac{(\bar{x}_1 - \bar{x}_2) - (\mu_1 - \mu_2)}{\sqrt{\dfrac{s_1^2}{n_1} + \dfrac{s_2^2}{n_2}}}$

24) Suppose you want to test the claim that $\mu_1 = \mu_2$. Two independent samples are randomly selected from populations that are normally distributed. The sample statistics are given below. Perform an F–test to determine which formula to use for the standardized test statistic, t. Use $\alpha = 0.05$.

$n_1 = 14 \qquad n_2 = 12$
$s_1 = 2.5 \qquad s_2 = 2.8$

A) $t = \dfrac{(\bar{x}_1 - \bar{x}_2) - (\mu_1 - \mu_2)}{\sqrt{\dfrac{s_1^2}{n_1} + \dfrac{s_2^2}{n_2}}}$

B) $t = \dfrac{(\bar{x}_1 - \bar{x}_2) - (\mu_1 - \mu_2)}{\sqrt{\dfrac{(n_1 - 1) s_1^2 + (n_2 - 1) s_2^2}{n_1 + n_2 - 2}} \cdot \sqrt{\dfrac{1}{n_1} + \dfrac{1}{n_2}}}$

25) A local bank claims that the variance of waiting time for its customers to be served is the lowest in the area. A competitor bank checks the waiting time at both banks. The sample statistics are listed below.Test the local bank's claim. Use $\alpha = 0.05$.

Local Bank   Competitor Bank
$n_1 = 13$ $n_2 = 16$

$s_1 = 1.1$ minutes $s_2 = 1.3$ minutes

26) A study was conducted to determine if the variances of elementary school teacher salaries from two neighboring districts were equal. A sample of 25 teachers from each district was selected. The first district had a standard deviation of $s_1 = \$3220$, and the second district had a standard deviation $s_2 = \$2940$. Test the claim that the variances of the salaries from both districts are equal. Use $\alpha = 0.05$

Elementary Statistics 198

27) A random sample of 21 women had blood pressure levels with a variance of 276.8. A random sample of 18 men had blood pressure levels with a variance of 184.32. Test the claim that the blood pressure levels for women have a larger variance than those for men. Use $\alpha = 0.01$.

28) The weights of a random sample of 121 women between the ages of 25 and 34 had a standard deviation of 84 pounds. The weights of 121 women between the ages of 55 and 64 had a standard deviation 63 pounds. Test the claim that the older women are from a population with a standard deviation less than that for women in the 25 to 34 age group. Use $\alpha = 0.05$.

29) At a college, 61 female students were randomly selected and it was found that their monthly income had a standard deviation of $133.65. For 121 male students, the standard deviation was $185.57. Test the claim that variance of monthly incomes is higher for male students than it is for female students. Use $\alpha = 0.01$.

30) A medical researcher suspects that the variance of the pulse rate of smokers is higher than the variance of the pulse rate of non–smokers. Use the sample statistics below to test the researcher's suspicion. Use $\alpha = 0.05$.

Smokers	Non–smokers
$n_1 = 61$	$n_2 = 121$
$s_1 = 7.8$	$s_2 = 5.3$

31) A statistics teacher believes that the variances of test scores of students in her evening statistics class are lower than the variances of test scores of students in her day class. The results of an exam, given to the day and evening students, are shown below. Can the teacher conclude that her evening students have a lower variance? Use $\alpha = 0.01$.

Day Students	Evening Students
$n_1 = 36$	$n_2 = 41$
$s_1 = 39.2$	$s_2 = 21.2$

32) A statistics teacher wants to see whether there is a significant difference in the variances of the ages between day students and night students. A random sample of 31 students is selected from each group. The data are given below. Test the claim that there is no difference in age between the two groups. Use $\alpha = 0.05$.

Day Students
22 24 24 23 19 19 23 22 18 21 21
18 18 25 29 24 23 22 22 21 20 20
20 27 17 19 18 21 20 23 26

Evening Students
18 23 25 23 21 21 23 24 27 31 34
20 20 23 19 25 24 27 23 20 20 21
25 24 23 28 20 19 23 24 20

33) A local bank claims that the variance of waiting time for its customers to be served is the lowest in the area. A competitor bank checks the waiting time at both banks. The sample statistics are listed below.Test the local bank's claim. Use $\alpha = 0.05$.

Local Bank

$n_1 = 41$

$s_1 = 0.55$ minutes

Competitor Bank

$n_2 = 61$

$s_2 = 1$ minutes

34) Find the left–tailed and right tailed critical F–values for a two-tailed test. Let $\alpha = 0.02$, d.f.$_N = 7$, and d.f.$_D = 5$.

35) Find the left–tailed and right tailed critical F–values for a two-tailed test. Use the sample statistics below. Let $\alpha = 0.05$.

$n_1 = 5$ $n_2 = 6$

$s_1^2 = 5.8$ $s_2^2 = 2.7$

36) The weights of a random sample of 25 women between the ages of 25 and 34 had a standard deviation of 28 pounds. The weights of a random sample of 41 women between the ages of 55 and 64 had a standard deviation of 21 pounds. Construct a 95% confidence interval for $\dfrac{\sigma_1^2}{\sigma_2^2}$, where σ_1^2 and σ_2^2 are the variances of the weights of women between the ages 25 and 34 and the weights of women between the ages of 55 and 64.

10.4 Analysis of Variance

Solve the problem.

1) Find the critical F_0–value to test the claim that the populations have the same mean. Use $\alpha = 0.05$.

Brand 1	Brand 2	Brand 3
$n = 8$	$n = 8$	$n = 8$
$\bar{x} = 3.0$	$\bar{x} = 2.6$	$\bar{x} = 2.6$
$s = 0.50$	$s = 0.60$	$s = 0.55$

A) 3.47   B) 2.819   C) 1.892   D) 3.210

2) Find the test statistic F to test the claim that the populations have the same mean.

Brand 1	Brand 2	Brand 3
$n = 8$	$n = 8$	$n = 8$
$\bar{x} = 3.0$	$\bar{x} = 2.6$	$\bar{x} = 2.6$
$s = 0.50$	$s = 0.60$	$s = 0.55$

A) 1.182   B) 0.832   C) 1.021   D) 1.403

3) Test the claim that the populations have the same mean. Use $\alpha = 0.05$.

Brand 1	Brand 2	Brand 3
$n = 8$	$n = 8$	$n = 8$
$\bar{x} = 3.0$	$\bar{x} = 2.6$	$\bar{x} = 2.6$
$s = 0.50$	$s = 0.60$	$s = 0.55$

4) A medical researcher wishes to try three different techniques to lower blood pressure of patients with high blood pressure. The subjects are randomly selected and assigned to one of three groups. Group 1 is given medication, Group 2 is given an exercise program, and Group 3 is assigned a diet program. At the end of six weeks, each subject's blood pressure is recorded. Find the critical value F_0 to test the claim that there is no difference among the means. Use $\alpha = 0.05$.

Group 1	Group 2	Group 3
13	8	6
12	3	12
9	5	4
15	2	8
11	4	9
8	0	4

    A) 39.43   B) 4.77   C) 3.68   D) 19.43

5) A medical researcher wishes to try three different techniques to lower blood pressure of patients with high blood pressure. The subjects are randomly selected and assigned to one of three groups. Group 1 is given medication, Group 2 is given an exercise program, and Group 3 is assigned a diet program. At the end of six weeks, each subject's blood pressure is recorded. Find the test statistic F to test the claim that there is no difference among the means.

Group 1	Group 2	Group 3
13	8	6
12	2	12
11	3	4
15	5	8
9	4	9
8	0	4

    A) 8.369   B) 12.162   C) 11.095   D) 9.812

6) A medical researcher wishes to try three different techniques to lower blood pressure of patients with high blood pressure. The subjects are randomly selected and assigned to one of three groups. Group 1 is given medication, Group 2 is given an exercise program, and Group 3 is assigned a diet program. At the end of six weeks, each subject's blood pressure is recorded. Test the claim that there is no difference among the means. Use $\alpha = 0.05$.

Group 1	Group 2	Group 3
9	8	6
12	2	12
13	3	4
15	5	4
11	4	9
8	0	8

7) Four different types of fertilizers are used on raspberry plants. The number of raspberries on each randomly selected plant is given below. Find the critical value F_0 to test the claim that the type of fertilizer makes no difference in the mean number of raspberries per plant. Use $\alpha = 0.01$.

Fertilizer 1	Fertilizer 2	Fertilizer 3	Fertilizer 4
6	8	6	3
5	5	3	5
6	5	4	3
7	5	2	4
7	5	3	5
6	6	3	4

A) 4.43   B) 26.69   C) 4.22   D) 4.94

8) Four different types of fertilizers are used on raspberry plants. The number of raspberries on each randomly selected plant is given below. Find the test statistic F to test the claim that the type of fertilizer makes no difference in the mean number of raspberries per plant.

Fertilizer 1	Fertilizer 2	Fertilizer 3	Fertilizer 4
6	5	6	3
7	8	3	5
5	5	4	3
6	5	2	4
7	5	3	4
6	6	3	5

A) 7.123   B) 6.912   C) 8.357   D) 8.123

9) Four different types of fertilizers are used on raspberry plants. The number of raspberries on each randomly selected plant is given below. Test the claim that the type of fertilizer makes no difference in the mean number of raspberries per plant. Use $\alpha = 0.01$.

Fertilizer 1	Fertilizer 2	Fertilizer 3	Fertilizer 4
6	8	6	3
5	5	3	5
6	5	2	3
7	5	4	4
7	5	3	5
6	6	3	4

10) A researcher wishes to determine whether there is a difference in the average age of elementary school, high school, and community college teachers. Teachers are randomly selected. Their ages are recorded below. Find the critical value F_0 to test the claim that there is no difference in the average age of each group. Use $\alpha = 0.01$.

Elementary Teachers	High School Teachers	Community College Teachers
23	36	36
28	41	45
27	38	39
25	47	61
52	42	45
37	31	35

A) 5.42   B) 9.43   C) 6.36   D) 5.09

11) A researcher wishes to determine whether there is a difference in the average age of elementary school, high school, and community college teachers. Teachers are randomly selected. Their ages are recorded below. Find the test statistic F to test the claim that there is no difference in the average age of each group.

Elementary Teachers	High School Teachers	Community College Teachers
23	38	39
28	36	45
27	41	45
52	47	61
25	42	36
37	31	35

A) 4.312   B) 3.189   C) 2.517   D) 2.913

12) A researcher wishes to determine whether there is a difference in the average age of elementary school, high school, and community college teachers. Teachers are randomly selected. Their ages are recorded below. Test the claim that there is no difference in the average age of each group. Use $\alpha = 0.01$.

Elementary Teachers	High School Teachers	Community College Teachers
23	38	39
28	41	45
27	36	36
25	47	61
37	42	45
52	31	35

13) The grade point averages of students participating in sports at a local college are to be compared. The data are listed below. Test the claim that there is no difference in the mean grade point averages of the 3 groups. Use $\alpha = 0.05$.

Tennis	Golf	Swimming
2.1	1.8	3.0
3.2	2.1	2.5
2.5	1.9	2.8
3.5	3.3	2.7
3.1		2.5
2.6		

14) The times (in minutes) to assemble a computer component for 3 different machines are listed below. Workers are randomly selected. Test the claim that there is no difference in the mean time for each machine. Use $\alpha = 0.01$.

Machine 1	Machine 2	Machine 3
32	40	25
32	29	31
31	38	29
30	33	28
33	35	
31	36	
	32	

15) A realtor wishes to compare the square footage of houses in 4 different cities, all of which are priced approximately the same. The data are listed below. Can the realtor conclude that the mean square footage in the four cities are equal?
Use $\alpha = 0.01$.

City #1	City #2	City #3	City #4
2150	1780	1530	2400
2210	1540	1600	2350
1980	1690	1580	2600
2000	1650	1750	2200
1900		1500	2000
		1670	2150
			2350

16) A medical researcher wishes to try three different techniques to lower blood pressure of patients with high blood-pressure. The subjects are randomly selected and assigned to one of three groups. Group 1 is given medication, Group 2 is given an exercise program, and Group 3 is assigned a diet program. At the end of six weeks, each subject's blood pressure is recorded. Perform a Scheffé Test to determine which means have a significance difference. Use $\alpha = 0.05$.

Group 1	Group 2	Group 3
9	8	6
12	2	12
13	3	4
15	5	4
11	4	9
8	0	8

17) Four different types of fertilizers are used on raspberry plants. The number of raspberries on each randomly selected plant is given below. Perform a Scheffé Test to determine which means have a significance difference. Use $\alpha = 0.01$.

Fertilizer 1	Fertilizer 2	Fertilizer 3	Fertilizer 4
6	8	6	3
6	5	3	5
7	5	2	3
5	5	4	4
7	5	3	4
6	6	3	5

Ch. 10 Chi–Square Tests and the F–Distribution
Answer Key

10.1 Goodness of Fit

1) B

2) D

3) critical value $\chi^2_0 = 11.070$; chi–square test statistic $\chi^2 \approx 6.750$; fail to reject H_0; There is not sufficient evidence to reject the claim. It seems that the probability of winning in different lanes is the same.

4) D

5) D

6) critical value $\chi^2_0 = 13.277$; chi–square test statistic $\chi^2 \approx 37.45$; reject H_0; There is sufficient evidence to reject the claim that customers show no preference for the brands.

7) C

8) A

9) critical value $\chi^2_0 = 13.277$; chi–square test statistic $\chi^2 \approx 5.25$; fail to reject H_0; There is not sufficient evidence to support the claim that the grades are different than expected.

10) A

11) D

12) critical value $\chi^2_0 = 9.236$; chi–square test statistic $\chi^2 \approx 3.067$; fail to reject H_0; There is not sufficient evidence to support the claim of a loaded die.

13) B

14) D

15) critical value $\chi^2_0 = 7.815$; chi–square test statistic $\chi^2 \approx 75.101$; reject H_0; There is sufficient evidence to reject the claim that all ages have the same crash rate.

16) 1.520

17) 4.605

18) Critical value $\chi_0^2 = 4.605$; chi–square test statistic $\chi^2 = 1.520$; fail to reject H_0; There is not enough evidence to support the claim that the distribution is not uniform.

19) 11, 27, 33, 20, and 6, respectively.

20) Critical value $\chi_0^2 = 9.448$; chi–square test statistic $\chi^2 = 1.954$; fail to reject H_0; The ages of employees are normally distributed.

21) 6, 12, 31, 57, 37, 38, and 11, respectively.

22) Critical value $\chi_0^2 = 12.592$; chi–square test statistic $\chi^2 = 75.239$; reject H_0; The heights of the trees are not normally distributed.

10.2 Independence

1) D

2) B

3) C

4) critical value $\chi^2_0 = 9.488$; chi–square test statistic $\chi^2 \approx 8.031$; fail to reject H_0; There is not enough evidence to conclude that the representative's opinion on a bill is related to their party affiliation.

5) A

6) A

7) D

8) critical value $\chi_0^2 = 7.815$; chi-square test statistic $\chi^2 \approx 18.146$; reject H_0; There is enough evidence to conclude that the number of minutes spent online per day is related to gender.

9) C

10) A

11) B

12) critical value $\chi_0^2 = 9.210$; chi-square test statistic $\chi^2 \approx 3.473$; fail to reject H_0; There is enough evidence to conclude that walking is not related to low, moderate, or high blood pressure.

13) C

14) A

15) D

16) critical value $\chi_0^2 = 11.345$; chi-square test statistic $\chi^2 \approx 3.290$; fail to reject H_0; There is enough evidence to conclude that home team wins and visiting team wins are independent of the sport.

17) critical value $\chi_0^2 = 16.919$; chi-square test statistic $\chi^2 \approx 91.097$; reject H_0; There is sufficient evidence to reject the claim of independence.

18) critical value $\chi_0^2 = 3.841$; chi-square test statistic $\chi^2 \approx 3.273$; fail to reject H_0; There is not sufficient evidence to reject the claim.

19) critical value $\chi_0^2 = 13.277$; chi-square test statistic $\chi^2 \approx 14.336$; reject H_0; There is sufficient evidence to reject the claim.

10.3 Comparing Two Variances

1) B

2) D

3) B

4) B

5) C

6) B

7) A

8) B

9) A

10) D

11) C

12) A

13) D

14) D

15) B

16) critical value $F_0 = 2.15$; test statistic $F \approx 1.604$; fail to reject H_0; There is not sufficient evidence to reject the claim.

17) critical value $F_0 = 4.40$; test statistic $F \approx 1.254$; fail to reject H_0; There is not sufficient evidence to reject the claim.

18) critical value $F_0 = 4.01$; test statistic $F \approx 2.560$; fail to reject H_0; There is not sufficient evidence to support the claim.

19) critical value $F_0 = 2.46$; test statistic $F \approx 1.073$; fail to reject H_0; There is not sufficient evidence to reject the claim.

20) critical value $F_0 = 3.59$; test statistic $F \approx 2.223$; fail to reject H_0; There is not sufficient evidence to support the claim.

21) B

22) A

23) B

24) B

25) critical value $F_0 = 2.48$; test statistic $F \approx 1.397$; fail to reject H_0; There is not sufficient evidence to reject the claim.

26) critical value $F_0 = 2.27$; test statistic $F \approx 1.200$; fail to reject H_0; There is not sufficient evidence to reject the claim.

27) critical value $F_0 = 3.16$; test statistic $F \approx 1.502$; fail to reject H_0; There is not sufficient evidence to support the claim.

28) critical value $F_0 = 1.35$; test statistic $F \approx 1.778$; reject H_0; There is sufficient evidence to support the claim.

29) critical value $F_0 = 1.73$; test statistic $F \approx 1.928$; reject H_0; There is sufficient evidence to support the claim.

30) critical value $F_0 = 1.43$; test statistic $F \approx 2.166$; reject H_0; There is sufficient evidence to support the claim.

31) critical value $F_0 = 2.153$; test statistic $F \approx 3.419$; reject H_0; There is sufficient evidence to support the claim.

32) critical value $F_0 = 2.07$; test statistic $F \approx 1.549$; fail to reject H_0; There is not sufficient evidence to reject the claim.

33) critical value $F_0 = 1.64$; test statistic $F \approx 3.306$; reject H_0; There is sufficient evidence to support the claim.

34) $F_L = 0.134$, $F_R = 10.46$

35) $F_L = 0.107$, $F_R = 7.39$

36) $0.827 < \dfrac{\sigma_1^2}{\sigma_2^2} < 3.573$

10.4 Analysis of Variance

1) A

2) D

3) critical value $F_0 = 3.47$; test statistic $F \approx 1.403$; fail to reject H_0; The data does not provide enough evidence to indicate that the means are unequal.

4) C

5) C

6) critical value $F_0 = 3.68$; test statistic $F \approx 11.095$; reject H_0; There is enough evidence that the sample means are different.

7) D

8) C

9) critical value $F_0 = 4.94$; test statistic $F \approx 8.357$; reject H_0; The data provides ample evidence that the sample means are unequal.

10) C

11) C

12) critical value $F_0 = 6.36$; test statistic $F \approx 2.517$; fail to reject H_0; There is not enough evidence to indicate that the means are different.

13) critical value $F_0 = 3.89$; test statistic $F \approx 1.560$; fail to reject H_0; The data does not provide enough evidence to indicate that the means are unequal.

14) critical value $F_0 = 6.52$; test statistic $F \approx 7.103$; reject H_0; There is enough evidence that the sample means are different.

15) critical value $F_0 = 5.09$; test statistic $F \approx 31.330$; reject H_0; There is enough evidence that the sample means are different.

16) critical value $F_0 = 7.36$; Test statistic $F \approx 22.0$ for Group #1 versus Group #2 indicating a significant difference. Test statistic $F \approx 6.5$ for Group #1 versus Group #3 indicating no difference. Test statistic $F \approx 4.6$ for Group #2 versus Group #3 indicating no difference.

17) critical value $F_0 = 14.82$; Test statistic $F \approx 0.634$ for #1 vs #2 indicating no difference. Test statistic $F \approx 18.03$ for #1 vs #3 indicating a significant difference. Test statistic $F \approx 11.90$ for #1 vs #4 indicating no difference. Test statistic $F \approx 11.90$ for #2 vs #3 indicating no difference. Test statistic $F \approx 7.04$ for #2 vs #4 indicating no difference. Test statistic $F \approx 0.634$ for #3 vs #4 indicating no difference.

11.1 The Sign Test

Solve the problem.

1) A convenience store owner believes that the median number of lottery tickets sold per day is 43. A random sample of 20 days yields the data below. Find the critical value to test the owner's claim. Use $\alpha = 0.05$.

```
26  42  53  58  25  49  64  21  27  32
41  48  48  38  38  43  43  53  48  32
```

   A) 2   B) 4   C) 5   D) 3

2) A convenience store owner believes that the median number of lottery tickets sold per day is 55. A random sample of 20 days yields the data below. Find the test statistic x to test the owner's claim.

```
38  54  65  70  37  61  76  33  39  44
53  60  60  50  50  55  55  65  60  44
```

   A) 8   B) 18   C) 10   D) 2

3) A convenience store owner believes that the median number of lottery tickets sold per day is 53. A random sample of 20 days yields the data below. Test the owner's claim. Use $\alpha = 0.05$.

```
36  52  63  68  35  59  74  31  37  42
51  58  58  48  48  53  53  63  58  42
```

4) A real estate agent surmises that the median rent for a one-bedroom apartment in a beach community in southern California is at least $1200 per month. The rents for a random sample of 15 one-bedroom apartments are listed below. Find the critical value to test the agent's claim. Use $\alpha = 0.01$.

```
$1500   $1450   $900    $1075   $935
$1950   $1375   $870    $1590   $2200
$1195   $1200   $1275   $1200   $980
```

   A) 2   B) 3   C) 1   D) 4

5) A real estate agent surmises that the median rent for a one-bedroom apartment in a beach community in southern California is at least $2000 per month. The rents for a random sample of 15 one-bedroom apartments are listed below. Find the test statistic x to test the agent's claim.

```
$2300   $2250   $1700   $1875   $1735
$2750   $2175   $1670   $2390   $3000
$1995   $2000   $2075   $2000   $1780
```

   A) 1   B) 6   C) 13   D) 7

6) A real estate agent surmises that the median rent for a one-bedroom apartment in a beach community in southern California is at least $1800 per month. The rents for a random sample of 15 one-bedroom apartments are listed below. Test the agent's claim. Use $\alpha = 0.01$.

```
$2100   $2050   $1500   $1675   $1535
$2550   $1975   $1470   $2190   $2800
$1795   $1800   $1875   $1800   $1580
```

7) A club professional at a major golf course claims that the course is so tough that even professional go..'ers rarely break par of 70. The scores from a random sample of 20 professional golfers are listed below. Find the critical value to test the club professional's claim. Use $\alpha = 0.05$.

69 67 70 70 73 72 64 76 70 75
67 69 71 71 78 76 70 72 73 63

   A) 1   B) 3   C) 2   D) 4

8) A club professional at a major golf course claims that the course is so tough that even professional golfers rarely break par of 73. The scores from a random sample of 20 professional golfers are listed below. Find the test statistic x to test the club professional's claim.

72 70 73 73 76 75 67 79 73 78
70 72 74 74 81 79 73 75 76 66

   A) 14   B) 10   C) 6   D) 4

9) A club professional at a major golf course claims that the course is so tough that even professional golfers rarely break par of 67. The scores from a random sample of 20 professional golfers are listed below. Test the club professional's claim. Use $\alpha = 0.05$.

66 64 67 67 70 69 61 73 67 72
64 66 68 68 75 73 67 69 70 60

10) A car dealer claims that its new model car still gets at least 25 miles per gallon of gas. Ten cars are tested. The results are given below. Test the dealer's claim. Use $\alpha = 0.05$.

19.8 17.6 23.8 18.9 22 24.2 27.3 21.9 16.7 23

11) A government agency claims that the median hourly wages for workers at fast food restaurants in the western U.S. is $6.80. In a random sample of 100 workers, 68 were paid less than $6.80, 10 were paid $6.80, and the rest more than $6.80. Find the critical values to test the government's claim. Use $\alpha = 0.05$.

   A) ±2.575   B) ±2.33   C) ±1.96   D) ±1.645

12) A government agency claims that the median hourly wages for workers at fast food restaurants in the western U.S. is $6.15. In a random sample of 100 workers, 68 were paid less than $6.15, 10 were paid $6.15, and the rest more than $6.15. Find the test statistic z to test the government's claim.

   A) −4.743   B) −2.386   C) −3.912   D) −3.187

13) A government agency claims that the median hourly wages for workers at fast food restaurants in the western U.S. is $6.45. In a random sample of 100 workers, 68 were paid less than $6.45, 10 were paid $6.45, and the rest more than $6.45. Test the government's claim. Use $\alpha = 0.05$.

14) Test the hypothesis that the median age of statistics teachers is 48 years. A random sample of 60 statistics teachers found 25 above 48 years and 35 below 48 years. Use $\alpha = 0.01$.

15) Nine students took the SAT test. Their scores are listed below. Later on, they took a test preparation course and retook the SAT. Their new scores are listed below. Use the sign test to test the claim that the test preparation had no effect on their scores. Use $\alpha = 0.05$.

Student	1	2	3	4	5	6	7	8	9
Before Score	840	930	890	860	900	1080	1170	970	870
After Score	860	930	880	900	930	1090	1160	1010	890

16) A weight–lifting coach claims that a weight–lifter can increase strength by taking vitamin E. To test the theory, the coach randomly selects 9 athletes and gives them a strength test using a bench press. The results are listed below. Thirty days later, after regular training supplemented by vitamin E, they are tested again. The new results are also listed below. Use the sign test to test the claim that the vitamin E supplement is effective in increasing the athletes' strength. Use $\alpha = 0.05$.

Athlete	1	2	3	4	5	6	7	8	9
Befor	216	238	247	193	231	199	239	218	215
After	226	243	247	191	238	214	244	213	220

17) A pharmaceutical company wishes to test a new drug with the expectation of lowering cholesterol levels. Ten subjects are randomly selected and their cholesterol levels are recorded. The results are listed below. The subjects were placed on the drug for a period of 6 months, after which their cholesterol levels were tested again. The results are listed below. (All units are milligrams per deciliter.) Use the sign test to test the company's claim that the drug lowers cholesterol levels. Use $\alpha = 0.01$.

Subject	1	2	3	4	5	6	7	8	9	10
Before	234	199	242	228	260	185	248	241	237	200
After	219	194	250	218	255	185	218	223	235	185

18) In a study of the effectiveness of physical exercise in weight loss, 20 people were randomly selected to participate in a program for 30 days. Use the sign test to test the claim that exercise has no bearing on weight loss. Use $\alpha = 0.02$.

Weight Before Program (in Pounds)	178	210	156	188	193	225	190	165	168	200
Weight After Program (in Pounds)	182	205	156	190	183	220	195	155	165	200

Weight Before Program (in Pounds)	186	172	166	184	225	145	208	214	148	174
Weight After Program (in Pounds)	180	173	165	186	240	138	203	203	142	170

19) A local school district is concerned about the number of school days missed by its teachers due to illness. A random sample of 10 teachers is selected. The numbers of days absent in one year are listed below. An incentive program is offered in an attempt to decrease the number of days absent. The numbers of days absent in one year after the incentive program are also listed below. Use the sign test to test the claim that the incentive program cuts down on the number of days missed by teachers. Use $\alpha = 0.05$.

Teacher	1	2	3	4	5	6	7	8	9	10
Days Absent Before Incentive	10	8	0	4	6	5	0	8	7	9
Days Absent After Incentive	9	7	0	2	5	3	1	7	5	9

20) A physician's group claims that a person's diastolic blood pressure can be lowered, if, instead of taking a drug, the person listens to a relaxation tape each evening. Ten subjects are randomly selected. Their blood pressures, measured in millimeters of mercury, are listed below. The 10 patients are given the tapes and told to listen to them each evening for one month. At the end of the month, their blood pressures are taken again. The data are listed below. Use the sign test to test the physician's claim. Use $\alpha = 0.01$.

Patient	1	2	3	4	5	6	7	8	9	10
Before	85	96	92	83	80	91	79	98	93	96
After	82	90	92	75	74	80	82	88	89	80

21) A college researcher claims that the median hours worked by full time students is at least 14 hours per week. In a random sample of 100 students, 62 worked more than 14 hours, 10 worked exactly 14 hours and the rest worked less than 14 hours. Find the critical value to test the researcher's claim. Use $\alpha = 0.05$.

    A) -2.33   B) -1.96   C) -1.645   D) -2.575

22) A college researcher claims that the median hours worked by full time students is at least 15 hours per week. In a random sample of 100 students, 61 worked more than 15 hours, 10 worked exactly 15 hours and the rest worked less than 15 hours. Find the test statistic to test the researcher's claim.

    A) -3.268   B) -4.2   C) -3.373   D) -4.1

23) A college researcher claims that the median hours worked by full time students is at least 13 hours per week. In a random sample of 100 students, 62 worked more than 13 hours, 10 worked exactly 13 hours and the rest worked less than 13 hours. Test the researcher's claim. Use $\alpha = 0.05$.

24) Test the hypothesis that the median age of statistics teachers is less than or equal to 45 years. A random sample of 60 statistics teachers found 25 above 45 years, 33 below 45 years, and the rest exactly 45 years. Use $\alpha = 0.01$.

25) A labor organization claims that the monthly earnings of farm workers are less than or equal to $912. To test the claim, 100 workers are randomly selected and asked to provide their monthly earnings. The data is shown below. Test the labor organization's claim. Use $\alpha = 0.05$.

Weekly Earnings	Number of Workers
Less than $912	45
$912	5
More than $912	50

26) One hundred people are placed on a special diet with the intent of losing weight. At the end of 6 weeks, 59 lost weight, 27 gained weight and the rest remained the same. Test the hypothesis that the diet is effective. Use $\alpha = 0.05$. (Note: The diet will be effective if at least 50% lose weight.)

11.2 The Wilcoxon Tests

Solve the problem.

1) Nine students took the SAT test. Their scores are listed below. Later on, they took a test preparation course and retook the SAT. Their new scores are listed below. Use the Wilcoxon signed-rank test to find the test statistic w_s to test the claim that the test preparation had no effect on their scores. Use $\alpha = 0.05$.

Student	1	2	3	4	5	6	7	8	9
Before Score	1150	1130	1120	1140	930	1110	1090	850	1020
After Score	1170	1130	1110	1180	960	1120	1080	890	1040

    A) 4   B) 41   C) -41   D) -4

2) Nine students took the SAT test. Their scores are listed below. Later on, they took a test preparation course and retook the SAT. Their new scores are listed below. Use the Wilcoxon signed-rank test to test the claim that the test preparation had no effect on their scores. Use $\alpha = 0.05$.

Student	1	2	3	4	5	6	7	8	9
Before Score	940	960	1170	920	1060	1070	930	1200	1020
After Score	960	960	1160	960	1090	1080	920	1240	1040

3) A weight-lifting coach claims that a weight-lifter can increase strength by taking vitamin E. To test the theory, the coach randomly selects 9 athletes and gives them a strength test using a bench press. The results are listed below. Thirty days later, after regular training supplemented by vitamin E, they are tested again. The new results are listed below. Use the Wilcoxon signed-rank test to find the critical value to test the claim that the vitamin E supplement is effective in increasing the athletes' strength. Use $\alpha = 0.05$.

Athlete	1	2	3	4	5	6	7	8	9
Befor	222	265	182	237	203	226	274	270	185
After	232	270	182	235	210	241	279	265	190

A) 6   B) 3   C) 2   D) 4

4) A weight-lifting coach claims that a weight-lifter can increase strength by taking vitamin E. To test the theory, the coach randomly selects 9 athletes and gives them a strength test using a bench press. The results are listed below. Thirty days later, after regular training supplemented by vitamin E, they are tested again. The new results are listed below. Use the Wilcoxon signed-rank test to find the critical value to test the claim that the vitamin E supplement is effective in increasing the athletes' strength. Use $\alpha = 0.05$.

Athlete	1	2	3	4	5	6	7	8	9
Befor	239	240	181	267	224	230	191	245	277
After	249	245	181	265	231	245	196	240	282

5) A pharmaceutical company wishes to test a new drug with the expectation of lowering cholesterol levels. Ten subjects are randomly selected and their cholesterol levels are recorded. The results are listed below. The subjects were placed on the drug for a period of 6 months, after which their cholesterol levels were tested again. The results are listed below. (All units are milligrams per deciliter.) Use the Wilcoxon signed-rank test to find the test statistic w_s to test the company's claim that the drug lowers cholesterol levels.

Subject	1	2	3	4	5	6	7	8	9	10
Before	226	243	200	232	210	245	234	263	221	202
After	211	238	208	222	205	245	204	245	219	187

A) –2   B) 4   C) 7.5   D) 5.5

6) A pharmaceutical company wishes to test a new drug with the expectation of lowering cholesterol levels. Ten subjects are randomly selected and their cholesterol levels are recorded. The results are listed below. The subjects were placed on the drug for a period of 6 months, after which their cholesterol levels were tested again. The results are listed below. (All units are milligrams per deciliter.) Use the Wilcoxon signed-rank test to test the company's claim that the drug lowers cholesterol levels. Use $\alpha = 0.05$.

Subject	1	2	3	4	5	6	7	8	9	10
Before	248	204	189	268	235	263	190	257	249	219
After	233	199	197	258	230	263	160	239	247	204

Elementary Statistics 212

7) A physician claims that a person's diastolic blood pressure can be lowered, if, instead of taking a drug, the person listens to a relaxation tape each evening. Ten subjects are randomly selected. Their blood pressures, measured in millimeters of mercury, are listed below. The 10 patients are given the tapes and told to listen to them each evening for one month. At the end of the month, their blood pressures are taken again. The data are listed below. Use the Wilcoxon signed-rank test to find the critical value to test the physician's claim. Use $\alpha = 0.05$.

Patient	1	2	3	4	5	6	7	8	9	10
Before	92	83	99	80	81	85	93	88	94	95
After	89	77	99	72	75	74	96	78	90	79

A) 8   B) 2   C) 4   D) 6

8) A physician claims that a person's diastolic blood pressure can be lowered, if, instead of taking a drug, the person listens to a relaxation tape each evening. Ten subjects are randomly selected. Their blood pressures, measured in millimeters of mercury, are listed below. The 10 patients are given the tapes and told to listen to them each evening for one month. At the end of the month, their blood pressures are taken again. The data are listed below. Use the Wilcoxon signed-rank test to test the physician's claim. Use $\alpha = 0.05$.

Patient	1	2	3	4	5	6	7	8	9	10
Before	84	83	87	97	93	86	94	98	88	81
After	81	77	87	89	87	75	97	88	84	65

9) In a study of the effectiveness of physical exercise on weight loss, 20 people were randomly selected to participate in a program for 30 days. Use the Wilcoxon signed-rank test to test the claim that exercise has no bearing on weight loss. Use $\alpha = 0.02$.

Weight Before Program (in Pounds)	178 210 156 188 193 225 190 165 168 200
Weight After Program (in Pounds)	182 205 156 190 183 220 195 155 165 200

Weight Before Program (in Pounds)	186 172 166 184 225 145 208 214 148 174
Weight After Program (in Pounds)	180 173 165 186 240 138 203 203 142 170

10) A local school district is concerned about the number of school days missed by its teachers due to illness. A random sample of 10 teachers is selected. The numbers of days absent in one year is listed below. An incentive program is offered in an attempt to decrease the number of days absent. The number of days absent in one year after the incentive program is listed below. Use the Wilcoxon signed-rank test to test the claim that the incentive program cuts down on the number of days missed by teachers. Use $\alpha = 0.05$.

Teacher	1	2	3	4	5	6	7	8	9	10
Days Absent Before Incentive	7	3	7	5	8	6	2	3	4	5
Days Absent After Incentive	5	2	7	3	7	4	0	4	2	5

11) Verbal SAT scores for students randomly selected from two different schools are listed below. Use the Wilcoxon rank sum test to find R to test the claim that there is no difference in the scores from each school.

School 1	School 2
550 520 770	490 440 680
480 750 530	430 710 590
580 780 610	690 550 530
590 730 750	630 640 540

A) 171.5   B) 128.5   C) 75.5   D) 38.5

12) Verbal SAT scores for students randomly selected from two different schools are listed below. Use the Wilcoxon rank sum test to test the claim that there is no difference in the scores from each school. Use $\alpha = 0.05$.

School 1	School 2
580 550 800	520 470 710
510 780 560	460 740 620
610 810 640	720 580 560
620 760 780	660 670 570

13) A researcher wants to know if the time spent in prison for a particular type of crime was the same for men and women. A random sample of men and women were each asked to give the length of sentence received. The data, in years, are listed below. What is the appropriate test to test the claim that there is no difference in the sentence received by each sex?

Men	14	26	20	22	23	30
Women	13	16	13	18	30	16

Men	18	26	16	23	27	28
Women	38	12	14	17	21	31

A) Wilcoxon signed-rank test   B) Wilcoxon rank sum test

C) Sign test   D) t-test

14) A researcher wants to know if the time spent in prison for a particular type of crime was the same for men and women. A random sample of men and women were each asked to give the length of sentence received. The data, in years, are listed below. Use the Wilcoxon rank sum test to find R, the sum of the ranks for the smaller sample, to test the claim that there is no difference in the sentence received by each gender.

Men	6	18	12	14	15	22
Women	5	8	5	10	22	8

Men	10	18	8	15	19	20
Women	30	4	6	9	13	23

A) 155.5   B) 173.5   C) 125.5   D) 115.5

15) A researcher wants to know if the time spent in prison for a particular type of crime was the same for men and women. A random sample of men and women were each asked to give the length of sentence received. The data, in years, are listed below. Use the Wilcoxon rank sum test to test the claim that there is no difference in the sentence received by each gender. Use α = 0.05.

Men	7	19	13	15	16	23
Women	6	9	6	11	23	9

Men	11	19	9	16	20	21
Women	31	5	7	10	14	24

16) A statistics teacher wanted to see whether there was a significant difference in age between day students and night students. A random sample of 35 students from each group was selected. The data are given below. Use the Wilcoxon rank sum test to test the claim that there is no difference in age between the two groups. Use α = 0.05.

Day Students

22	24	24	23	19	19	23	22	18	21	21
18	18	25	29	24	23	22	22	21	20	20
20	27	17	19	18	21	20	23	26	30	24
21	25

Evening Students

18	23	25	23	21	21	23	24	27	31	34
20	20	23	19	25	24	27	23	20	20	21
25	24	23	28	20	19	23	24	20	27	21
29	30

11.3 The Kruskal–Wallis Test

Solve the problem.

1) A medical researcher wishes to try three different techniques to lower blood pressure of patients with high blood pressure. The subjects are randomly selected and assigned to one of three groups. Group 1 is given medication, Group 2 is given an exercise program, and Group 3 is assigned a diet program. At the end of six weeks, the reduction in each subject's blood pressure is recorded. Use the Kruskal–Wallis test to find the critical value to test the claim that there is no difference in the distribution of the populations. Use α = 0.05.

Group 1	Group 2	Group 3
15	12	10
16	9	16
13	6	8
19	7	12
17	8	13
12	4	8

A) 5.991   B) 1.960   C) 3.195   D) 4.153

2) A medical researcher wishes to try three different techniques to lower blood pressure of patients with high blood pressure. The subjects are randomly selected and assigned to one of three groups. Group 1 is given medication, Group 2 is given an exercise program, and Group 3 is assigned a diet program. At the end of six weeks, the reduction in each subject's blood pressure is recorded. Use the Kruskal–Wallis test to find the test statistic H to test the claim that there is no difference in the distribution of the populations.

Group 1	Group 2	Group 3
16	13	11
17	10	17
14	7	9
20	8	13
18	9	14
13	5	9

A) 6.813   B) 10.187   C) 8.312   D) 5.321

3) A medical researcher wishes to try three different techniques to lower blood pressure of patients with high blood pressure. The subjects are randomly selected and assigned to one of three groups. Group 1 is given medication, Group 2 is given an exercise program, and Group 3 is assigned a diet program. At the end of six weeks, the reduction in each subject's blood pressure is recorded. Use the Kruskal–Wallis test to test the claim that there is no difference in the distribution of the populations. Use $\alpha = 0.05$.

Group 1	Group 2	Group 3
16	13	11
17	10	17
14	7	9
20	8	13
18	9	14
13	5	9

4) Four different types of fertilizers are used on raspberry plants. The number of raspberries on each randomly selected plant is given below. Use the Kruskal–Wallis test to find the test statistic H to test the claim that there is no difference in the distribution of the populations.

Fertilizer 1	Fertilizer 2	Fertilizer 3	Fertilizer 4
6	5	6	3
5	8	3	5
6	5	4	3
7	5	3	4
7	5	2	5
6	6	3	4

A) 10.922   B) 15.364   C) 12.833   D) 14.818

5) Four different types of fertilizers are used on raspberry plants. The number of raspberries on each randomly selected plant is given below. Use the Kruskal–Wallis test to find the critical value H to test the claim that there is no difference in the distribution of the populations. Use $\alpha = 0.05$.

Fertilizer 1	Fertilizer 2	Fertilizer 3	Fertilizer 4
8	7	8	5
7	10	5	7
8	7	6	5
9	7	5	6
9	7	4	7
8	8	5	6

A) 7.352   B) 7.815   C) 6.531   D) 5.198

6) Four different types of fertilizers are used on raspberry plants. The number of raspberries on each randomly selected plant is given below. Use the Kruskal–Wallis test to test the claim that there is no difference in the distribution of the populations. Use $\alpha = 0.05$.

Fertilizer 1	Fertilizer 2	Fertilizer 3	Fertilizer 4
8	7	8	5
7	10	5	7
8	7	6	5
9	7	5	6
9	7	4	7
8	8	5	6

7) A researcher wishes to determine whether there is a difference in the average age of elementary school, high school, and community college teachers. Teachers are randomly selected. Their ages are recorded below. Use the Kruskal–Wallis test to test the claim that there is no difference in the distribution of the populations. Use $\alpha = 0.05$.

Elementary School Teachers	High School Teachers	Community College Teachers
27	40	43
32	45	49
31	42	40
56	51	65
41	46	49
29	35	39

8) The grade point averages of students participating in sports at a college are to be compared. The data are listed below. Use the Kruskal–Wallis test to test the claim that there is no difference in the distribution of the populations. Use $\alpha = 0.05$.

Tennis	Golf	Swimming
3.7	2.3	3.2
3.1	2.6	3.5
3	3.8	3.3
4	2.4	3
3.6	2.8	3
2.6	2.5	2.9

9) The time (in minutes) it takes to assemble a computer component for 3 different machines is listed below. Workers are randomly selected. Use the Kruskal–Wallis test to test the claim that there is no difference in the distribution of the populations. Use $\alpha = 0.05$.

Machine 1	Machine 2	Machine 3
44	52	40
43	41	37
44	50	41
42	45	43
45	47	42
43	44	39
44	48	49

10) A realtor wishes to compare the square footage of houses in 4 different cities, all of which are priced approximately the same. The data are listed below. Use the Kruskal–Wallis test to test the claim that there is no difference in the distribution of the populations. Use $\alpha = 0.05$.

City 1	City 2	City 3	City 4
2160	1790	1540	2410
1990	1550	1680	2360
2010	1700	1590	2610
2220	1660	1610	2160
1910	1710	1510	2010
2060		1760	2210
		1660	2360
			2260

11) Four different types of fertilizers are used on raspberry plants. The number of raspberries on each randomly selected plant is given below. Test the claim using (a) a Kurskal–Wallis test and (b) a one–way ANOVA test that the type of fertilizer makes no difference in the mean number of raspberries per plant. Compare the results. Use $\alpha = 0.01$.

Fertilizer 1	Fertilizer 2	Fertilizer 3	Fertilizer 4
6	5	6	3
5	8	3	5
6	5	4	3
7	5	3	4
7	5	2	5
6	6	3	4

12) A researcher claims that the lifetimes (in hours) of fluorescent light bulbs are the same regardless of manufacturer. Random samples are selected from 3 different manufacturers. The data are listed below. Test the claim that the samples come from identical populations by using (a) a one–way ANOVA test and (b) a Kruskal–Wallis test. Compare the results. Use $\alpha = 0.05$.

Manufacturer 1	Manufacturer 2	Manufacturer 3
190 220	180 170	200 210
235 215	200 175	195 205
225 230	175 180	200 205
215 220	190 185	205 205

11.4 Rank Correlation

Solve the problem.

1) The table below lists the verbal and math SAT scores of 10 students selected at random. Find the critical values to test the claim of no correlation between verbal and math SAT scores. Use $\alpha = 0.05$.

Verbal	445	530	535	440	520
Math	530	600	625	560	610

Verbal	550	450	500	570	460
Math	575	660	580	450	460

    A) ± 0.745   B) ± 0.564   C) ± 0.648   D) ± 0.794

2) The table below lists the verbal and math SAT scores of 10 students selected at random. Find the test statistic r_s, to test the claim of no correlation between verbal and math SAT scores.

Verbal	335	420	425	330	410
Math	420	490	515	450	500

Verbal	440	340	390	460	350
Math	465	550	470	340	350

    A) −0.006   B) −0.0192   C) −0.326   D) −0.218

3) The table below lists the verbal and math SAT scores of 10 students selected at random. Test the claim of no correlation between verbal and math SAT scores. Use $\alpha = 0.05$.

Verbal	295	380	385	290	370
Math	380	450	475	410	460

Verbal	400	300	350	420	310
Math	425	510	430	300	310

4) The drama department at a college asked professors and students in the drama department to rank 8 actors according to their performance. The data are listed below. A 10 is the highest ranking and a 1 the lowest ranking. Find the critical values to test the claim of no correlation between the rankings. Use $\alpha = 0.05$.

Actor	1	2	3	4	5	6	7	8
Professors	2	3	6	10	8	1	5	4
Students	4	3	1	4	5	7	9	6

    A) ±0.643   B) ±0.881   C) ±0.833   D) ±0.738

5) The drama department at a college asked professors and students in the drama department to rank 8 actors according to their performance. The data are listed below. A 10 is the highest ranking and a 1 the lowest ranking. Find the test statistic to test the claim of no correlation between the rankings.

Actor	1	2	3	4	5	6	7	8
Professors	2	3	6	10	8	1	5	4
Students	4	3	1	4	5	7	9	6

    A) −0.354   B) −0.250   C) −0.278   D) −0.198

6) The drama department at a college asked professors and students in the drama department to rank 8 actors according to their performance. The data are listed below. A 10 is the highest ranking and a 1 the lowest ranking. Test the claim of no correlation between the rankings. Use $\alpha = 0.05$.

Actor	1	2	3	4	5	6	7	8
Professors	2	3	6	10	8	1	5	4
Students	4	3	1	4	5	7	9	6

7) The final exam scores of 10 randomly selected statistics students and the number of hours they studied for the exam are given below. Can you conclude that there is a correlation between the scores on the test and the times spend studying?
Use $\alpha = 0.01$.

Hours	3	5	2	8	2	4	4	5	6	3
Scores	65	80	60	88	66	78	85	90	90	71

8) The temperatures on randomly chosen days during a summer class and the number of absences from class on those days are listed below. Can you conclude that there is a correlation between the temperature and the number absent?
Use $\alpha = 0.01$.

Temp	73	86	92	91	89	99	76	101	81
Absences	4	8	11	11	9	16	5	16	6

9) The ages and systolic blood pressures (measured in millimeters of mercury) of 9 randomly selected adults are given below. Can you conclude that there is a correlation between age and blood pressure? Use $\alpha = 0.05$.

Age	38	41	45	48	51	53	57	61	65
Pressure	116	120	123	131	142	145	148	150	152

10) The number of absences and the final grades of 9 randomly selected students from a statistics class are given below. Can you conclude that there is a correlation between the final grade and the number of absences?
Use $\alpha = 0.01$.

Number of Absences	0	3	6	4	9	2	15	8	5
Final Grade	98	86	80	82	71	92	55	76	82

11) A manager wishes to determine the relationship between the number of miles (in hundreds of miles) the manager's sales representatives travel per month and the amount of sales (in thousands of dollars) per month. Can you conclude that there is a correlation between the miles traveled and sales generated? Use $\alpha = 0.05$.

Miles	8	9	16	13	14	21	9	7	17
Sales	37	39	84	68	71	67	54	61	126

12) In an area of the Midwest, records were kept on the relationship between the rainfall (in inches) and the yield of wheat (bushels per acre). Can you conclude that there is a correlation between rainfall and yield per acre?
Use $\alpha = 0.01$.

Rainfall	10.5	8.8	13.4	12.5	18.8	10.3	7.0	15.6	16.0
Yield	50.5	46.2	58.8	59.0	82.4	49.2	31.9	76.0	78.8

13) The table below lists the verbal and math SAT scores of 35 students selected at random. Find the critical values to test the claim of no correlation between verbal and math SAT scores. Use $\alpha = 0.05$.

Verbal	295	380	385	290	370	400	300	350	420	310
Math	380	450	475	410	460	425	510	430	300	310
Verbal	295	340	410	520	360	400	660	530	700	610
Math	440	500	400	480	410	380	500	540	580	620
Verbal	290	470	510	380	390	550	420	430	330	370
Math	380	480	490	510	440	560	440	500	410	300
Verbal	430	390	530	380	390					
Math	430	410	560	400	360					

A) ±0.442   B) ±0.282   C) ±0.336   D) ±0.400

14) The table below lists the verbal and math SAT scores of 35 students selected at random. Find the test statistic, r_S, to test the claim of no correlation between verbal and math SAT scores.

Verbal	295	380	385	290	370	400	300	350	420	310
Math	380	450	475	410	460	45	510	430	300	310
Verbal	295	340	410	520	360	400	660	530	700	610
Math	440	500	400	480	410	380	500	540	580	620
Verbal	290	470	510	380	390	550	420	430	330	370
Math	380	480	490	510	440	560	440	500	410	300
Verbal	430	390	530	380	390					
Math	430	410	560	400	360					

A) 0.819   B) 0.731   C) 0.616   D) 0.545

15) The table below lists the verbal and math SAT scores of 35 students selected at random. Test the claim of no correlation between verbal and math SAT scores. Use $\alpha = 0.05$.

Verbal	295	380	385	290	370	400	300	350	420	310
Math	380	450	475	410	460	45	510	430	300	310
Verbal	295	340	410	520	360	400	660	530	700	610
Math	440	500	400	480	410	380	500	540	580	620
Verbal	290	470	510	380	390	550	420	430	330	370
Math	380	480	490	510	440	560	440	500	410	300
Verbal	430	390	530	380	390					
Math	430	410	560	400	360					

11.5   The Runs Test

Solve the problem.

1) Two poker players are dealt cards in the sequence shown, where B represents a black card and R represents a red card. Find the test statistic G to test for randomness.

B   B   B   R   B   R   B
R   R   B   B   B   R   R

2) Two poker players are dealt cards in the sequence shown, where B represents a black card and R represents a red card. Can you conclude that the dealing of cards was not random? Use $\alpha = 0.05$.

B   B   B   R   B   R   B
R   R   B   B   B   R   R

3) A telemarketer solicited households to change their long-distance carrier. The results for one afternoon are shown, where C represents the households that changed their carrier and S represents the households that kept their same carrier. Find the test statistic G to test for randomness.

C   C   C   S   C   S   C   S   S   C   C
S   C   S   C   S   C   S   S   C   S   C

4) A telemarketer solicited households to change their long-distance carrier. The results for one afternoon are shown, where C represents the households that changed their carrier and S represents the households that kept their same carrier. Can you conclude that the sequence is random? Use $\alpha = 0.05$.

C   C   C   S   C   S   C   S   S   C   C
S   C   S   C   S   C   S   S   C   S   C

5) An airport security officer manually searched carry-on bags of people boarding a plane in the sequence shown, where S represents a searched bag and N represents a bag not searched. Find the test statistic z to test for randomness.

N   N   N   N   N   S   N   N   S   S
N   N   N   N   N   N   N   S   N   N
N   N   S   S   S   N   N   N   S   N
N   S   N   N   N   N   S   S   N   N
N   N   N   N   N   N   S   N   N   N

6) An airport security officer manually searched carry-on bags of people boarding a plane in the sequence shown, where S represents a searched bag and N represents a bag not searched. Can you conclude that the officer conducted a random search? Use $\alpha = 0.05$.

N   N   N   N   N   S   N   N   S   S
N   N   N   N   N   N   N   S   N   N
N   N   S   S   S   N   N   N   S   N
N   S   N   N   N   N   S   S   N   N
N   N   N   N   N   N   S   N   N   N

7) A pitching machine throws baseballs that are either strikes (S) or balls (B). A coach records whether each ball thrown during batting practice is a strike or a ball. Find the standardized test statistic z to test for randomness.

```
B   B   S   B   S   S   B   B   S   B
B   B   B   S   B   S   S   S   S   S
B   B   B   B   S   B   B   S   B   B
B   S   S   S   B   S   S   S   B   B
B   B   B   S   S   S   S   S   S   S
```

8) A pitching machine throws baseballs that are either strikes (S) or balls (B). A coach records whether each ball thrown during batting practice is a strike or a ball. Can you conclude that the sequence of pitches was random? Use α = 0.05.

```
B   B   S   B   S   S   B   B   S   B
B   B   B   S   B   S   S   S   S   S
B   B   B   B   S   B   B   S   B   B
B   S   S   S   B   S   S   S   B   B
B   B   B   S   S   S   S   S   S   S
```

9) The sequence shows a company's daily sales, in thousands of dollars, for the business days during the month of September. Find the standardized test statistic, G to test for randomness.

```
10   10   15   12.5   20   12.5   10     10     12.5   20
 8   10   10   20     15    9     12.5   12.5   20     17.5
```

10) The sequence shows a company's daily sales, in thousands of dollars, for the business days during the month of September. Find the standardized test statistic, G to test for randomness.

```
10   10   15   12.5   20   12.5   10     10     12.5   20
 8   10   10   20     15    9     12.5   12.5   20     17.5
```

11.1 The Sign Test

1) C

2) A

3) critical value 4; test statistic x = 8; fail to reject H_0; There is not sufficient evidence to reject the claim.

4) C

5) B

6) critical value 1; test statistic x = 6; fail to reject H_0; There is not sufficient evidence to reject the claim.

7) D

8) C

9) claim: median > 67; critical value 4; test statistic x = 6; fail to reject H_0; There is not sufficient evidence to support the claim.

10) critical value 1; test statistic x = 1; reject H_0; There is sufficient evidence to reject the claim.

11) C

12) A

13) critical values ±1.96; test statistic z ≈ −4.743; reject H_0; There is sufficient evidence to reject the claim.

14) critical values ±2.575; test statistic z ≈ −1.162; fail to reject H_0; There is not sufficient evidence to reject the claim.

15) claim: The test preparation had no effect on SAT scores. (H_0); critical value 0; test statistic x = 2; fail to reject H_0; There is not sufficient evidence to reject claim.

16) claim: Viatmin E supplements increase athletes' strength. (H_a); critical value 1; test statistic x = 2; fail to reject H_0; There is not sufficient evidence to support claim.

17) claim: The drug reduces cholesterol levels. (H_a); critical value 0; test statistic x = 1; fail to reject H_0; There is not sufficient evidence to support claim.

18) claim: Exercise has no bearing on weight loss. (H_0); critical value = 3; test statistic x = 6; fail to reject H_0; There is not sufficient evidence to reject claim.

19) claim: The incentive program reduces the number of teacher absences. (H_a); critical value 1; test statistic x = 1; reject H_0; There is sufficient evidence to support claim.

20) claim: The relaxation tape lowers diastolic blood pressure. (H_a); critical value 0; test statistic x = 1; fail to reject H_0; There is not sufficient evidence to reject the claim.

21) C

22) A

23) critical value −1.645; test statistic z ≈ −3.479; reject H_0; There is sufficient evidence to reject the claim.

24) critical value −2.33; test statistic z ≈ −0.919; Fail to reject H_0; There is not sufficient evidence to reject the claim.

25) claim: median ≤ $912; critical value −1.645; test statistic z ≈ −0.41; fail to reject H_0; There is not sufficient evidence to reject the claim.

26) claim: diet is effective; critical value −1.645; test statistic z ≈ −3.343; reject H_0; There is sufficient evidence to reject the claim.

11.2 The Wilcoxon Tests

1) A

2) critical value 4; test statistic w_s = 4; reject H_0; There is sufficient evidence to reject claim. The course is effective.

3) A

4) critical value 6; test statistic w_s = 4.5; reject H_0; There is sufficient evidence to support the claim.

5) B

6) critical value 8; test statistic w_s = 4; reject H_0; There is sufficient evidence to support the claim.

7) A

8) critical value 8; test statistic w_s = 1.5; reject H_0; There is sufficient evidence to support the claim.

9) critical value 33; test statistic w_s = 42.5; fail to reject H_0; There is not sufficient evidence to reject the claim.

10) critical value 6; test statistic w_s = 2; reject H_0; There is sufficient evidence to support the claim.

11) B

12) critical values ±1.96; test statistic $z \approx 1.241$; fail to reject H_0; There is not sufficient evidence to reject the claim.

13) B

14) C

15) critical values ±1.96; test statistic $z \approx 1.415$; fail to reject H_0; There is not sufficient evidence to reject the claim.

16) critical values ±1.96; test statistic $z \approx -1.75$; fail to reject H_0; There is not sufficient evidence to reject the claim.

11.3 The Kruskal–Wallis Test

1) A

2) B

3) critical value 5.991; test statistic $H \approx 10.187$; reject H_0; The data provide ample evidence that there is a difference in the distribution of the populations.

4) C

5) B

6) critical value 7.815; test statistic $H \approx 12.833$; reject H_0; There is enough evidence to conclude that there is a difference in the distribution of the populations.

7) critical value 5.991; test statistic $H \approx 4.056$; fail to reject H_0; There is not enough evidence to conclude that there is difference in the distribution of the populations.

8) critical value 5.991; test statistic $H \approx 5.108$; fail to reject; There is enough evidence to conclude that there is a difference in the distribution of the populations.

9) critical value 5.991; test statistic $H \approx 7.482$; reject H_0; There is enough evidence to conclude that there is a difference in the distribution of the populations.

10) critical value 7.815; test statistic $H \approx 20.657$; reject H_0; There is enough evidence to conclude that there is a difference in the distribution of the populations.

11) a) critical value 7.815; test statistic $H \approx 12.833$; reject H_0; There is enough evidence to conclude that there is a difference in the distribution of the populations.
b) critical value 4.938; Test statistic $F \approx 8.357$; reject H_0; There is enough evidence to conclude that there is a difference in the distribution of the populations.

The decisions are the same in (a) and (b).

12) a) critical value 3.467; test statistic $F \approx 27.653$; reject H_0; The data provides sample evidence that the means are unequal.
b) critical value 5.991; test statistic $H \approx 16.666$; reject H_0; The data provides evidence that the samples come from different populations.

The decision is the same in parts (a) and (b).

11.4 Rank Correlation

1) C

2) A

3) critical values ±0.648; test statistic $r_s \approx -0.006$; fail to reject H_0; There is not enough evidence to conclude that there is a significant correlation between verbal and math SAT scores.

4) D

5) B

6) critical values ±0.738; test statistic $r_s \approx -0.250$; fail to reject H_0; There is not enough evidence to conclude that there is a significant correlation between the rankings.

7) critical values ±0.794; test statistic $r_s \approx 0.889$; reject H_0; There is enough evidence to conclude that there is a significant correlation between the scores and the time spent studying.

8) critical values ±0.833; test statistic $r_s \approx 0.992$; reject H_0; There is enough evidence to conclude that there is a significant correlation between the temperature and the number of absences.

9) critical values ±0.683; test statistic $r_s \approx 1.0$; reject H_0; There is enough evidence to conclude that there is a significant correlation between age and blood pressure.

10) critical values ±0.883; test statistic $r_s \approx -0.996$; reject H_0; There is enough evidence to conclude that there is a significant correlation between the final grade and the number of absences.

11) critical values ±0.683; test statistic $r_s \approx 0.728$; reject H_0; There is enough evidence to conclude that there is significant correlation between miles traveled and sales generated.

12) critical values ±0.833; test statistic $r_s \approx 0.983$; reject H_0; There is enough evidence to conclude that there is a significant correlation between rainfall and yield per acre.

13) C

14) D

15) critical values ±0.336; test statistic $r_s \approx 0.545$; reject H_0; There is enough evidence to conclude that there is a significant correlation between verbal and math SAT scores.

11.5   The Runs Test

1) $G = 8$

2) Lower critical value = 3; upper critical value = 12; standardized test statistic = 8; fail to reject H_0; The cards were dealt randomly.

3) $G = 17$

4) Lower critical value = 7; upper critical value = 17; standardized test statistic = 17; reject H_0; The sequence was not random.

5) $z = -0.88$

6) Critical $z_0 = \pm 1.96$; standardized test statistic $z \approx -0.88$; fail to reject H_0; The search was random.

7) $z = -2.44$

8) Critical $z_0 = \pm 1.96$; standardized test statistic $z \approx -2.44$; reject H_0; The pitches were not random.

9) $G = 8$

10) Lower critical value = 4; upper critical value = 13; standardized test statistic = 8; fail to reject H_0; The daily sales are random.